THE abc OF BRITISH RAILWAYS LOCOMOTIVES

COMBINED VOLUME

PARTS 1—4

Nos. 1-99999

ALSO DIESEL AND ELECTRIC LOCOMOTIVES AND MULTIPLE UNITS

SUMMER 1960 EDITION

LONDON:

Ian Allan Ltd

NOTES ON THE USE OF THIS BOOK

THE following notes are a guide to the system of reference marks and other details given in the lists of dimensions shown for each class.

1. Many of the classes listed are sub-divided by reason of mechanical or constructional differences (on the Eastern and North Eastern Regions the sub-divisions are denoted in some cases by "Parts," shown thus : D16/3). At the head of each class will be found a list of such sub-divisions, if any, usually arranged in order of introduction. Each part is given there a reference mark by which its relevant dimensions, if differing from those of other parts, and the locomotives included in this sub-division, or part, may be indentified. Any other differences between locomotives are also indicated, with reference marks, below the details of the class's introduction.

2. The lists of dimensions at the head of each class show locomotives fitted with two inside cylinders, Stephenson valve gear and slide valves, unless otherwise stated, e.g. (O) = two outside cylinders, P.V. = piston valves.

3. The following method is used to denote superheated locomotives, the letters being inserted, where applicable, after the boiler pressure details : Su = All engines superheated.
SS = Some engines superheated.

4. The date on which the first locomotive of a class was built or modified is denoted by " Introduced."

5. S. denotes Service (Departmental) locomotive still carrying B.R. number. This reference letter is introduced only for the reader's guidance and is not borne by the locomotive concerned.

Note :

On the Southern Region the letters " DS " preceding a number indicate a Service Locomotive. On the S.R. (only) this marking appears on the locomotive.

BRITISH RAILWAYS LOCOMOTIVE SHEDS AND SHED CODES

AND PRINCIPAL SIGNING-ON POINTS

ALL B.R. LOCOMOTIVES CARRY THE CODE OF THEIR HOME DEPOT ON A SMALL PLATE AFFIXED TO THE SMOKEBOX DOOR.

LONDON MIDLAND REGION

1A **Willesden**
1B Camden
1C Watford
1D Devons Road (Bow)
1E Bletchley
  Leighton Buzzard

2A **Rugby**
2B Nuneaton
2D Coventry
2E Northampton
2F Woodford Halse

3A **Bescot**
3B Bushbury
3C Walsall
3D Aston
3E Monument Lane

5A **Crewe North**
  Crewe (Gresty Lane)
5B Crewe South
5C Stafford
5D Stoke
5E Alsager
5F Uttoxeter

6A **Chester (Midland)**
6B Mold Junction
6C Birkenhead
6E Chester (West)
6F Bidston
6G Llandudno Junction
6H Bangor
6J Holyhead
6K Rhyl

8A **Edge Hill**
8B Warrington (Dallam)
  Warrington (Arpley)
8C Speke Junction
8D Widnes
8E Northwich
8F Springs Branch (Wigan)
8G Sutton Oak

9A **Longsight (Manchester)**
9B Stockport (Edgeley)
9C Macclesfield
9D Buxton
9E Trafford Park
  Glazebrook
9F Heaton Mersey
  Gowhole
9G Gorton
  Ardwick
  Dinting
  Guide Bridge
  Mottram
  Reddish

11A **Barrow**
11B Workington
11C Oxenholme
11D Tebay

12A **Carlisle (Kingmoor)**
12B Carlisle (Upperby)
  Penrith
12C Carlisle (Canal)
12D Kirkby Stephen

14A **Cricklewood**
14B Kentish Town
14C St. Albans
14D Neasden
  Aylesbury
  Chesham
  Marylebone
  Rickmansworth
14E Bedford

15A **Wellingborough**
15B Kettering
15C Leicester (Midland)
15D Coalville
15E Leicester (Central)
15F Market Harborough
  Seaton

16A **Nottingham**
16B Kirkby-in-Ashfield
16C Mansfield
16D Annesley
  Nottingham (Victoria)
  Kirkby Bentinck

17A **Derby**
Derby (Friargate)
17B Burton
Horninglow
Overseal
17C Rowsley
Cromford
Middleton
Sheep Pasture

18A **Toton (Stapleford & Sandiacre)**
18B Westhouses
18C Hasland

21A **Saltley**
21B Bournville

24A **Accrington**
24B Rose Grove
24C Lostock Hall
24D Lower Darwen
24E Blackpool
24F Fleetwood
24G Skipton
24H Hellifield
24J Lancaster (Green Ayre)
24K Preston
24L Carnforth

26A **Newton Heath**
26B Agecroft
26C Bolton
26D Bury
26E Lees (Oldham)
26F Patricroft

27A **Bank Hall**
27B Aintree
27C Southport
27D Wigan
27E Walton-on-the-Hill
27F Brunswick (Liverpool)
Warrington (Central)

EASTERN REGION

30A **Stratford**
Chelmsford
Enfield Town
Southend (Victoria)
Wood St. (Walthamstow)
30B Hertford East
Buntingford
30C Bishops Stortford
30E Colchester
Clacton
Maldon
Walton-on-Naze
30F Parkeston

31A **Cambridge**
Ely
31B March
31C Kings Lynn
31E Sudbury (Suffolk)

32A **Norwich (Thorpe)**
Cromer Beach
32B Ipswich
32C Lowestoft Central
32D Yarmouth South Town

33B **Tilbury**
33C **Shoeburyness**

34A **Kings Cross**
34B Hornsey
34C Hatfield
34D Hitchin
34E New England
34F Grantham

36A **Doncaster**
36C Frodingham
36E Retford

40A **Lincoln**
40B Immingham
Grimsby
New Holland
40E Colwick
40F Boston
Sleaford

41A **Sheffield (Darnall)**
41B Sheffield (Grimesthorpe)
41C Millhouses
41D Canklow
41E Staveley (Barrow Hill)
41F Mexborough
41H Staveley (ex-G.C.)
41J Langwith

NORTH EASTERN REGION

50A **York**
50B Hull (Dairycoates)
Hull (Alexandra Dock)
50C Hull (Botanic Gardens)
50D Goole
50E Scarborough
50F Malton

51A **Darlington**
51C West Hartlepool
51F West Auckland
51J Northallerton
51L Thornaby

52A **Gateshead**
Bowes Bridge
52B Heaton
52C Blaydon
Alston
52D Tweedmouth
Alnmouth
52E Percy Main
52F North and South Blyth
52G Sunderland
52H Tyne Dock
Pelton Level
52K Consett

55A **Leeds (Holbeck)**
55B Stourton
55C Farnley
55D Royston
55E Normanton
55F Bradford (Manningham)
Keighley
55G Huddersfield
55H Leeds (Neville Hill)

56A **Wakefield**
Knottingley
56B Ardsley
56C Copley Hill
56D Mirfield
56E Sowerby Bridge
56F Low Moor
56G Bradford (Hammerton St.)

SCOTTISH REGION

60A **Inverness**
Dingwall
Kyle of Lochalsh
60B Aviemore
Boat of Garten
60C Helmsdale
Dornoch
Tain
60D Wick
Thurso
60E Forres

61A **Kittybrewster**
Ballater
Fraserburgh
Inverurie
Peterhead
61B Aberdeen (Ferryhill)
61C Keith
Banff
Elgin

62A **Thornton**
Anstruther
Burntisland
Kirkcaldy
Ladybank
Methil
62B **Dundee (Tay Bridge)**
Arbroath
Montrose
St. Andrews
62C Dunfermline
Alloa
Kelty

63A **Perth**
Aberfeldy
Blair Atholl
Crieff
Forfar
63B Stirling
Killin
63C Oban
Ballachulish

64A **St. Margarets (Edinburgh)**
Dunbar
Galashiels
Hardengreen
Longniddry
North Berwick
Seafield
South Leith
64B Haymarket
64C Dairy Road
64D Carstairs
64E Polmont
64F Bathgate

64G Hawick
Riccarton Junction
St. Boswells
64H Leith Central

65A **Eastfield (Glasgow)**
Arrochar
65B St. Rollox
65C Parkhead
65D Dawsholm
Dumbarton
65E Kipps
65F Grangemouth
65G Yoker
65H Helensburgh
65I Balloch
65J Fort William
Mallaig

66A **Polmadie (Glasgow)**
66B Motherwell
66C Hamilton
66D Greenock (Ladyburn)

67A **Corkerhill (Glasgow)**
67B Hurlford
Beith
Muirkirk
67C Ayr
67D Ardrossan

68B Dumfries
68C Stranraer
Newton Stewart
68D Beattock

SOUTHERN REGION

70A **Nine Elms**
70B Feltham
70C Guildford
Reading South
70D Basingstoke
70H Ryde (I.O.W.)

71A **Eastleigh**
Andover Junction
Lymington
Southampton Terminus
Winchester City
71B Bournemouth Central
Branksome
71G Weymouth
Bridport
71I Southampton Docks

72A **Exmouth Junction**
Bude
Callington
Exmouth
Lyme Regis
Okehampton
Seaton

72B Salisbury
72C Yeovil
72E Barnstaple Junction
Ilfracombe
Torrington
72F Wadebridge

73A **Stewarts Lane**
73B Bricklayers Arms
73C Hither Green
73E Faversham
73F Ashford (Kent)
Gillingham (Kent)
Ramsgate
73H Dover
Folkestone
73J Tonbridge

75A **Brighton**
Newhaven
75B Redhill
75C Norwood Junction
75E Three Bridges
Horsham
75F Tunbridge Wells West

WESTERN REGION

81A **Old Oak Common**
81B Slough
Marlow
81C Southall
81D Reading
81E Didcot
81F Oxford
Fairford

82A **Bristol (Bath Road)**
Bath
Wells
Weston-super-Mare
Yatton
82B St. Philip's Marsh
82C Swindon
Chippenham

82D Westbury
Frome
82E Bristol (Barrow Rd.)
82F Bath (Green Park)
Radstock West
82G Templecombe

83A **Newton Abbot**
Kingsbridge
83B Taunton
Bridgwater
83C Exeter
Tiverton Junction
83D Laira (Plymouth)
Launceston
83E St. Blazey
Bodmin
Moorswater
83F Truro
83G Penzance
Helston
St. Ives
83H Plymouth (Friary)

84A **Wolverhampton (Stafford Road)**
84B Oxley
84C Banbury
84D Leamington Spa
84E Tyseley
Stratford-on-Avon
84F Stourbridge Junction
84G Shrewsbury
Craven Arms
Knighton
Builth Road
84H Wellington (Salop)
84J Croes Newydd
Bala
Penmaenpool
Trawstynydd

85A **Worcester**
Evesham
Kingham
85B Gloucester
Brimscombe
Cheltenham (Malvern Rd.)
Lydney
85C Hereford
Leominster
Ross
85D Kidderminster
85E Gloucester (Barnwood)
Dursley
Tewkesbury

85F Bromsgrove
Redditch

86A **Newport (Ebbw Junction)**
86B Newport (Pill)
86C Cardiff (Canton)
86D Llantrisant
86E Severn Tunnel Junction
86F Tondu
86G Pontypool Road
86H Aberbeeg
86J Aberdare
86K Tredegar

87A **Neath**
Glyn Neath
Neath (N. & B.
87B Duffryn Yard
87C Danygraig
87D Swansea East Dock
Gurnos
Upper Bank
87E Landore
87F Llanelly
Burry Port
Llandovery
Pantyffynnon
87G Carmarthen
87H Neyland
Cardigan
Milford Haven
Pembroke Dock
Whitland
87J Goodwick

88A **Cardiff (Radyr)**
Cathays
88B Cardiff East Dock
88C Barry
88D Merthyr
Dowlais Cae Harris
Dowlais Central
Rhymney
88E Abercynon
88F Treherbert
Ferndale

89A **Oswestry**
Llanidloes
Moat Lane
89B Brecon
89C Machynlleth
Aberystwyth
Aberystwyth (V. of R.)
Portmadoc
Pwllheli

SUMMARY OF WESTERN REGION STEAM LOCOMOTIVE CLASSES WITH HISTORICAL NOTES AND DIMENSIONS

The code given in smaller bold type at the head of each Class, e.g. "6MT" denotes its British Railways power classification.

The numbers of locomotives in service have been checked to February 27th, 1960

4-6-0 6MT 1000 Class "County"

Introduced 1945. Hawksworth design.
*Fitted with double chimney.
Weight: Loco. 76 tons 17 cwt.
Tender 49 tons 0 cwt.
Pressure: 280 lb. Su.
Cyls.: (O) 18½" × 30".
Driving Wheels: 6' 3".
T.E.: 32,580 lb. P.V.

*1000–4/6–16/8/20/2–4/6–9
1005/17/9/21/5 **Total 30**

4-6-0 7P 4073 Class "Castle"

*Introduced 1923. Collett design, developed from "Star" (4037, 5083–92 converted from "Star").
†Introduced 1946. Fitted with 3-row superheater.
‡Introduced 1947. Fitted with 4-row superheater.
¶Introduced 1956. Fitted with double chimney.
Weight: Loco. 79 tons 17 cwt.
Tender 46 tons 14 cwt.
Pressure: 225 lb. Su.
Cyls.: (4) 16" × 26".
Driving Wheels: 6' 8½".
T.E.: 31,625 lb.
Inside Walschaerts valve gear and rocking shafts. P.V.

*4037/73/5–7/9/81–6/9/92/4–6/8/9, 5001–4/6–9/11–25/7–32/4/5/7–42/4–8/51–6/8–60/2/6–70/6/8/80/4/5/7/9–92
†5000/50/63/5/72/4/5/7/9/81/2/93/6–9, 7000–3/5–12/4–7/20/1/5–8/31–3/5/7
‡4074/8, 5026/33/6/49/71/3/94/5, 7019/24/9/30/4/6
†¶7023
‡¶4080/7/8/90/3/7, 5043/57/61/4/88, 7004/13/8/22 **Total 161**

4-6-0 5MT 4900 Class "Hall"

Introduced 1928. Modified design of Collett rebuild with 6' 0" driving wheels of "Saint" (built 1907) for new construction, with higher-pitched boiler, modified footplating and detail differences.
Weight: Loco. 75 tons 0 cwt.
Tender 46 tons 14 cwt.
Pressure: 225 lb. Su.
Cyls.: (O) 18½" × 30".
Driving Wheels: 6' 0".
T.E.: 27,275 lb.
P.V.

4901–10/2–39/41–99, 5900–14/6–99, 6900–58 **Total 255**

4-6-0 8P 6000 Class "King"

Introduced 1927. Collett design.
All engines modified since 1947 with 4-row superheater and since 1955 with double chimney.
Weight: Loco. 89 tons 0 cwt.
Tender 46 tons 14 cwt.
Pressure: 250 lb. Su.
Cyls.: (4) 16¼" × 28".
Driving Wheels: 6' 6".
T.E.: 40,285 lb.
Inside Walschaerts valve gear and rocking shafts. P.V.

6000–29 **Total 30**

4-6-0 5MT 6800 Class "Grange"

Introduced 1936. Collett design, variation of "Hall" with smaller wheels, incorporating certain parts of withdrawn 4300 2-6-0 locos.
Weight: Loco. 74 tons 0 cwt.
Tender 40 tons 0 cwt.
Pressure: 225 lb. Su.
Cyls.: (O) 18½" × 30".
Driving Wheels: 5' 8".
T.E.: 28,875 lb.
P.V.

6800–79 **Total 80**

4-6-0 5MT 6959 Class "Modified Hall"

ntroduced 1944. Hawksworth development of "Hall," with larger superheater, "one-piece" main frames and plate-framed bogie.
Weight: Loco. 75 tons 16 cwt.
Tender 46 tons 14 cwt.
Pressure: 225 lb. Su.
Cyls.: (O) 18½" × 30".
Driving Wheels: 6' 0".
T.E.: 27,275 lb.
P.V

6959–99, 7900–29 **Total 71**

4-6-0 5MT 7800 Class "Manor"

Introduced 1938. Collett design for secondary lines, incorporating certain parts of withdrawn 4300 2-6-0 locos.
Weight: Loco. 68 tons 18 cwt.
Tender 40 tons 0 cwt.
Pressure: 225 lb. Su.
Cyls.: (O) 18" × 30".
Driving Wheels: 5' 8".
T.E.: 27,340 lb.
P.V.

7800–29 **Total 30**

4-4-0 "City" Class

Introduced 1903. Churchward design.
Weight: Loco. 55 tons 6 cwt.
Tender 36 tons 15 cwt.
Pressure: 200 lb. Su.
Cyls.: 18" × 26".
Driving Wheels: 6' 8½".
T.E.: 17,790 lb.

3440

Withdrawn 1931 and preserved in York Museum. Returned to service 1957.

Total 1

4-4-0 2P 9000 Class

Introduced 1936. Collett rebuild, incorporating "Duke" type boiler and "Bulldog" frames for light lines.
Weight: Loco. 49 tons 0 cwt.
Tender {40 tons 0 cwt. / 36 tons 15 cwt.}
Pressure: 180 lb. SS.
Cyls.: 18" × 26".
Driving Wheels: 5' 8".
T.E.: 18,955 lb.

9004/14/5/7/8 **Total 5**

2-8-0 8F 2800 Class

*Introduced 1903. Churchward design, earlier locos. subsequently fitted with new boiler and superheater.
†Introduced 1938. Collett locos., with side-window cab and detail alterations.
Weight: Loco. {75 tons 10 cwt.* / 76 tons 5 cwt.†}
Tender 40 tons 0 cwt.
Pressure: 225 lb. Su.
Cyls.: (O) 18½" × 30".
Driving Wheels: 4' 7½".
T.E.: 35,380 lb.
P.V.

*2805–7/13/8/9/21/2/34–7/9/41/2/4–7/9/51–62/5–7/71–6/9/82/3
†2884–99, 3800–66 **Total 127**

2-8-0 7F 4700 Class

Introduced 1919. Churchward mixed traffic design (4700 built with smaller boiler and later rebuilt).
Weight: Loco. 82 tons 0 cwt.
Tender 46 tons 14 cwt.
Pressure: 225 lb. Su.
Cyls.: (O) 19" × 30".
Driving Wheels: 5' 8".
T.E.: 30,460 lb.
P.V.

4700–8 **Total 9**

2-6-0 4MT 4300 Class

*Introduced 1911. Churchward design.
†Introduced 1925. Locos. with detail alteration affecting weight.
‡Introduced 1932. Locos. with side window cab and detail alterations.
Weight: Loco. {62 tons 0 cwt.* / 64 tons 0 cwt.† / 65 tons 6 cwt.‡}
Tender 40 tons 0 cwt.
Pressure: 200 lb. Su.
Cyls.: (O) 18½" × 30".
Driving Wheels: 5' 8".
T.E.: 25,670 lb.
P.V.

*5306/11/8/22/4/6/30–3/6/7/9/51/3/7/8/69/70/6/80/4/5/96/9, 6300–2/4/6/7/9/10/2–4/6/7/9/20/3/4/6/7/9/30/2/3/5–53/6/7/60–82/4–92/4/5/8, 7305–21

†7300–4

‡7322–41 **Total 146**

0-6-0 3MT 2251 Class

Introduced 1930. Collett design.
Weight:
Loco. 43 tons 8 cwt.
Tender {36 tons 15 cwt. / 47 tons 6 cwt. (ex-R.O.D. tender from 3000 Class 2-8-0).}
Pressure: 200 lb. Su.
Cyls.: 17½" × 24".
Driving Wheels: 5' 2".
T.E.: 20,155 lb.

2200–4/6/7/9–24/7/9–34/6/9–51/3/5–7/60/1/4/5/7/8/71/3/4/6/7/82/3/6–9/91/2/4/5/7/8, 3200–19

Total 91

2-8-2T 8F 7200 Class

Introduced 1934. Collett rebuild, with extended bunker and trailing wheels, of Churchward 4200 class 2-8-0T.
Weight: 92 tons 2 cwt.
Pressure: 200 lb. Su.
Cyls.: (O) 19" × 30".
Driving Wheels: 4' 7½".
T.E.: 33,170 lb.
P.V.

7200–53 **Total 54**

2-8-0T {7F* / 8F†} 4200 Class

*Introduced 1910. Churchward design.
†**5205 class.** Introduced 1923. With enlarged cyls. and detail alterations.
Weight: {81 tons 12 cwt.* / 82 tons 2 cwt.†}
Pressure: 200 lb. Su.
Cyls.: {(O) 18½" × 30"*. / (O) 19" × 30"†.}
Driving Wheels: 4' 7½".
T.E.: {31,450 lb.* / 33,170 lb.†}
P.V.

*4203/7/13/4/8/22/5/7–30/2/3/5–8/41–3/6–8/50–9/62–99, 5200–4

†5205–64 **Total 136**

2-6-2T 4MT 4500 Class

*Introduced 1906. Churchward design for light branches, developed from 4400 class with larger wheels, earlier locos. subsequently fitted with superheater.
†**4575 class.** Introduced 1927. With detail alterations and increased weight.
‡Introduced 1953. Push-and-pull fitted.
Weight: {57 tons 0 cwt.* / 61 tons 0 cwt.†‡}
Pressure: 200 lb. Su.
Cyls.: (O) 17" × 24".
Driving Wheels: 4' 7½".
T.E.: 21,250 lb.
P.V.

*4507/49/50/2/5–9/61–7/9–71/3/4

†4575/87/8/91/3/4, 5503/4/8–10/4–6/8–21/3/5–7/31/2/6–44/6–50/2–4/7/8/61–5/9–71/3

‡4589, 5511/24/9/34/45/55/60/8/72

Total 83

2-6-2T 4MT 5101 & 6100 Classes

***5101 class.** Introduced 1929. Modified design for new construction of Collett rebuild, with detail alterations and increased weight, of Churchward 3100 class (introduced 1903 and subsequently fitted with superheater).
†**6100 class.** Introduced 1931. Locos. for London suburban area with increased boiler pressure.
Weight: 78 tons 9 cwt.
Pressure: {200 lb. Su.* / 225 lb. Su.†}
Cyls.: (O) 18" × 30".
Driving Wheels: 5' 8".
T.E.: {24,300 lb.* / 27,340 lb.†}
P.V.

*4100–37/40–63/5–79, 5101–4/6/10/50–5/8/64/6/7/9/73–85/7/8/90–5/7–9

†6101/3–69 **Total 186**

2-6-2T 4MT 8100 Class

Introduced 1938. Collett rebuild, with higher pressure and smaller wheels, of Churchward locos. in 5100 class.
Weight: 76 tons 11 cwt.
Pressure: 225 lb. Su.
Cyls.: (O) 18″ × 30″.
Driving Wheels: 5′ 6″.
T.E.: 28,165 lb.
P.V.

8100–4/6–9 **Total 9**

2-6-2T unclass. V. of R.

*Introduced 1902. Davies and Metcalfe design for V. of R. 1′ 11½″ gauge.
†Introduced 1923. G.W. development of V. of R. design.
Weight: 25 tons 0 cwt.
Gauge: 1′ 11½″.
Pressure: 165 lb.
Cyls.: (O) {11″ × 17″.* / 11½″ × 17″.†}
Driving Wheels: 2′ 6″.
T.E.: {9,615 lb.* / 10,510 lb.†}
Walschaerts valve gear.

*9 †7/8 **Total 3**

NOTE

The following abbreviations are used to indicate the pre-grouping owners of certain Western Region locomotives:

Car.R.	Cardiff Railway.
P. & M.	Powlesland & Mason (Contractor).
S.H.T.	Swansea Harbour Trust.
V. of R.	Cambrian Railways (Vale of Rheidol).
W. & L.	Cambrian Railways (Welshpool & Llanfair).

0-6-2T 5MT 5600 Class

*Introduced 1924. Collett design for service in Welsh valleys.
†Introduced 1927. Locos. with detail alterations.
Weight: {68 tons 12 cwt.* / 69 tons 7 cwt.†}
Pressure: 200 lb. Su.
Cyls.: 18″ × 26″.
Driving Wheels: 4′ 7½″.
T.E.: 25,800 lb.
P.V

*5600–99

†6600–99 **Total 200**

0-6-0ST 0F 1361 Class

Introduced 1910. Churchward design for dock shunting.
Weight: 35 tons 4 cwt.
Pressure: 150 lb.
Cyls.: (O) 16″ × 20″.
Driving Wheels: 3′ 8″.
T.E.: 14,835 lb.

1361–5 **Total 5**

0-6-0PT 1F 1366 Class

Introduced 1934. Collett development of 1361 class, with pannier tanks.
Weight: 35 tons 15 cwt.
Pressure: 165 lb.
Cyls.: (O) 16″ × 20″.
Driving Wheels: 3′ 8″.
T.E.: 16,320 lb.

1366–9/71 **Total 5**

0-6-0PT 4F 1500 Class

Introduced 1949. Hawksworth short-wheelbase heavy shunting design.
Weight: 58 tons 4 cwt.
Pressure: 200 lb.
Cyls.: (O) 17½″ × 24″.
Driving Wheels: 4′ 7½″.
T.E.: 22,515 lb.
Walschaerts valve gear. P.V.

1500–8 **Total 9**

0-6-0PT 2F 1600 Class

Introduced 1949. Hawksworth light branch line and shunting design.
Weight: 41 tons 12 cwt.
Pressure: 165 lb.
Cyls.: $16\frac{1}{2}'' \times 24''$.
Driving Wheels: $4' 1\frac{1}{2}''$.
T.E.: 18,515 lb.

1601/2/4–9/11–5/7–34/6–43/5–51/3–69 **Total 63**

0-6-0PT 1P 5400 Class

Introduced 1931. Collett design for light passenger work, push-and-pull fitted.
Weight: 46 tons 12 cwt.
Pressure: 165 lb.
Cyls.: $16\frac{1}{2}'' \times 24''$.
Driving Wheels: 5′ 2″.
T.E.: 14,780 lb.

5407/10/2/6–8/20–2 **Total 9**

0-6-0PT 3F 5700 Class

*Introduced 1929. Collett design for shunting and light goods work developed from 2021 class.
†Introduced 1930. Locos. with steam brake and no A.T.C. fittings, for shunting only.
§Introduced 1933. Locos. with detail alterations, modified cab (except 8700) and increased weight.
‡Introduced 1933. Locos. with condensing apparatus for working over L.T. Metropolitan line.
¶Introduced 1948. Steam brake locos. with increased weight.
Weight: { 47 tons 10 cwt.*† / 50 tons 15 cwt.‡ / 49 tons 0 cwt.§¶ }
Pressure: 200 lb.
Cyls.: $17\frac{1}{2}'' \times 24''$.
Driving Wheels: $4' 7\frac{1}{2}''$.
T.E.: 22,515 lb.

*5702/4/6/9/17/20/7/8/31/44/6/8–50/4–9/61/3/4/6/8–71/3–6/8–80/3/7/9/91/3/5/8, 7700/2–4/6–9/12/3/5/7–26/8/9/32/3/6/7/9–41/4/5/7–9/52/3/5–62/4–7/71/2/5–7/80–8/90/3/4/6/8/9, 8701/2/5–49

†6700/2/12/4/9/20/4/8/38/9/41/2/9

§3600–3739/41–92/4–9, 4600–85/7–99, 8700/50–4/6/7/9–99, 9600–82, 9711–71/3–99

‡9700–7/9/10

¶6751–70/2/5–8 **Total 723**

0-6-0PT 2P* 2F† 6400 & 7400 Classes

***6400 class.** Introduced 1932. Collett design for light passenger work, variation of 5400 class with smaller wheels, push-and-pull fitted.
†7400 class. Introduced 1936. Non-push-and-pull fitted locos.
Weight: { 45 tons 12 cwt.* / 45 tons 9 cwt.† }
Pressure: 180 lb.
Cyls.: $16\frac{1}{2}'' \times 24''$.
Driving Wheels: $4' 7\frac{1}{2}''$.
T.E.: 18,010 lb.

*6400/1/3/6/8/10–3/5/6/8/9/21/2/4–6/9–31/3–9

†7400/2–10/2–4/7–9/21–37/9–46/8/9

Total : 6400 Class 28
7400 Class 43

0-6-0PT 4F 9400 Class

*Introduced 1947. Hawksworth taper boiler design for heavy shunting.
†Introduced 1949. Locos. with non-superheated boiler.
Weight: 55 tons 7 cwt.
Pressure: 200 lb. SS.
Cyls.: $17\frac{1}{2}'' \times 24''$.
Driving Wheels: $4' 7\frac{1}{2}''$.
T.E.: 22,515 lb.

*9401/4–9

†3400–9, 8400–7/9/11/3–6/8–20/2/4–8/30/1/3/5–41/4–6/9/51–61/4–84/6–91/3–9, 9410–6/8–26/8–31/3–7/40–2/4/6–58/60–90/3–5/7/8 **Total 177**

0-6-0T Unclass. W. & L.

(Line closed: locos. stored.)

Introduced 1902. Beyer Peacock design for 2′ 6″ gauge W. & L. Section, Cambrian Railways.

Weight: 19 tons 18 cwt.
Gauge: 2′ 6″.
Pressure: 150 lb.
Cyls.: (O) $11\frac{1}{2}$″ × 16″.
Driving Wheels: 2′ 9″.
T.E.: 8,175 lb.
Walschaerts valve gear.

822/3 **Total 2**

0-4-2T 1P
1400 & 5800 Classes

***1400 class** introduced 1932. Collett design for light branch work (originally designated 4800 class). Push-and-pull fitted.
†**5800 class** introduced 1933. Non-push-and-pull fitted locos.
Weight: 41 tons 6 cwt.
Pressure: 165 lb.
Cyls.: 16″ × 24″.
Driving Wheels: 5′ 2″.
T.E.: 13,900 lb.

*1407/9/10/2/9–21/4/6/7/31–5/8/40–2/4/5/7–55/8/62–4/6/8/70–4

†5815 **Total 42**

0-4-0ST OF Cardiff Rly.

Introduced 1893. Kitson design for Cardiff Railway.
Weight: 25 tons 10 cwt.
Pressure: 160 lb.
Cyls.: (O) 14″ × 21″.
Driving Wheels: 3′ $2\frac{1}{2}$″.
T.E.: 14,540 lb.
Hawthorn Kitson valve gear.

1338 **Total 1**

0-4-0ST OF P. & M.

Introduced 1907. Peckett design for P. & M.
Weight: 33 tons 10 cwt.
Pressure: 150 lb.
Cyls.: (O) 15″ × 21″.
Driving Wheels: 3′ 7″.
T.E.: 14,010 lb.

1151/2 **Total 2**

0-4-0ST S.H.T.

Introduced 1906. Peckett design for S.H.T. (similar to 1151/2).
Weight: 33 tons 10 cwt.
Pressure: 150 lb.
Cyls.: (O) 15″ × 21″.
Driving Wheels: 3′ 7″.
T.E.: 14,010 lb.

1143 **Total 1**

LOCOMOTIVE SUPERINTENDENTS AND CHIEF MECHANICAL ENGINEERS OF THE G.W.R. & W.R.

Sir Daniel Gooch	1837–1864
Joseph Armstrong	1854–1864* 1864–1877
George Armstrong (*Bro. of J. Armstrong*)	1864–1896*
William Dean	1877–1902
G. J. Churchward	1902–1921
Charles B. Collett	1922–1941
F. W. Hawksworth	1941–1949

* In charge of standard gauge locomotives at Stafford Road Works, Wolverhampton, with wide powers in design and construction.

NUMERICAL LIST OF WESTERN REGION STEAM LOCOMOTIVES

Locomotives are of G.W. origin except where indicated by other initials

2-6-2T — V. of R.

7 Owain Glyndŵr
8 Llywelyn
9 Prince of Wales

0-6-0T — W. & L.

822 823
(Line closed : locos. stored.)

4-6-0 — 1000 Class "County"

1000 County of Middlesex
1001 County of Bucks
1002 County of Berks
1003 County of Wilts
1004 County of Somerset
1005 County of Devon
1006 County of Cornwall
1007 County of Brecknock
1008 County of Cardigan
1009 County of Carmarthen
1010 County of Caernarvon
1011 County of Chester
1012 County of Denbigh
1013 County of Dorset
1014 County of Glamorgan
1015 County of Gloucester
1016 County of Hants
1017 County of Hereford
1018 County of Leicester
1019 County of Merioneth
1020 County of Monmouth
1021 County of Montgomery
1022 County of Northampton
1023 County of Oxford
1024 County of Pembroke
1025 County of Radnor
1026 County of Salop
1027 County of Stafford
1028 County of Warwick
1029 County of Worcester

0-4-0ST — S.H.T.

1143

0-4-0ST — P.M.

1151 1152

0-4-0ST — Car. R.

1338

0-6-0ST — 1361 Class

1361	1363	1365
1362	1364	

0-6-0PT — 1366 Class

1366	1368	1371
1367	1369	

0-4-2T — 1400 Class

1407	1420	1431	1438
1409	1421	1432	1440
1410	1424	1433	1441
1412	1426	1434	1442
1419	1427	1435	1444

1445	1452	1463	1472
1447	1453	1464	1473
1448	1454	1466	1474
1449	1455	1468	
1450	1458	1470	
1451	1462	1471	

0-6-0PT 1500 Class

1500	1503	1505	1507
1501	1504	1506	1508
1502			

0-6-0PT 1600 Class

1601	1620	1637	1655
1602	1621	1638	1656
1604	1622	1639	1657
1605	1623	1640	1658
1606	1624	1641	1659
1607	1625	1642	1660
1608	1626	1643	1661
1609	1627	1645	1662
1611	1628	1646	1663
1612	1629	1647	1664
1613	1630	1648	1665
1614	1631	1649	1666
1615	1632	1650	1667
1617	1633	1651	1668
1618	1634	1653	1669
1619	1636	1654	

0-6-0 2251 Class

2200	2212	2222	2236
2201	2213	2223	2239
2202	2214	2224	2240
2203	2215	2227	2241
2204	2216	2229	2242
2206	2217	2230	2243
2207	2218	2231	2244
2209	2219	2232	2245
2210	2220	2233	2246
2211	2221	2234	2247

2248	2260	2274	2289
2249	2261	2276	2291
2250	2264	2277	2292
2251	2265	2282	2294
2253	2267	2283	2295
2255	2268	2286	2297
2256	2271	2287	2298
2257	2273	2288	

2-8-0 2800 Class

2805	2844	2861	2885
2806	2845	2862	2886
2807	2846	2865	2887
2813	2847	2866	2888
2818	2849	2867	2889
2819	2851	2871	2890
2821	2852	2872	2891
2822	2853	2873	2892
2834	2854	2874	2893
2835	2855	2875	2894
2836	2856	2876	2895
2837	2857	2879	2896
2839	2858	2882	2897
2841	2859	2883	2898
2842	2860	2884	2899

0-6-0 2251 Class

3200	3205	3210	3215
3201	3206	3211	3216
3202	3207	3212	3217
3203	3208	3213	3218
3204	3209	3214	3219

0-6-0PT 9400 Class

3400	3403	3406	3408
3401	3404	3407	3409
3402	3405		

4-4-0 "City" Class

3440 City of Truro

0-6-0PT 5700 Class

3600	3640	3680	3720
3601	3641	3681	3721
3602	3642	3682	3722
3603	3643	3683	3723
3604	3644	3684	3724
3605	3645	3685	3725
3606	3646	3686	3726
3607	3647	3687	3727
3608	3648	3688	3728
3609	3649	3689	3729
3610	3650	3690	3730
3611	3651	3691	3731
3612	3652	3692	3732
3613	3653	3693	3733
3614	3654	3694	3734
3615	3655	3695	3735
3616	3656	3696	3736
3617	3657	3697	3737
3618	3658	3698	3738
3619	3659	3699	3739
3620	3660	3700	3741
3621	3661	3701	3742
3622	3662	3702	3743
3623	3663	3703	3744
3624	3664	3704	3745
3625	3665	3705	3746
3626	3666	3706	3747
3627	3667	3707	3748
3628	3668	3708	3749
3629	3669	3709	3750
3630	3670	3710	3751
3631	3671	3711	3752
3632	3672	3712	3753
3633	3673	3713	3754
3634	3674	3714	3755
3635	3675	3715	3756
3636	3676	3716	3757
3637	3677	3717	3758
3638	3678	3718	3759
3639	3679	3719	3760

3761	3771	3781	3790
3762	3772	3782	3791
3763	3773	3783	3792
3764	3774	3784	3794
3765	3775	3785	3795
3766	3776	3786	3796
3767	3777	3787	3797
3768	3778	3788	3798
3769	3779	3789	3799
3770	3780		

2-8-0 2800 Class

3800	3817	3834	3851
3801	3818	3835	3852
3802	3819	3836	3853
3803	3820	3837	3854
3804	3821	3838	3855
3805	3822	3839	3856
3806	3823	3840	3857
3807	3824	3841	3858
3808	3825	3842	3859
3809	3826	3843	3860
3810	3827	3844	3861
3811	3828	3845	3862
3812	3829	3846	3863
3813	3830	3847	3864
3814	3831	3848	3865
3815	3832	3849	3866
3816	3833	3850	

4-6-0 4073 Class

"Castle"

4037 The South Wales Borderers
4073 Caerphilly Castle
4074 Caldicot Castle
4075 Cardiff Castle
4076 Carmarthen Castle
4077 Chepstow Castle
4078 Pembroke Castle
4079 Pendennis Castle
4080 Powderham Castle
4081 Warwick Castle

4082 Windsor Castle
4083 Abbotsbury Castle
4084 Aberystwyth Castle
4085 Berkeley Castle
4086 Builth Castle
4087 Cardigan Castle
4088 Dartmouth Castle
4089 Donnington Castle
4090 Dorchester Castle
4092 Dunraven Castle
4093 Dunster Castle
4094 Dynevor Castle
4095 Harlech Castle
4096 Highclere Castle
4097 Kenilworth Castle
4098 Kidwelly Castle
4099 Kilgerran Castle

2-6-2T 5100 Class

4100	4120	4141	4160
4101	4121	4142	4161
4102	4122	4143	4162
4103	4123	4144	4163
4104	4124	4145	4165
4105	4125	4146	4166
4106	4126	4147	4167
4107	4127	4148	4168
4108	4128	4149	4169
4109	4129	4150	4170
4110	4130	4151	4171
4111	4131	4152	4172
4112	4132	4153	4173
4113	4133	4154	4174
4114	4134	4155	4175
4115	4135	4156	4176
4116	4136	4157	4177
4117	4137	4158	4178
4118	4140	4159	4179
4119			

2-8-0T 4200 Class

4203	4214	4225	4229
4207	4218	4227	4230
4213	4222	4228	4232

4233	4254	4271	4286
4235	4255	4272	4287
4236	4256	4273	4288
4237	4257	4274	4289
4238	4258	4275	4290
4241	4259	4276	4291
4242	4262	4277	4292
4243	4263	4278	4293
4246	4264	4279	4294
4247	4265	4280	4295
4248	4266	4281	4296
4250	4267	4282	4297
4251	4268	4283	4298
4252	4269	4284	4299
4253	4270	4285	

2-6-2T 4500 Class

4507	4558	4566	4575
4549	4559	4567	4587
4550	4561	4569	4588
4552	4562	4570	4589
4555	4563	4571	4591
4556	4564	4573	4593
4557	4565	4574	4594

0-6-0PT 5700 Class

4600	4615	4630	4645
4601	4616	4631	4646
4602	4617	4632	4647
4603	4618	4633	4648
4604	4619	4634	4649
4605	4620	4635	4650
4606	4621	4636	4651
4607	4622	4637	4652
4608	4623	4638	4653
4609	4624	4639	4654
4610	4625	4640	4655
4611	4626	4641	4656
4612	4627	4642	4657
4613	4628	4643	4658
4614	4629	4644	4659

4660	4670	4680	4691
4661	4671	4681	4692
4662	4672	4682	4693
4663	4673	4683	4694
4664	4674	4684	4695
4665	4675	4685	4696
4666	4676	4687	4697
4667	4677	4688	4698
4668	4678	4689	4699
4669	4679	4690	

2-8-0 4700 Class

4700	4703	4705	4707
4701	4704	4706	4708
4702			

4-6-0 " Hall " 4900 Class

4901 Adderley Hall
4902 Aldenham Hall
4903 Astley Hall
4904 Binnegar Hall
4905 Barton Hall
4906 Bradfield Hall
4907 Broughton Hall
4908 Broome Hall
4909 Blakesley Hall
4910 Blaisdon Hall
4912 Berrington Hall
4913 Baglan Hall
4914 Cranmore Hall
4915 Condover Hall
4916 Crumlin Hall
4917 Crosswood Hall
4918 Dartington Hall
4919 Donnington Hall
4920 Dumbleton Hall
4921 Eaton Hall
4922 Enville Hall
4923 Evenley Hall
4924 Eydon Hall
4925 Eynsham Hall
4926 Fairleigh Hall
4927 Farnborough Hall
4928 Gatacre Hall
4929 Goytrey Hall
4930 Hagley Hall
4931 Hanbury Hall
4932 Hatherton Hall
4933 Himley Hall
4934 Hindlip Hall
4935 Ketley Hall
4936 Kinlet Hall
4937 Lanelay Hall
4938 Liddington Hall
4939 Littleton Hall
4941 Llangedwyn Hall
4942 Maindy Hall
4943 Marrington Hall
4944 Middleton Hall
4945 Milligan Hall
4946 Moseley Hall
4947 Nanhoran Hall
4948 Northwick Hall
4949 Packwood Hall
4950 Patshull Hall
4951 Pendeford Hall
4952 Peplow Hall
4953 Pitchford Hall
4954 Plaish Hall
4955 Plaspower Hall
4956 Plowden Hall
4957 Postlip Hall
4958 Priory Hall
4959 Purley Hall
4960 Pyle Hall
4961 Pyrland Hall
4962 Ragley Hall
4963 Rignall Hall
4964 Rodwell Hall
4965 Rood Ashton Hall
4966 Shakenhurst Hall
4967 Shirenewton Hall
4968 Shotton Hall
4969 Shrugborough Hall
4970 Sketty Hall
4971 Stanway Hall
4972 Saint Brides Hall
4973 Sweeney Hall
4974 Talgarth Hall
4975 Umberslade Hall
4976 Warfield Hall
4977 Watcombe Hall

4978 Westwood Hall
4979 Wootton Hall
4980 Wrottesley Hall
4981 Abberley Hall
4982 Acton Hall
4983 Albert Hall
4984 Albrighton Hall
4985 Allesley Hall
4986 Aston Hall
4987 Brockley Hall
4988 Bulwell Hall
4989 Cherwell Hall
4990 Clifton Hall
4991 Cobham Hall
4992 Crosby Hall
4993 Dalton Hall
4994 Downton Hall
4995 Easton Hall
4996 Eden Hall
4997 Elton Hall
4998 Eyton Hall
4999 Gopsal Hall

4-6-0 4073 Class "Castle"

5000 Launceston Castle
5001 Llandovery Castle
5002 Ludlow Castle
5003 Lulworth Castle
5004 Llanstephan Castle
5006 Tregenna Castle
5007 Rougemont Castle
5008 Raglan Castle
5009 Shrewsbury Castle
5011 Tintagel Castle
5012 Berry Pomeroy Castle
5013 Abergavenny Castle
5014 Goodrich Castle
5015 Kingswear Castle
5016 Montgomery Castle
5017 The Gloucestershire Regiment 28th, 61st
5018 St. Mawes Castle
5019 Treago Castle
5020 Trematon Castle
5021 Whittington Castle
5022 Wigmore Castle
5023 Brecon Castle
5024 Carew Castle
5025 Chirk Castle
5026 Criccieth Castle
5027 Farleigh Castle
5028 Llantilio Castle
5029 Nunney Castle
5030 Shirburn Castle
5031 Totnes Castle
5032 Usk Castle
5033 Broughton Castle
5034 Corfe Castle
5035 Coity Castle
5036 Lyonshall Castle
5037 Monmouth Castle
5038 Morlais Castle
5039 Rhuddlan Castle
5040 Stokesay Castle
5041 Tiverton Castle
5042 Winchester Castle
5043 Earl of Mount Edgcumbe
5044 Earl of Dunraven
5045 Earl of Dudley
5046 Earl Cawdor
5047 Earl of Dartmouth
5048 Earl of Devon
5049 Earl of Plymouth
5050 Earl of St. Germans
5051 Earl Bathurst
5052 Earl of Radnor
5053 Earl Cairns
5054 Earl of Ducie
5055 Earl of Eldon
5056 Earl of Powis
5057 Earl Waldegrave
5058 Earl of Clancarty
5059 Earl St. Aldwyn
5060 Earl of Berkeley
5061 Earl of Birkenhead
5062 Earl of Shaftesbury
5063 Earl Baldwin
5064 Bishop's Castle
5065 Newport Castle

5066 Sir Felix Pole
5067 St. Fagans Castle
5068 Beverston Castle
5069 Isambard Kingdom Brunel
5070 Sir Daniel Gooch
5071 Spitfire
5072 Hurricane
5073 Blenheim
5074 Hampden
5075 Wellington
5076 Gladiator
5077 Fairey Battle
5078 Beaufort
5079 Lysander
5080 Defiant
5081 Lockheed Hudson
5082 Swordfish
5084 Reading Abbey
5085 Evesham Abbey
5087 Tintern Abbey
5088 Llanthony Abbey
5089 Westminster Abbey
5090 Neath Abbey
5091 Cleeve Abbey
5092 Tresco Abbey
5093 Upton Castle
5094 Tretower Castle
5095 Barbury Castle
5096 Bridgwater Castle
5097 Sarum Castle
5098 Clifford Castle
5099 Compton Castle

2-6-2T 5100 Class

5101	5154	5177	5188
5102	5158	5178	5190
5103	5164	5179	5191
5104	5166	5180	5192
5106	5167	5181	5193
5110	5169	5182	5194
5150	5173	5183	5195
5151	5174	5184	5197
5152	5175	5185	5198
5153	5176	5187	5199✓

2-8-0T 4200 Class

5200	5217	5233	5249
5201	5218	5234	5250
5202	5219	5235	5251
5203	5220	5236	5252
5204	5221	5237	5253
5205	5222	5238	5254
5206	5223	5239	5255
5207	5224	5240	5256
5208	5225	5241	5257
5209	5226	5242	5258
5210	5227	5243	5259
5211	5228	5244	5260
5212	5229	5245	5261
5213	5230	5246	5262
5214	5231	5247	5263
5215	5232	5248	5264
5216			

2-6-0 4300 Class

5306	5331	5351	5376
5311	5332	5353	5380
5318	5333	5357	5384
5322	5336	5358	5385
5324	5337	5369	5396
5326	5339	5370	5399
5330			

0-6-0PT 5400 Class

5407	5416	5418	5421
5410	5417	5420	5422
5412			

2-6-2T 4500 Class

5503	5514	5521	5529
5504	5515	5523	5531
5508	5516	5524	5532
5509	5518	5525	5534
5510	5519	5526	5536
5511	5520	5527	5537

5538	5546	5555	5565
5539	5547	5557	5568
5540	5548	5558	5569
5541	5549	5560	5570
5542	5550	5561	5571
5543	5552	5562	5572
5544	5553	5563	5573
5545	5554	5564	

0-6-2T 5600 Class

5600	5625	5650	5675
5601	5626	5651	5676
5602	5627	5652	5677
5603	5628	5653	5678
5604	5629	5654	5679
5605	5630	5655	5680
5606	5631	5656	5681
5607	5632	5657	5682
5608	5633	5658	5683
5609	5634	5659	5684
5610	5635	5660	5685
5611	5636	5661	5686
5612	5637	5662	5687
5613	5638	5663	5688
5614	5639	5664	5689
5615	5640	5665	5690
5616	5641	5666	5691
5617	5642	5667	5692
5618	5643	5668	5693
5619	5644	5669	5694
5620	5645	5670	5695
5621	5646	5671	5696
5622	5647	5672	5697
5623	5648	5673	5698
5624	5649	5674	5699

0-6-0PT 5700 Class

5702	5717	5744	5754
5704	5720	5746	5755
5706	5727	5748	5756
5709	5728	5749	5757
5713	5731	5750	5758
5759	5769	5776	5789
5761	5770	5778	5791
5763	5771	5779	5793
5764	5773	5780	5795
5766	5774	5783	5798
5768	5775	5787	

0-4-2T 5800 Class

5815

4-6-0 4900 Class
"Hall"

5900 Hinderton Hall
5901 Hazel Hall
5902 Howick Hall
5903 Keele Hall
5904 Kelham Hall
5905 Knowsley Hall
5906 Lawton Hall
5907 Marble Hall
5908 Moreton Hall
5909 Newton Hall
5910 Park Hall
5911 Preston Hall
5912 Queen's Hall
5913 Rushton Hall
5914 Ripon Hall
5916 Trinity Hall
5917 Westminster Hall
5918 Walton Hall
5919 Worsley Hall
5920 Wycliffe Hall
5921 Bingley Hall
5922 Caxton Hall
5923 Colston Hall
5924 Dinton Hall
5925 Eastcote Hall
5926 Grotrian Hall
5927 Guild Hall
5928 Haddon Hall

5929 Hanham Hall
5930 Hannington Hall
5931 Hatherley Hall
5932 Haydon Hall
5933 Kingsway Hall
5934 Kneller Hall
5935 Norton Hall
5936 Oakley Hall
5937 Stanford Hall
5938 Stanley Hall
5939 Tangley Hall
5940 Whitbourne Hall
5941 Campion Hall
5942 Doldowlod Hall
5943 Elmdon Hall
5944 Ickenham Hall
5945 Leckhampton Hall
5946 Marwell Hall
5947 Saint Benet's Hall
5948 Siddington Hall
5949 Trematon Hall
5950 Wardley Hall
5951 Clyffe Hall
5952 Cogan Hall
5953 Dunley Hall
5954 Faendre Hall
5955 Garth Hall
5956 Horsley Hall
5957 Hutton Hall
5958 Knolton Hall
5959 Mawley Hall
5960 Saint Edmund Hall
5961 Toynbee Hall
5962 Wantage Hall
5963 Wimpole Hall
5964 Wolseley Hall
5965 Woollas Hall
5966 Ashford Hall
5967 Bickmarsh Hall
5968 Cory Hall
5969 Honington Hall
5970 Hengrave Hall
5971 Merevale Hall
5972 Olton Hall
5973 Rolleston Hall
5974 Wallsworth Hall
5975 Winslow Hall
5976 Ashwicke Hall
5977 Beckford Hall
5978 Bodinnick Hall
5979 Cruckton Hall
5980 Dingley Hall
5981 Frensham Hall
5982 Harrington Hall
5983 Henley Hall
5984 Linden Hall
5985 Mostyn Hall
5986 Arbury Hall
5987 Brocket Hall
5988 Bostock Hall
5989 Cransley Hall
5990 Dorford Hall
5991 Gresham Hall
5992 Horton Hall
5993 Kirby Hall
5994 Roydon Hall
5995 Wick Hall
5996 Mytton Hall
5997 Sparkford Hall
5998 Trevor Hall
5999 Wollaton Hall

4-6-0 6000 Class
" King "

6000 King George V
6001 King Edward VII
6002 King William IV
6003 King George IV
6004 King George III
6005 King George II
6006 King George I
6007 King William III
6008 King James II
6009 King Charles II
6010 King Charles I
6011 King James I
6012 King Edward VI
6013 King Henry VIII
6014 King Henry VII
6015 King Richard III
6016 King Edward V
6017 King Edward IV

6018 King Henry VI
6019 King Henry V
6020 King Henry IV
6021 King Richard II
6022 King Edward III
6023 King Edward II
6024 King Edward I
6025 King Henry III
6026 King John
6027 King Richard I
6028 King George VI
6029 King Edward VIII

2-6-2T 6100 Class

6101	6119	6136	6153
6103	6120	6137	6154
6104	6121	6138	6155
6105	6122	6139	6156
6106	6123	6140	6157
6107	6124	6141	6158
6108	6125	6142	6159
6109	6126	6143	6160
6110	6127	6144	6161
6111	6128	6145	6162
6112	6129	6146	6163
6113	6130	6147	6164
6114	6131	6148	6165
6115	6132	6149	6166
6116	6133	6150	6167
6117	6134	6151	6168
6118	6135	6152	6169

2-6-0 4300 Class

6300	6314	6330	6342
6301	6316	6332	6343
6302	6317	6333	6344
6304	6319	6335	6345
6306	6320	6336	6346
6307	6323	6337	6347
6309	6324	6338	6348
6310	6326	6339	6349
6312	6327	6340	6350
6313	6329	6341	6351

6352	6366	6376	6387
6353	6367	6377	6388
6356	6368	6378	6389
6357	6369	6379	6390
6360	6370	6380	6391
6361	6371	6381	6392
6362	6372	6382	6394
6363	6373	6384	6395
6364	6374	6385	6398
6365	6375	6386	

0-6-0PT 6400 Class

6400	6412	6422	6433
6401	6413	6424	6434
6403	6415	6425	6435
6406	6416	6426	6436
6408	6418	6429	6437
6410	6419	6430	6438
6411	6421	6431	6439

0-6-2T 5600 Class

6600	6620	6640	6660
6601	6621	6641	6661
6602	6622	6642	6662
6603	6623	6643	6663
6604	6624	6644	6664
6605	6625	6645	6665
6606	6626	6646	6666
6607	6627	6647	6667
6608	6628	6648	6668
6609	6629	6649	6669
6610	6630	6650	6670
6611	6631	6651	6671
6612	6632	6652	6672
6613	6633	6653	6673
6614	6634	6654	6674
6615	6635	6655	6675
6616	6636	6656	6676
6617	6637	6657	6677
6618	6638	6658	6678
6619	6639	6659	6679

6680	6685	6690	6695
6681	6686	6691	6696
6682	6687	6692	6697
6683	6688	6693	6698
6684	6689	6694	6699

0-6-0PT 5700 Class

6700	6741	6758	6767
6702	6742	6759	6768
6712	6749	6760	6769
6714	6751	6761	6770
6719	6752	6762	6772
6720	6753	6763	6775
6724	6754	6764	6776
6728	6755	6765	6777
6738	6756	6766	6778
6739	6757		

4-6-0 6800 Class
"Grange"

6800 Arlington Grange
6801 Aylburton Grange
6802 Bampton Grange
6803 Bucklebury Grange
6804 Brockington Grange
6805 Broughton Grange
6806 Blackwell Grange
6807 Birchwood Grange
6808 Beenham Grange
6809 Burghclere Grange
6810 Blakemere Grange
6811 Cranbourne Grange
6812 Chesford Grange
6813 Eastbury Grange
6814 Enborne Grange
6815 Frilford Grange
6816 Frankton Grange
6817 Gwenddwr Grange
6818 Hardwick Grange
6819 Highnam Grange
6820 Kingstone Grange
6821 Leaton Grange
6822 Manton Grange
6823 Oakley Grange
6824 Ashley Grange
6825 Llanvair Grange
6826 Nannerth Grange
6827 Llanfrechfa Grange
6828 Trellech Grange
6829 Burmington Grange
6830 Buckenhill Grange
6831 Bearley Grange
6832 Brockton Grange
6833 Calcot Grange
6834 Dummer Grange
6835 Eastham Grange
6836 Estevarney Grange
6837 Forthampton Grange
6838 Goodmoor Grange
6839 Hewell Grange
6840 Hazeley Grange
6841 Marlas Grange
6842 Nunhold Grange
6843 Poulton Grange
6844 Penhydd Grange
6845 Paviland Grange
6846 Ruckley Grange
6847 Tidmarsh Grange
6848 Toddington Grange
6849 Walton Grange
6850 Cleeve Grange
6851 Hurst Grange
6852 Headbourne Grange
6853 Morehampton Grange
6854 Roundhill Grange
6855 Saighton Grange
6856 Stowe Grange
6857 Tudor Grange
6858 Woolston Grange
6859 Yiewsley Grange
6860 Aberporth Grange
6861 Crynant Grange
6862 Derwent Grange
6863 Dolhywel Grange
6864 Dymock Grange

6865 Hopton Grange
6866 Morfa Grange
6867 Peterston Grange
6868 Penrhos Grange
6869 Resolven Grange
6870 Bodicote Grange
6871 Bourton Grange
6872 Crawley Grange
6873 Caradoc Grange
6874 Haughton Grange
6875 Hindford Grange
6876 Kingsland Grange
6877 Llanfair Grange
6878 Longford Grange
6879 Overton Grange

4-6-0 4900 Class "Hall"

6900 Abney Hall
6901 Arley Hall
6902 Butlers Hall
6903 Belmont Hall
6904 Charfield Hall
6905 Claughton Hall
6906 Chicheley Hall
6907 Davenham Hall
6908 Downham Hall
6909 Frewin Hall
6910 Gossington Hall
6911 Holker Hall
6912 Helmster Hall
6913 Levens Hall
6914 Langton Hall
6915 Mursley Hall
6916 Misterton Hall
6917 Oldlands Hall
6918 Sandon Hall
6919 Tylney Hall
6920 Barningham Hall
6921 Borwick Hall
6922 Burton Hall
6923 Croxteth Hall
6924 Grantley Hall
6925 Hackness Hall
6926 Holkham Hall
6927 Lilford Hall
6928 Underley Hall
6929 Whorlton Hall
6930 Aldersey Hall
6931 Aldborough Hall
6932 Burwarton Hall
6933 Birtles Hall
6934 Beachamwell Hall
6935 Browsholme Hall
6936 Breccles Hall
6937 Conyngham Hall
6938 Corndean Hall
6939 Calveley Hall
6940 Didlington Hall
6941 Fillongley Hall
6942 Eshton Hall
6943 Farnley Hall
6944 Fledborough Hall
6945 Glasfryn Hall
6946 Heatherden Hall
6947 Helmingham Hall
6948 Holbrooke Hall
6949 Haberfield Hall
6950 Kingsthorpe Hall
6951 Impney Hall
6952 Kimberley Hall
6953 Leighton Hall
6954 Lotherton Hall
6955 Lydcott Hall
6956 Mottram Hall
6957 Norcliffe Hall
6958 Oxburgh Hall

4-6-0 6959 Class "Modified Hall"

6959 Peatling Hall
6960 Raveningham Hall
6961 Stedham Hall
6962 Soughton Hall
6963 Throwley Hall
6964 Thornbridge Hall
6965 Thirlestaine Hall
6966 Witchingham Hall

6967 Willesley Hall
6968 Woodcock Hall
6969 Wraysbury Hall
6970 Whaddon Hall
6971 Athelhampton Hall
6972 Beningbrough Hall
6973 Bricklehampton Hall
6974 Bryngwyn Hall
6975 Capesthorne Hall
6976 Graythwaite Hall
6977 Grundisburgh Hall
6978 Haroldstone Hall
6979 Helperly Hall
6980 Llanrumney Hall
6981 Marbury Hall
6982 Melmerby Hall
6983 Otterington Hall
6984 Owsden Hall
6985 Parwick Hall
6986 Rydal Hall
6987 Shervington Hall
6988 Swithland Hall
6989 Wightwick Hall
6990 Witherslack Hall
6991 Acton Burnell Hall
6992 Arborfield Hall
6993 Arthog Hall
6994 Baggrave Hall
6995 Benthall Hall
6996 Blackwell Hall
6997 Bryn-Ivor Hall
6998 Burton Agnes Hall
6999 Capel Dewi Hall

4-6-0 4073 Class
"Castle"

7000 Viscount Portal
7001 Sir James Milne
7002 Devizes Castle
7003 Elmley Castle
7004 Eastnor Castle
7005 Sir Edward Elgar
7006 Lydford Castle
7007 Great Western
7008 Swansea Castle
7009 Athelney Castle
7010 Avondale Castle
7011 Banbury Castle
7012 Barry Castle
7013 Bristol Castle
7014 Caerhays Castle
7015 Carn Brea Castle
7016 Chester Castle
7017 G. J. Churchward
7018 Drysllwyn Castle
7019 Fowey Castle
7020 Gloucester Castle
7021 Haverfordwest Castle
7022 Hereford Castle
7023 Penrice Castle
7024 Powis Castle
7025 Sudeley Castle
7026 Tenby Castle
7027 Thornbury Castle
7028 Cadbury Castle
7029 Clun Castle
7030 Cranbrook Castle
7031 Cromwell's Castle
7032 Denbigh Castle
7033 Hartlebury Castle
7034 Ince Castle
7035 Ogmore Castle
7036 Taunton Castle
7037 Swindon

2-8-2T 7200 Class

7200	7214	7228	7241
7201	7215	7229	7242
7202	7216	7230	7243
7203	7217	7231	7244
7204	7218	7232	7245
7205	7219	7233	7246
7206	7220	7234	7247
7207	7221	7235	7248
7208	7222	7236	7249
7209	7223	7237	7250
7210	7224	7238	7251
7211	7225	7239	7252
7212	7226	7240	7253
7213	7227		

2-6-0 4300 Class

7300	7311	7322	7333
7301	7312	7323	7334
7302	7313	7324	7335
7303	7314	7325	7336
7304	7315	7326	7337
7305	7316	7327	7338
7306	7317	7328	7339
7307	7318	7329	7340
7308	7319	7330	7341
7309	7320	7331	
7310	7321	7332	

0-6-0PT 7400 Class

7400	7413	7427	7439
7402	7414	7428	7440
7403	7417	7429	7441
7404	7418	7430	7442
7405	7419	7431	7443
7406	7421	7432	7444
7407	7422	7433	7445
7408	7423	7434	7446
7409	7424	7435	7448
7410	7425	7436	7449
7412	7426	7437	

0-6-0PT 5700 Class

7700	7720	7740	7760
7702	7721	7741	7761
7703	7722	7744	7762
7704	7723	7745	7764
7706	7724	7747	7765
7707	7725	7748	7766
7708	7726	7749	7767
7709	7728	7752	7771
7712	7729	7753	7772
7713	7732	7755	7775
7715	7733	7756	7776
7717	7736	7757	7777
7718	7737	7758	7780
7719	7739	7759	7781

7782	7786	7790	7796
7783	7787	7793	7798
7784	7788	7794	7799
7785			

4-6-0 7800 Class
"Manor"

7800 Torquay Manor
7801 Anthony Manor
7802 Bradley Manor
7803 Barcote Manor
7804 Baydon Manor
7805 Broome Manor
7806 Cockington Manor
7807 Compton Manor
7808 Cookham Manor
7809 Childrey Manor
7810 Draycott Manor
7811 Dunley Manor
7812 Erlestoke Manor
7813 Freshford Manor
7814 Fringford Manor
7815 Fritwell Manor
7816 Frilsham Manor
7817 Garsington Manor
7818 Granville Manor
7819 Hinton Manor
7820 Dinmore Manor
7821 Ditcheat Manor
7822 Foxcote Manor
7823 Hook Norton Manor
7824 Iford Manor
7825 Lechlade Manor
7826 Longworth Manor
7827 Lydham Manor
7828 Odney Manor
7829 Ramsbury Manor

4-6-0 6959 Class
"Modified Hall"

7900 Saint Peter's Hall
7901 Dodington Hall
7902 Eaton Mascot Hall
7903 Foremarke Hall
7904 Fountains Hall

7905 Fowey Hall
7906 Fron Hall
7907 Hart Hall
7908 Henshall Hall
7909 Heveningham Hall
7910 Hown Hall
7911 Lady Margaret Hall
7912 Little Linford Hall
7913 Little Wyrley Hall
7914 Lleweni Hall
7915 Mere Hall
7916 Mobberley Hall
7917 North Aston Hall
7918 Rhose Wood Hall
7919 Runter Hall
7920 Coney Hall
7921 Edstone Hall
7922 Salford Hall
7923 Speke Hall
7924 Thornycroft Hall
7925 Westol Hall
7926 Willey Hall
7927 Willington Hall
7928 Wolf Hall
7929 Wyke Hall

2-6-2T 8100 Class

8100	8103	8106	8108
8101	8104	8107	8109
8102			

0-6-0PT 9400 Class

8400	8413	8427	8440
8401	8414	8428	8441
8402	8415	8430	8444
8403	8416	8431	8445
8404	8418	8433	8446
8405	8420	8435	8449
8406	8422	8436	8451
8407	8424	8437	8452
8409	8425	8438	8453
8411	8426	8439	8454

8456	8468	8478	8489
8457	8469	8479	8490
8458	8470	8480	8491
8459	8471	8481	8493
8460	8472	8482	8494
8461	8473	8483	8495
8464	8474	8484	8496
8465	8475	8486	8497
8466	8476	8487	8498
8467	8477	8488	8499

0-6-0PT 5700 Class

8700	8727	8752	8779
8701	8728	8753	8780
8702	8729	8754	8781
8705	8730	8756	8782
8706	8731	8757	8783
8707	8732	8759	8784
8708	8733	8760	8785
8709	8734	8761	8786
8710	8735	8762	8787
8711	8736	8763	8788
8712	8737	8764	8789
8713	8738	8765	8790
8714	8739	8766	8791
8715	8740	8767	8792
8716	8741	8768	8793
8717	8742	8769	8794
8718	8743	8770	8795
8719	8744	8771	8796
8720	8745	8772	8797
8721	8746	8773	8798
8722	8747	8774	8799
8723	8748	8775	
8724	8749	8776	
8725	8750	8777	
8726	8751	8778	

4-4-0 9000 Class

9004	9015	9017	9018
9014			

0-6-0PT 9400 Class

9401	9426	9453	9475
9404	9428	9454	9476
9405	9429	9455	9477
9406	9430	9456	9478
9407	9431	9457	9479
9408	9433	9458	9480
9409	9434	9460	9481
9410	9435	9461	9482
9411	9436	9462	9483
9412	9437	9463	9484
9413	9440	9464	9485
9414	9441	9465	9486
9415	9442	9466	9487
9416	9444	9467	9488
9418	9446	9468	9489
9419	9447	9469	9490
9420	9448	9470	9493
9421	9449	9471	9494
9422	9450	9472	9495
9423	9451	9473	9497
9424	9452	9474	9498
9425			

0-6-0PT 5700 Class

9600	9616	9632	9648
9601	9617	9633	9649
9602	9618	9634	9650
9603	9619	9635	9651
9604	9620	9636	9652
9605	9621	9637	9653
9606	9622	9638	9654
9607	9623	9639	9655
9608	9624	9640	9656
9609	9625	9641	9657
9610	9626	9642	9658
9611	9627	9643	9659
9612	9628	9644	9660
9613	9629	9645	9661
9614	9630	9646	9662
9615	9631	9647	9663

9664	9712	9742	9773
9665	9713	9743	9774
9666	9714	9744	9775
9667	9715	9745	9776
9668	9716	9746	9777
9669	9717	9747	9778
9670	9718	9748	9779
9671	9719	9749	9780
9672	9720	9750	9781
9673	9721	9751	9782
9674	9722	9752	9783
9675	9723	9753	9784
9676	9724	9754	9785
9677	9725	9755	9786
9678	9726	9756	9787
9679	9727	9757	9788
9680	9728	9758	9789
9681	9729	9759	9790
9682	9730	9760	9791
9700	9731	9761	9792
9701	9732	9762	9793
9702	9733	9763	9794
9703	9734	9764	9795
9704	9735	9765	9796
9705	9736	9766	9797
9706	9737	9767	9798
9707	9738	9768	9799
9709	9739	9769	
9710	9740	9770	
9711	9741	9771	

SERVICE LOCOMOTIVES

Diesel Mechanical

20	PWM 651	PWM 653
PWM 650	PWM 652	PWM 654

Total 6

Petrol

24 27

Total 2

SUMMARY OF SOUTHERN REGION STEAM LOCOMOTIVE CLASSES

IN ALPHABETICAL ORDER WITH HISTORICAL NOTES AND DIMENSIONS

The Code given in smaller bold type at the head of each Class, e.g. "2F" denotes its British Railways power classification.
The number of locomotives in service has been checked to April 5th, 1960.

0-6-0T 0P Classes A1 & A1X

*A1. Introduced 1872. Stroudley L.B.S.C. "Terrier," later fitted with Marsh boiler, retaining original type smokebox.

†A1X. Introduced 1911. Rebuild of A1 with Marsh boiler and extended smokebox.

‡A1X. Loco. with increased cylinder diameter.

Weight: { 27 tons 10 cwt.* / 28 tons 5 cwt.†‡
Pressure: 150 lb.
Cyls.: { 12" × 20".*† / $14\frac{3}{16}$" × 20".‡
Driving Wheels: 4' 0".
T.E.: { 7,650 lb.*† / 10,695 lb.‡

*DS680
†DS681, 32635/40/6/50/5/61/2/70/8
‡32636 **Total A1 1**
A1X 11

0-4-0T 1F Class B4

Introduced 1891. Adams L.S.W. design for dock shunting.

Weight: 33 tons 9 cwt.
Pressure: 140 lb. Cyls. (O): 16" × 22"
Driving Wheels: 3' $9\frac{3}{4}$".
T.E.: 14,650 lb.

30089/93/6, 30102 **Total 4**

0-6-0 2F Class C

Introduced 1900. Wainwright S.E.C. design.
Weight: Loco. 43 tons 16 cwt.
Pressure: 160 lb.
Cyls.: $18\frac{1}{2}$" × 26".
Driving Wheels: 5' 2".
T.E.: 19,520 lb.

31004/37/54/61/8/86, 31102/12/3/50, 31218/23/9/42/4/55/6/67/8/71/80/7/93/8, 31317, 31480/1/95/8, 31510/73/5/8/9/83/4/8–90/2, 31682/4/6/9–95, 31714–7/9–25 **Total 61**

0-6-0 2F Class C2X

Introduced 1908. Marsh rebuild of R. J. Billinton L.B.S.C. C2 with larger C3-type boiler, extended smokebox, etc.
Weight: Loco. 45 tons 5 cwt.
Pressure: 170 lb.
Cyls.: $17\frac{1}{2}$" × 26".
Driving Wheels: 5' 0".
T.E.: 19,175 lb.

32438/41/3/5/6/8–51, 32521–3/5/7/8/32/4–6/8/9/41/3–50/2/3 **Total 32**

0-4-0T 0P Class C14

Introduced 1923. Urie rebuild as shunting loco. of Drummond L.S.W. motor-train 2-2-0T (originally introduced 1906).
Weight: 25 tons 15 cwt.
Pressure: 150 lb.
Cyls.: (O) 14" × 14".
Driving Wheels: 3' 0".
T.E.: 9,720 lb.
Walschaerts valve gear.

DS77 **Total 1**

4-4-0 3P Class D1

Introduced 1921. Maunsell rebuild of Wainwright S.E.C. D, with larger superheated boiler. Belpaire firebox and long-travel piston valves.
Weight: Loco. 52 tons 4 cwt.
Pressure: 180 lb. Su.
Cyls.: 19" × 26".
Driving Wheels: 6' 8".
T.E.: 17,950 lb.

31145, 31246/7, 31487/9/94, 31505/9/45, 31727/35/9/49

Total 13

4-4-0 3P Class E1

Introduced 1919. Maunsell rebuild of Wainwright S.E.C. E, with larger superheated boiler, Belpaire firebox and long-travel piston valves.
Weight: Loco. 53 tons 9 cwt.
Pressure: 180 lb.
Cyls.: 19" × 26".
Driving Wheels: 6' 6".
T.E.: 18,410 lb.

31019/67, 31497, 31507

Total 4

0-6-0T 2F Class E1

Introduced 1874. Stroudley L.B.S.C. design, reboilered by Marsh.
Weight: 44 tons 3 cwt.
Pressure: 170 lb.
Cyls.: 17" × 24".
Driving Wheels: 4' 6".
T.E.: 18,560 lb.

4, 32694

Total 2

0-6-0T 3F Class E2

*Introduced 1913. L. B. Billinton L.B.S.C. design.
†Introduced 1915. Later locos. with tanks extended further forward.
Weight: { 52 tons 15 cwt.* / 53 tons 10 cwt.† }
Pressure: 170 lb.
Cyls.: 17½" × 26".
Driving Wheels: 4' 6".
T.E.: 21,305 lb.

*32100–4
†32105–9

Total 10

0-6-2T 2P2F Class E4

Introduced 1897. R. J. Billinton L.B.S.C. design, development of E3 with larger wheels, reboilered with Marsh boiler and extended smokebox, cylinder diameter reduced from 18" by S.R.
Weight: 57 tons 10 cwt.
Pressure: 170 lb.
Cyls.: 17½" × 26".
Driving Wheels: 5' 0".
T.E.: 19,175 lb.

32468–70/2–5/9/84/7/91/5/8, 32500/3–6/9/10/2/5/56/7/9/62–5/78/80/1

Total 32

0-6-2T 3F Class E6

Introduced 1904. R. J. Billinton L.B.S.C. design, development of E5 with smaller wheels, some with higher pressure.
Weight: 61 tons.
Pressure: 160 lb. or 175 lb.
Cyls.: 18" × 26".
Driving Wheels: 4' 6".
T.E.: 21,215 lb. or 23,205 lb.

32408/10/5–8

Total 6

0-6-0T 2F Class G6

*Introduced 1894. Adams L.S.W. design, later additions by Drummond, but with Adams type boiler.
†Introduced 1925. Fitted with Drummond type boiler.
Weight: 47 tons 13 cwt.
Pressure: 160 lb.
Cyls.: 17½" × 24".
Driving Wheels: 4' 10".
T.E.: 17,235 lb.

*30238/58/66/77, 30349, DS3152
†30274

Total 7

4-8-0T 8F Class G16

Introduced 1921. Urie L.S.W. "Hump" loco.
Weight: 95 tons 2 cwt.
Pressure: 180 lb. Su.
Cyls.: (O) 22" × 28".
Driving Wheels: 5' 1"
T.E.: 33,990 lb.
Walschaerts valve gear. P.V.

30494/5 **Total 2**

0-4-4T 1P Class H

Introduced 1904. Wainwright S.E.C. design.

*Introduced 1949. Fitted for push-and-pull working.

Weight: 54 tons 8 cwt.
Pressure: 160 lb.
Cyls.: 18" × 26".
Driving Wheels: 5' 6".
T.E.: 17,360 lb.

31261/5, 31305/7/24/6/8, 31542/50–2
*31005, 31161/2/77/93, 31263/6/76/8, 31306/8/10/22/31500/12/7–22/30/3/43/4/53
Total 38

4-6-0 4P5F Class H15

*Introduced 1914. Urie L.S.W. design, fitted with Maunsell superheater from 1927, replacing earlier types.

†Introduced 1924. Maunsell locos. with N15-type boiler and smaller tender.

‡Introduced 1924. Maunsell rebuild of Drummond F13 4-cyl. 4-6-0 introduced 1905, with detail differences from rebuild of E14.

§Introduced 1927. Urie loco. (built 1914 saturated), rebuilt with later N15-type boiler, with smaller firebox.

Weight: Loco. { 81 tons 5 cwt.* / 79 tons 19 cwt.†§ / 80 tons 11 cwt.‡ }
Pressure: { 180 lb. Su.*†§ / 175 lb. Su.‡ }
Cyls.: (O) 21" × 28".
Driving Wheels: 6' 0".
T.E. { 26,240 lb.*†§ / 25,510 lb.‡ }
Walschaerts valve gear. P.V.

*30489 †30474–6, 30521–4
‡30331 §30491
Total 10

4-6-2T 6F Class H16

Introduced 1921. Urie L.S.W. design for heavy freight traffic.
Weight: 96 tons 8 cwt.
Pressure: 180 lb. Su.
Cyls.: (O) 21" × 28".
Driving Wheels: 5' 7".
T.E.: 28,200 lb.
Walschaerts valve gear. P.V.

30516–20 **Total 5**

2-6-0 4P5F Class K

Introduced 1913. L. B. Billinton L.B.S.C. design.
Weight: Loco. 63 tons 15 cwt.
Pressure: 180 lb. Su.
Cyls.: (O) 21" × 26".
Driving Wheels: 5'6".
T.E.: 26,580 lb.
P.V.

32337-53 **Total 17**

4-4-0 3P Class L

Introduced 1914. Wainwright S.E.C. design, with detail alterations by Maunsell.
Weight: Loco. 57 tons 9 cwt.
Pressure: 160 lb. Su.
Cyls.: 20½" × 26".
Driving Wheels: 6' 8".
T.E.: 18,575 lb.
P.V.

31760/3-6/8/71/6/80
Total 9

Ex-Cardiff Railway 0-4-0ST No. 1338 [R. C. Riley

Ex-S.H.T. 0-4-0ST No. 1144 [J. B. Bucknall

Ex-P.M. 0-4-0ST No. 1151 [J. B. Bucknall

1361 Class 0-6-0ST No. 1365 [R. C. Riley

1366 Class 0-6-0PT No. 1369 [A. R. Carpenter

1500 Class 0-6-0PT No. 1508 [N Fields

1400 Class 0-4-2T No. 1463 *[J. Davenport*

5800 Class 0-4-2T No. 5815 *[L. King*

1101 Class 0-4-0T No. 1102 *[A. R. Carpenter*

Left: 1600 Class 0-6-0PT No. 1629 (fitted with spark arrester) [*R. C. Riley*

Centre: 5400 Class 0-6-0PT No. 5410 [*K. L. Cook*

Bottom: 5700 Class 0-6-0PT No. 6724 [*A. A. Delicata*

5600 Class 0-6-2T No. 6631 [P. H. Groom

9400 Class 0-6-0PT No. 8426 [R. E. Vincent

6400 Class 0-6-0PT No. 6419 [G. Wheeler

Above: 2800 Class 2-8-0 No. 3848 (with side-window cab)
[*A. W. Martin*

Left: 2800 Class 2-8-0 No. 2834 [*R. A. Panting*

Below: 4700 Class 2-8-0 No. 4707 [*R. C. Riley*

2251 Class 0-6-0 No. 2253 [*C. P. Boocock*

4300 Class 2-6-0 No. 6374 [*G. Wheeler*

4300 Class 2-6-0 No. 7331 (with side-window cab and large tender) [*G. Wheeler*

4073 Class 4-6-0 No. 5031 *Totnes Castle* (fitted with double chimney) [G. Wheeler

4073 Class 4-6-0 No. 7010 *Avondale Castle* [G. Wheeler

6000 Class 4-6-0 No. 6010 *King Charles I* [J. A. Coiley

4-4-0 3P Class L1

Introduced 1926. Maunsell post-grouping development of L, with long-travel valves, side window cab and detail alterations.
Weight: Loco. 57 tons 16 cwt.
Pressure: 180 lb. Su.
Cyls.: 19½" × 26".
Driving Wheels: 6' 8".
T.E.: 18,910 lb.
P.V.

31753/4/6/7/9/82/3/6/7/9

Total 10

4-6-0 7P Class LN

*Introduced 1926. Maunsell design, cylinders and tender modified by Bulleid from 1938, and fitted with multiple-jet blastpipe and large-diameter chimney.
†Introduced 1929. Loco. fitted experimentally with smaller driving wheels.
‡Introduced 1929. Loco. fitted experimentally with longer boiler.
Weight: Loco. {83 tons 10 cwt.*† / 84 tons 16 cwt.‡}
Pressure: 220 lb. Su.
Cyls.: (4) 16½" × 26".
Driving Wheels: {6' 7".*‡ / 6' 3".†}
T.E.: {33,510 lb.*‡ / 35,300 lb.†}
Walschaerts valve gear. P.V.

*30850–8/61–5

†30859 ‡30860

Total 16

0-4-4T 2P Class M7

*Introduced 1897. Drummond L.S.W. M7 design.
†Introduced 1903. Drummond X14 design, with increased front overhang, steam reverser and detail alterations, now classified M7 (30254 originally M7).
‡Introduced 1925. X14 design fitted for push-and-pull working.
Weight: {60 tons 4 cwt.* / 60 tons 3 cwt.† / 62 tons 0 cwt.‡}
Pressure: 175 lb.
Cyls.: 18½" × 26".
Driving Wheels: 5' 7".
T.E.: 19,755 lb.

*30023–5/31–6/9/40/3/4, 30112, 30241/5–9/51/3/5, 30320/1/57, 30667–70/3/4/6

†30124/7/32, 30254, 30375/7/8, 30479

‡30021/8/9/45/8–53/5–60, 30104–11/25/8/9/31/3, 30328/79, 30480

Total 73

4-6-2 8P Class MN

Introduced 1941. Bulleid design originally with 280 lb. pressure, multiple-jet blastpipe and Bulleid Valve gear. Rebuilt since 1956 with Walschaerts valve gear, modified details and air-smoothed casing removed.

Weight: Loco. 97 tons 18 cwt.
Pressure: 250 lb.
Cyls: (3) 18" × 24".
Driving Wheels: 6' 2".
T.E.: 33,495 lb.
P.V.

35001–30

Total 30

2-6-0 4P5F Classes N & N1

*N. Introduced 1917. Maunsell S.E.C. mixed traffic design.
†N1. Introduced 1922. 3-cylinder development of N.
Weight: Loco. {61 tons 4 cwt.* / 64 tons 5 cwt.†}
Pressure: 200 lb. Su.
Cyls.: {(O) 19" × 28".* / (3) 16" × 28".†}
Driving Wheels: 5' 6".
T.E.: {26,035 lb.* / 27,695 lb.†}
Walschaerts valve gear. P.V.

*31400–14, 31810–21/3–75

†31822/76–80

Total N 80
N1 6

4-6-0 5P Class N15

*Introduced 1925. Maunsell locos. with long-travel valves, increased boiler pressure, smaller fireboxes, and tenders from Drummond G14 4-6-0s.
†Introduced 1925. Later locos, with detail alterations and increased weight.
‡Introduced 1925. Locos. with modified cabs to suit Eastern Section, and new bogie tenders.
§Introduced 1926. Locos. with detail alterations and most with six-wheeled tenders for Central Section.
Weight: Loco. { 79 tons 18 cwt.* / 80 tons 19 cwt.†‡ / 81 tons 17 cwt.§ }
Pressure: 200 lb. Su.
Cyls.: (O) $20\frac{1}{2}'' \times 28''$.
Driving Wheels: 6′ 7″.
T.E.: 25,320 lb.
Walschaerts valve gear. P.V.

*30453/6/7 †30448/50/1

†30763–5/8/70–3/7/81–3/8/90/1

§30793–6/8–30800/2–4/6

Total 32

0-6-0 2F Class O1

*Introduced 1903. Wainwright rebuild with domed boiler and new cab of Stirling S.E. Class O 0-6-0 (introduced 1878).
†Introduced 1903. Loco. with smaller driving wheels.
Weight: Loco. 41 tons 1 cwt.
Pressure: 150 lb.
Cyls.: $18'' \times 26''$.
Driving Wheels: { 5′ 2″.* / 5′ 1″.† }
T.E.: { 17,325 lb.* / 17,610 lb.† }

*31065, 31258

†31048 **Total 3**

0-4-4T 0P Class O2

*Introduced 1889. Adams L.S.W. design.
†Introduced 1923. Fitted with Westinghouse brake for I.O.W. Bunkers enlarged from 1932.
‡Fitted with Drummond-type boiler.
§Fitted for push-and-pull working.
Weight: { 46 tons 18 cwt.*‡ / 48 tons 8 cwt.† }
Pressure: 160 lb.
Cyls.: $17\frac{1}{2}'' \times 24''$.
Driving Wheels: 4′ 10″.
T.E.: 17,235 lb.

*30192/3/9, 30200/25/9
†14/6–8/20–2/4–33
†§35/6
‡30223 ‡§30183

Total 27

0-6-0T Unclass. Class P

Introduced 1909. Wainwright S.E.C. design for push-and-pull work, now used for shunting.
Weight: 28 tons 10 cwt.
Pressure: 160 lb.
Cyls.: $12'' \times 18''$.
Driving Wheels: 3′ $9\frac{1}{8}''$.
T.E.: 7,810 lb.

31027, 31323, 31556

Total 3

0-6-0 4F Class Q

Introduced 1938. Maunsell design, later fitted with multiple-jet blastpipe and large-diameter chimney.
Weight: Loco. 49 tons 10 cwt.
Pressure 200 lb. Su.
Cyls.: $19'' \times 26''$.
Driving Wheels: 5′ 1″.
T.E.: 26,160 lb.
P.V.

30530–49 **Total 20**

0-6-0 5F Class Q1

Introduced 1942. Bulleid "Austerity" design.
Weight: Loco. 51 tons 5 cwt.
Pressure: 230 lb. Su.
Cyls.: $19'' \times 26''$.
Driving Wheels: 5′ 1″
T.E.: 30,080 lb.
P.V.

33001–40 **Total 40**

4-6-0 6F Class S15

*Introduced 1920. Urie L.S.W. design, development of N15 for mixed traffic work.
†Introduced 1927. Maunsell design, with higher pressure, smaller grate, modified footplating and other detail differences. 30833–7 with 6-wheel tenders for Central Section.
‡Introduced 1936. Later locos, with detail differences and reduced weight.

Weight: Loco. { 79 tons 16 cwt.* / 80 tons 14 cwt.† / 79 tons 5 cwt.‡
Pressure: { 180 lb. Su.* / 200 lb. Su.†‡
Cyls.: { (O) 21" × 28".* / (O) 20½" × 28".†‡
Driving Wheels: 5' 7".
T.E. { 28,200 lb.* / 29,855 lb.†‡
Walschaerts valve gear. P.V.

*30496–30515 †30823–37
‡30838–47

Total 45

4-4-0 3P Class T9

*Introduced 1899. Drummond L.S.W. design, fitted with superheater and larger cylinders by Urie from 1922.
†Introduced 1899. Locos. with detail differences (originally fitted with firebox watertubes).
‡Introduced 1900. Locos. with wider cab and splashers, without coupling rod splashers and originally fitted with firebox watertubes.

Weight: Loco. { 51 tons 18 cwt.* / 51 tons 16 cwt.† / 51 tons 7 cwt.‡
Pressure: 175 lb. Su.
Cyls.: 19" × 26".
Driving Wheels: 6' 7".
T.E.: 17,675 lb.

*30117/20, 30287/8
†30707/9/15/7–9/29
‡30300/13/38

Total 14

2-6-0 4P3F Classes U & U1

*U. Introduced 1928. Rebuild of Maunsell S.E.C. Class K ("River") 2-6-4T (introduced 1917).
†U. Introduced 1928. Locos. built as Class U, with smaller splashers and detail alterations.
‡U1. Introduced 1928. 3-cylinder development of Class U (prototype 31890, rebuilt from 2-6-4T, originally built 1925).

Weight: Loco. { 63 tons.* / 62 tons 6 cwt.† / 65 tons 6 cwt.‡
Pressure: 200 lb. Su.
Cyls.: { (O) 19" × 28".*† / (3) 16" × 28".‡
Driving Wheels: 6' 0".
T.E.: { 23,865 lb.*† / 25,385 lb.‡
Walschaerts valve gear. P.V.

*31790–31809 †31610–39
‡31890–31910

Total Class U 50
Class U1 21

0-6-0T 3F Class USA

Introduced 1942. U.S. Army Transportation Corps design, purchased by S.R. 1946, and fitted with modified cab and bunker and other detail alterations.
Weight: 46 tons 10 cwt.
Pressure: 210 lb.
Cyls.: (O) 16½" × 24".
Driving Wheels: 4' 6".
T.E.: 21,600 lb.
Walschaerts valve gear. P.V.

30061–74 **Total 14**

4-4-0 5P Class V

*Introduced 1930. Maunsell design.
†Introduced 1938. Fitted with multiple-jet blastpipe and large-diameter chimney by Bulleid.
Weight: Loco. 67 tons 2 cwt.
Pressure: 220 lb. Su.
Cyls.: (3) 16½" × 26".
Driving Wheels: 6' 7".
T.E.: 25,135 lb.
Walschaerts valve gear. P.V.

*30902–6/8/10–2/6/22/3/5–8/32/5/6
†30900/1/7/9/13–5/7–21/4/29–31/3/4/7–9 **Total 40**

2-6-4T 6F Class W

Introduced 1931. Maunsell design, developed from Class N1 2-6-0.
Weight: 90 tons 14 cwt.
Pressure: 200 lb. Su.
Cyls.: (3) 16½" × 28".
Driving Wheels: 5' 6".
T.E.: 29,450 lb.
Walschaerts valve gear. P.V.

31911–25 **Total 15**

4-6-2 7P5F Classes WC & BB

*Introduced 1945. Bulleid "West Country" Class, with Bulleid valve gear.
†Introduced 1946. Bulleid "Battle of Britain" Class, with Bulleid valve gear.
‡Introduced 1957. Rebuilt with Walschaerts valve gear, modified details and air-smoothed casing removed.
Weight: Loco. {86 tons 0 cwt.*† / 90 tons 1 cwt.‡}
Pressure: 250 lb. Su.
Cyls.: (3) 16⅜" × 24".
Driving Wheels: 6' 2".
T.E.: 27,715 lb.
Bulleid valve gear. P.V.

*34002/6–9/11/5/9/20/3/4/30/2–6/8/40/1/3/4/91–9, 34100–8
†34049/51/4–8/60/1/3–81/3–7/9/90, 34109/10
*‡34001/3–5/10/2–4/6–8/21/2/5–9/31/7/9/42/4–8
†‡34050/2/3/9/62/82/8
Total 110

0-8-0T 6F Class Z

Introduced 1929. Maunsell design for heavy shunting.
Weight: 71 tons 12 cwt.
Pressure: 180 lb.
Cyls.: (3) 16" × 28".
Driving Wheels: 4' 8".
T.E.: 29,375 lb.
Walschaerts valve gear. P.V.

30950–7 **Total 8**

0-6-0 3F Class 700

Introduced 1897. Drummond L.S.W. design, superheated from 1921.
Weight: Loco. 46 tons 14 cwt.
Pressure: 180 lb. Su.
Cyls.: 19" × 26".
Driving Wheels: 5' 1".
T.E.: 23,540 lb.

30306/8/9/15–7/25–7/39/46/50/5/68, 30687/9–30701
Total 28

2-4-0WT 0P Class 0298

Introduced 1874. Beattie L.S.W. design, rebuilt by Adams (1884–92), Urie (1921–2) and Maunsell (1931–5).
Weight: 37 tons 16 cwt.
Pressure: 160 lb.
Cyls.: (O) 16½" × 20".
Driving Wheels: 5' 7".
T.E.: 11,050 lb.

30585–7 **Total 3**

4-4-2T 1P Class 0415

Introduced 1882. Adams L.S.W. design, later reboilered.
Weight: 55 tons 2 cwt.
Pressure: 160 lb.
Cyls.: (O) 17½" × 24".
Driving Wheels: 5' 7".
T.E.: 14,920 lb.

30582–4 **Total 3**

BRITISH RAILWAYS LOCOMOTIVES

Nos. 30021-35030

Named Engines are indicated by an asterisk (*)

No.	Class	No.	Class	No.	Class	No.	Class
30021	M7	30068	U.S.A.	30229	O2	30350	700
30023	M7	30069	U.S.A.	30238	G6	30355	700
30024	M7	30070	U.S.A.	30241	M7	30357	M7
30025	M7	30071	U.S.A.	30245	M7	30368	700
30028	M7	30072	U.S.A.	30246	M7	30375	M7
30029	M7	30073	U.S.A.	30247	M7	30377	M7
30031	M7	30074	U.S.A.	30248	M7	30378	M7
30032	M7	30089	B4	30249	M7	30379	M7
30033	M7	30093	B4	30251	M7	30448*	N15
30034	M7	30096	B4	30253	M7	30450*	N15
30035	M7	30102	B4	30254	M7	30451*	N15
30036	M7	30104	M7	30255	M7	30453*	N15
30039	M7	30105	M7	30258	G6	30456*	N15
30040	M7	30106	M7	30266	G6	30457*	N15
30043	M7	30107	M7	30274	G6	30474	H15
30044	M7	30108	M7	30277	G6	30475	H15
30045	M7	30109	M7	30287	T9	30476	H15
30048	M7	30110	M7	30288	T9	30479	M7
30049	M7	30111	M7	30300	T9	30480	M7
30050	M7	30112	M7	30306	700	30489	H15
30051	M7	30117	T9	30308	700	30491	H15
30052	M7	30120	T9	30309	700	30494	G16
30053	M7	30124	M7	30313	T9	30495	G16
30055	M7	30125	M7	30315	700	30496	S15
30056	M7	30127	M7	30316	700	30497	S15
30057	M7	30128	M7	30317	700	30498	S15
30058	M7	30129	M7	30320	M7	30499	S15
30059	M7	30131	M7	30321	M7	30500	S15
30060	M7	30132	M7	30325	700	30501	S15
30061	U.S.A.	30133	M7	30326	700	30502	S15
30062	U.S.A.	30183	O2	30327	700	30503	S15
30063	U.S.A.	30192	O2	30328	M7	30504	S15
30064	U.S.A.	30193	O2	30331	H15	30505	S15
30065	U.S.A.	30199	O2	30338	T9	30506	S15
30066	U.S.A.	30200	O2	30339	700	30507	S15
30067	U.S.A.	30223	O2	30346	700	30508	S15
		30225	O2	30349	G6		

No.	Class	No.	Class	No.	Class	No.	Class
30509	S15	30670	M7	30799*	N15	30864*	LN
30510	S15	30673	M7	30800*	N15	30865*	LN
30511	S15	30674	M7	30802*	N15	30900*	V
30512	S15	30676	M7	30803*	N15	30901*	V
30513	S15	30687	700	30804*	N15	30902*	V
30514	S15	30689	700	30806*	N15	30903*	V
30515	S15	30690	700	30823	S15	30904*	V
30516	H16	30691	700	30824	S15	30905*	V
30517	H16	30692	700	30825	S15	30906*	V
30518	H16	30693	700	30826	S15	30907*	V
30519	H16	30694	700	30827	S15	30908*	V
30520	H16	30695	700	30828	S15	30909*	V
30521	H15	30696	700	30829	S15	30910*	V
30522	H15	30697	700	30830	S15	30911*	V
30523	H15	30698	700	30831	S15	30912*	V
30524	H15	30699	700	30832	S15	30913*	V
30530	Q	30700	700	30833	S15	30914*	V
30531	Q	30701	700	30834	S15	30915*	V
30532	Q	30707	T9	30835	S15	30916*	V
30533	Q	30709	T9	30836	S15	30917*	V
30534	Q	30715	T9	30837	S15	30918*	V
30535	Q	30717	T9	30838	S15	30919*	V
30536	Q	30718	T9	30839	S15	30920*	V
30537	Q	30719	T9	30840	S15	30921*	V
30538	Q	30729	T9	30841	S15	30922*	V
30539	Q	30763*	N15	30842	S15	30923*	V
30540	Q	30764*	N15	30843	S15	30924*	V
30541	Q	30765*	N15	30844	S15	30925*	V
30542	Q	30768*	N15	30845	S15	30926*	V
30543	Q	30770*	N15	30846	S15	30927*	V
30544	Q	30771*	N15	30847	S15	30928*	V
30545	Q	30772*	N15	30850*	LN	30929*	V
30546	Q	30773*	N15	30851*	LN	30930*	V
30547	Q	30777*	N15	30852*	LN	30931*	V
30548	Q	30781*	N15	30853*	LN	30932*	V
30549	Q	30782*	N15	30854*	LN	30933*	V
30582	0415	30783*	N15	30855*	LN	30934*	V
30583	0415	30788*	N15	30856*	LN	30935*	V
30584	0415	30790*	N15	30857*	LN	30936*	V
30585	0298	30791*	N15	30858*	LN	30937*	V
30586	0298	30793*	N15	30859*	LN	30938*	V
30587	0298	30794*	N15	30860*	LN	30939*	V
30667	M7	30795*	N15	30861*	LN	30950	Z
30668	M7	30796*	N15	30862*	LN	30951	Z
30669	M7	30798*	N15	30863*	LN	30952	Z

No.	Class	No.	Class	No.	Class	No.	Class
30953	Z	31280	C	31518	H	31629	U
30954	Z	31287	C	31519	H	31630	U
30955	Z	31293	C	31520	H	31631	U
30956	Z	31298	C	31521	H	31632	U
30957	Z	31305	H	31522	H	31633	U
31004	C	31306	H	31530	H	31634	U
31005	H	31307	H	31533	H	31635	U
31019	EI	31308	H	31542	H	31636	U
31027	P	31310	H	31543	H	31637	U
31037	C	31317	C	31544	H	31638	U
31048	OI	31322	H	31545	DI	31639	U
31054	C	31323	P	31550	H	31682	C
31061	C	31324	H	31551	H	31684	C
31065	OI	31326	H	31552	H	31686	C
31067	EI	31328	H	31553	H	31689	C
31068	C	31400	N	31556	P	31690	C
31086	C	31401	N	31573	C	31691	C
31102	C	31402	N	31575	C	31692	C
31112	C	31403	N	31578	C	31693	C
31113	C	31404	N	31579	C	31694	C
31145	DI	31405	N	31583	C	31695	C
31150	C	31406	N	31584	C	31714	C
31161	H	31407	N	31588	C	31715	C
31162	H	31408	N	31589	C	31716	C
31177	H	31409	N	31590	C	31717	C
31193	H	31410	N	31592	C	31719	C
31218	C	31411	N	31610	U	31720	C
31223	C	31412	N	31611	U	31721	C
31229	C	31413	N	31612	U	31722	C
31242	C	31414	N	31613	U	31723	C
31244	C	31480	C	31614	U	31724	C
31246	DI	31481	C	31615	U	31725	C
31247	DI	31487	DI	31616	U	31727	DI
31255	C	31489	DI	31617	U	31735	DI
31256	C	31494	DI	31618	U	31739	DI
31258	OI	31495	C	31619	U	31749	DI
31261	H	31497	EI	31620	U	31753	LI
31263	H	31498	C	31621	U	31754	LI
31265	H	31500	H	31622	U	31756	LI
31266	H	31505	DI	31623	U	31757	LI
31267	C	31507	EI	31624	U	31759	LI
31268	C	31509	DI	31625	U	31760	L
31271	C	31510	C	31626	U	31763	L
31276	H	31512	H	31627	U	31764	L
31278	H	31517	H	31628	U	31765	L

No.	Class	No.	Class	No.	Class	No.	Class
31766	L	31825	N	31870	N	31924	W
31768	L	31826	N	31871	N	31925	W
31771	L	31827	N	31872	N	32100	E2
31776	L	31828	N	31873	N	32101	E2
31780	L	31829	N	31874	N	32102	E2
31782	L1	31830	N	31875	N	32103	E2
31783	L1	31831	N	31876	N1	32104	E2
31786	L1	31832	N	31877	N1	32105	E2
31787	L1	31833	N	31878	N1	32106	E2
31789	L1	31834	N	31879	N1	32107	E2
31790	U	31835	N	31880	N1	32108	E2
31791	U	31836	N	31890	U1	32109	E2
31792	U	31837	N	31891	U1	32151	E1
31793	U	31838	N	31892	U1	32337	K
31794	U	31839	N	31893	U1	32338	K
31795	U	31840	N	31894	U1	32339	K
31796	U	31841	N	31895	U1	32340	K
31797	U	31842	N	31896	U1	32341	K
31798	U	31843	N	31897	U1	32342	K
31799	U	31844	N	31898	U1	32343	K
31800	U	31845	N	31899	U1	32344	K
31801	U	31846	N	31900	U1	32345	K
31802	U	31847	N	31901	U1	32346	K
31803	U	31848	N	31902	U1	32347	K
31804	U	31849	N	31903	U1	32348	K
31805	U	31850	N	31904	U1	32349	K
31806	U	31851	N	31905	U1	32350	K
31807	U	31852	N	31906	U1	32351	K
31808	U	31853	N	31907	U1	32352	K
31809	U	31854	N	31908	U1	32353	K
31810	N	31855	N	31909	U1	32408	E6
31811	N	31856	N	31910	U1	32410	E6
31812	N	31857	N	31911	W	32415	E6
31813	N	31858	N	31912	W	32416	E6
31814	N	31859	N	31913	W	32417	E6
31815	N	31860	N	31914	W	32418	E6
31816	N	31861	N	31915	W	32438	C2X
31817	N	31862	N	31916	W	32441	C2X
31818	N	31863	N	31917	W	32443	C2X
31819	N	31864	N	31918	W	32445	C2X
31820	N	31865	N	31919	W	32446	C2X
31821	N	31866	N	31920	W	32448	C2X
31822	N1	31867	N	31921	W	32449	C2X
31823	N	31868	N	31922	W	32450	C2X
31824	N	31869	N	31923	W	32451	C2X

No.	Class	No.	Class	No.	Class	No.	Class
32468	E4	32556	E4	33025	Q1	34030*	WC
32469	E4	32557	E4	33026	Q1	34031*	WC
32470	E4	32559	E4	33027	Q1	34032*	WC
32472	E4	32562	E4	33028	Q1	34033*	WC
32473	E4	32563	E4	33029	Q1	34034*	WC
32474	E4	32564	E4	33030	Q1	34035*	WC
32475	E4	32565	E4	33031	Q1	34036*	WC
32479	E4	32578	E4	33032	Q1	34037*	WC
32484	E4	32580	E4	33033	Q1	34038*	WC
32487	E4	32581	E4	33034	Q1	34039*	WC
32491	E4	32635	A1X	33035	Q1	34040*	WC
32495	E4	32636	A1X	33036	Q1	34041*	WC
32498	E4	32640	A1X	33037	Q1	34042*	WC
32500	E4	32646	A1X	33038	Q1	34043*	WC
32503	E4	32650	A1X	33039	Q1	34044*	WC
32504	E4	32655	A1X	33040	Q1	34045*	WC
32505	E4	32661	A1X	34001*	WC	34046*	WC
32506	E4	32662	A1X	34002*	WC	34047*	WC
32509	E4	32670	A1X	34003*	WC	34048*	WC
32510	E4	32678	A1X	34004*	WC	34049*	BB
32512	E4	32694	E1	34005*	WC	34050*	BB
32515	E4	33001	Q1	34006*	WC	34051*	BB
32521	C2X	33002	Q1	34007*	WC	34052*	BB
32522	C2X	33003	Q1	34008*	WC	34053*	BB
32523	C2X	33004	Q1	34009*	WC	34054*	BB
32525	C2X	33005	Q1	34010*	WC	34055*	BB
32527	C2X	33006	Q1	34011*	WC	34056*	BB
32528	C2X	33007	Q1	34012*	WC	34057*	BB
32532	C2X	33008	Q1	34013*	WC	34058*	BB
32534	C2X	33009	Q1	34014*	WC	34059*	BB
32535	C2X	33010	Q1	34015*	WC	34060*	BB
32536	C2X	33011	Q1	34016*	WC	34061*	BB
32538	C2X	33012	Q1	34017*	WC	34062*	BB
32539	C2X	33013	Q1	34018*	WC	34063*	BB
32541	C2X	33014	Q1	34019*	WC	34064*	BB
32543	C2X	33015	Q1	34020*	WC	34065*	BB
32544	C2X	33016	Q1	34021*	WC	34066*	BB
32545	C2X	33017	Q1	34022*	WC	34067*	BB
32546	C2X	33018	Q1	34023*	WC	34068*	BB
32547	C2X	33019	Q1	34024*	WC	34069*	BB
32548	C2X	33020	Q1	34025*	WC	34070*	BB
32549	C2X	33021	Q1	34026*	WC	34071*	BB
32550	C2X	33022	Q1	34027*	WC	34072*	BB
32552	C2X	33023	Q1	34028*	WC	34073*	BB
32553	C2X	33024	Q1	34029*	WC	34074*	BB

No.	Class	No.	Class	No.	Class	No.	Class
34075*	BB	34092*	WC	34109*	BB	35016*	MN
34076*	BB	34093*	WC	34110*	BB	35017*	MN
34077*	BB	34094*	WC	35001*	MN	35018*	MN
34078*	BB	34095*	WC	35002*	MN	35019*	MN
34079*	BB	34096*	WC	35003*	MN	35020*	MN
34080*	BB	34097*	WC	35004*	MN	35021*	MN
34081*	BB	34098*	WC	35005*	MN	35022*	MN
34082*	BB	34099*	WC	35006*	MN	35023*	MN
34083*	BB	34100*	WC	35007*	MN	35024*	MN
34084*	BB	34101*	WC	35008*	MN	35025*	MN
34085*	BB	34102*	WC	35009*	MN	35026*	MN
34086*	BB	34103*	WC	35010*	MN	35027*	MN
34087*	BB	34104*	WC	35011*	MN	35028*	MN
34088*	BB	34105*	WC	35012*	MN	35029*	MN
34089*	BB	34106*	WC	35013*	MN	35030*	MN
34090*	BB	34107*	WC	35014*	MN		
34091*	WC	34108*	WC	35015*	MN		

Isle of Wight Locomotives

For details see named engines.

SOUTHERN REGION SERVICE LOCOMOTIVES

No.	Old No.	Class	Station
*DS 74	—	Bo-Bo	Durnsford Road Power Station
*DS 75	—	Bo	Waterloo & City
DS 77	0745	C14	Redbridge Sleeper Depot
DS 600	—	0-4-0 Diesel	Eastleigh Carriage Works
DS 680	L.B.S.C. 654 S.E.C. 751	A1	Lancing Carriage Works
DS 681	L.B.S.C. 659	A1X	Lancing Carriage Works
DS 1169	—	0-4-0 Diesel	Broad Clyst
DS 1173	2217	0-6-0 Diesel	Engineer's Department
DS 3152	30272	G6	Meldon Quarry

* Electric.

NAMED LOCOMOTIVES

CLASS N15 "KING ARTHUR" 4-6-0

30448	Sir Tristram	30782	Sir Brian
30450	Sir Kay	30783	Sir Gillemere
30451	Sir Lamorak	30788	Sir Urre of the Mount
30453	King Arthur	30790	Sir Villiars
30456	Sir Galahad	30791	Sir Uwaine
30457	Sir Bedivere	30793	Sir Ontzlake
30763	Sir Bors de Ganis	30794	Sir Ector de Maris
30764	Sir Gawain	30795	Sir Dinadan
30765	Sir Gareth	30796	Sir Dodinas le Savage
30768	Sir Balin	30798	Sir Hectimere
30770	Sir Prianius	30799	Sir Ironside
30771	Sir Sagramore	30800	Sir Meleaus de Lile
30772	Sir Percivale	30802	Sir Durnore
30773	Sir Lavaine	30803	Sir Harry le Fise Lake
30777	Sir Lamiel	30804	Sir Cador of Cornwall
30781	Sir Aglovale	30806	Sir Galleron

CLASS LN "LORD NELSON" 4-6-0

30850	Lord Nelson	30858	Lord Duncan
30851	Sir Francis Drake	30859	Lord Hood
30852	Sir Walter Raleigh	30860	Lord Hawke
30853	Sir Richard Grenville	30861	Lord Anson
30854	Howard of Effingham	30862	Lord Collingwood
30855	Robert Blake	30863	Lord Rodney
30856	Lord St. Vincent	30864	Sir Martin Frobisher
30857	Lord Howe	30865	Sir John Hawkins

CLASS V "SCHOOLS" 4-4-0

30900	Eton	30906	Sherborne
30901	Winchester	30907	Dulwich
30902	Wellington	30908	Westminster
30903	Charterhouse	30909	St. Paul's
30904	Lancing	30910	Merchant Taylors
30905	Tonbridge	30911	Dover

30912	Downside
30913	Christ's Hospital
30914	Eastbourne
30915	Brighton
30916	Whitgift
30917	Ardingly
30918	Hurstpierpoint
30919	Harrow
30920	Rugby
30921	Shrewsbury
30922	Marlborough
30923	Bradfield
30924	Haileybury
30925	Cheltenham
30926	Repton
30927	Clifton
30928	Stowe
30929	Malvern
30930	Radley
30931	King's Wimbledon
30932	Blundells
30933	King's Canterbury
30934	St. Lawrence
30935	Sevenoaks
30936	Cranleigh
30937	Epsom
30938	St. Olave's
30939	Leatherhead

CLASSES WC & BB 4-6-2

"WEST COUNTRY" and "BATTLE OF BRITAIN"

34001	Exeter
34002	Salisbury
34003	Plymouth
34004	Yeovil
34005	Barnstaple
34006	Bude
34007	Wadebridge
34008	Padstow
34009	Lyme Regis
34010	Sidmouth
34011	Tavistock
34012	Launceston
34013	Okehampton
34014	Budleigh Salterton
34015	Exmouth
34016	Bodmin
34017	Ilfracombe
34018	Axminster
34019	Bideford
34020	Seaton
34021	Dartmoor
34022	Exmoor
34023	Blackmore Vale
34024	Tamar Valley
34025	Whimple
34026	Yes Tor
34027	Taw Valley
34028	Eddystone
34029	Lundy
34030	Watersmeet
34031	Torrington
34032	Camelford
34033	Chard
34034	Honiton
34035	Shaftesbury
34036	Westward Ho
34037	Clovelly
34038	Lynton
34039	Boscastle
34040	Crewkerne
34041	Wilton
34042	Dorchester
34043	Combe Martin
34044	Woolacombe
34045	Ottery St. Mary
34046	Braunton
34047	Callington
34048	Crediton
34049	Anti-Aircraft Command
34050	Royal Observer Corps
34051	Winston Churchill
34052	Lord Dowding
34053	Sir Keith Park
34054	Lord Beaverbrook
34055	Fighter Pilot
34056	Croydon

34057	Biggin Hill
34058	Sir Frederick Pile
34059	Sir Archibald Sinclair
34060	25 Squadron
34061	73 Squadron
34062	17 Squadron
34063	229 Squadron
34064	Fighter Command
34065	Hurricane
34066	Spitfire
34067	Tangmere
34068	Kenley
34069	Hawkinge
34070	Manston
34071	601 Squadron
34072	257 Squadron
34073	249 Squadron
34074	46 Squadron
34075	264 Squadron
34076	41 Squadron
34077	603 Squadron
34078	222 Squadron
34079	141 Squadron
34080	74 Squadron
34081	92 Squadron
34082	615 Squadron
34083	605 Squadron
34084	253 Squadron
34085	501 Squadron
34086	219 Squadron
34087	145 Squadron
34088	213 Squadron
34089	602 Squadron
34090	Sir Eustace Missenden, Southern Railway
34091	Weymouth
34092	City of Wells
34093	Saunton
34094	Mortehoe
34095	Brentor
34096	Trevone
34097	Holsworthy
34098	Templecombe
34099	Lynmouth
34100	Appledore
34101	Hartland
34102	Lapford
34103	Calstock
34104	Bere Alston
34105	Swanage
34106	Lydford
34107	Blandford Forum
34108	Wincanton
34109	Sir Trafford Leigh-Mallory
34110	66 Squadron

CLASS MN "MERCHANT NAVY" 4–6–2

35001	Channel Packet
35002	Union Castle
35003	Royal Mail
35004	Cunard White Star
35005	Canadian Pacific
35006	Peninsular & Oriental S.N. Co.
35007	Aberdeen Commonwealth
35008	Orient Line
35009	Shaw Savill
35010	Blue Star
35011	General Steam Navigation
35012	United States Lines
35013	Blue Funnel
35014	Nederland Line
35015	Rotterdam Lloyd
35016	Elders Fyffes
35017	Belgian Marine
35018	British India Line
35019	French Line CGT
35020	Bibby Line
35021	New Zealand Line
35022	Holland-America Line
35023	Holland-Afrika Line
35024	East Asiatic Company
35025	Brocklebank Line
35026	Lamport & Holt Line
35027	Port Line
35028	Clan Line
35029	Ellerman Lines
35030	Elder Dempster Lines

ISLE OF WIGHT LOCOMOTIVES

CLASS E1 0-6-0T

4 Wroxall

CLASS O2 0-4-4T

14 Fishbourne
16 Ventnor
17 Seaview
18 Ningwood
20 Shanklin
21 Sandown
22 Brading
24 Calbourne
25 Godshill
26 Whitwell
27 Merstone
28 Ashey
29 Alverstone
30 Shorwell
31 Chale
32 Bonchurch
33 Bembridge
35 Freshwater
36 Carisbrooke

SOUTHERN RAILWAY LOCOMOTIVE SUPERINTENDENTS AND CHIEF MECHANICAL ENGINEERS OF CONSTITUENT COMPANIES

LONDON & SOUTH WESTERN RAILWAY

J. Woods	1835–1841
J. V. Gooch	1841–1850
J. Beattie	1850–1871
W. G. Beattie	1871–1878
W. Adams	1878–1895
D. Drummond	1895–1912
R. W. Urie...	1912–1922

LONDON, BRIGHTON AND SOUTH COAST RAILWAY

—. Statham	? –1845
J. Gray	1845–1847
S. Kirtley	1847
J. C. Craven	1847–1869
W. Stroudley	1870–1889
R. J. Billinton	1890–1904
D. Earle Marsh	1905–1911
L. B. Billinton	1911–1922

SOUTH EASTERN RAILWAY

B. Cubitt	1842–1845
J. Cudworth	1845–1876
A. M. Watkin	1876
R. Mansell	1877–1878
J. Stirling	1878–1898

LONDON, CHATHAM AND DOVER RAILWAY

W. Cubitt	1853–1860
W. Martley	1860–1874
W. Kirtley	1874–1898

SOUTH EASTERN AND CHATHAM RAILWAY

H. S. Wainwright	1899–1913
R. E. L. Maunsell	1913–1922

SOUTHERN RAILWAY

R. E. L. Maunsell	1923–1937
O. V. Bulleid	1937–1949

BRITISH RAILWAYS LOCOMOTIVES

Nos. 40000-59999

The code given in bold type to the right of each Class heading, e.g. "2P" denotes its British Railways power classification.

The numbers of locomotives in service have been checked to March 12th, 1960.

2-6-2T **3**

Introduced 1930. Fowler L.M.S. design with parallel boiler.
*Introduced 1930. Condensing locos. for working to Moorgate, London.
Weight: { 70 tons 10 cwt. / 71 tons 16 cwt.* }
Pressure: 200 lb. Su.
Cyls.: (O) 17½" × 26".
Driving Wheels: 5' 3".
T.E.: 21,485 lb.
Walschaerts valve gear. P.V.

40001	40015	40031*	40042
40003	40016	40032*	40049
40006	40018	40033*	40050
40007	40020	40034*	40051
40009	40022*	40035*	40053
40010	40024*	40036*	40054
40011	40026*	40037*	40062
40012	40028*	40038*	40063
40014	40029*	40041	40064

Total 36

2-6-2T **3**

Introduced 1935. Stanier L.M.S. taper boiler development of Fowler design (*above*).
*Introduced 1941. Rebuilt with larger boiler.
Weight: { 71 tons 5 cwt. / 72 tons 10 cwt.* }
Pressure: 200 lb. Su.
Cyls.: (O) 17½" × 26".
Driving Wheels: 5' 3".
T.E.: 21,485 lb.
Walschaerts valve gear. P.V.

40071	40106	40141	40177
40072	40107	40142	40178
40073	40108	40143	40179
40074	40109	40144	40180
40075	40110	40145	40181
40076	40111	40146	40182
40077	40112	40147	40183
40078	40113	40148*	40184
40079	40114	40149	40185
40080	40115	40150	40186
40081	40116	40151	40187
40082	40117	40152	40188
40083	40118	40153	40189
40085	40119	40154	40190
40086	40120	40155	40191
40087	40121	40156	40192
40088	40122	40157	40193
40089	40123	40158	40194
40090	40124	40159	40195
40091	40126	40161	40196
40092	40128	40162	40197
40093	40129	40164	40198
40094	40130	40165	40199
40095	40131	40166	40200
40097	40132	40167*	40201
40098	40133	40168	40202
40099	40134	40170	40203*
40100	40135	40171	40205
40101	40136	40173	40206
40102	40137	40174	40207
40103	40138	40175	40208
40104	40140	40176	40209
40105			

Total 129

4-4-0 2P

Introduced 1912. Fowler rebuild of Johnson locos. with superheater and piston valves.

Weight: Loco. 53 tons 7 cwt.
Pressure: 160 lb. Su.
Cyls.: 20½" × 26".
Driving Wheels: 7′ 0½".
T.E.: 17,585 lb.
P.V.

40396	40452	40501	40540
40402	40453	40502	40543
40411	40454	40504	40548
40421	40487	40511	40552
40439	40489	40537	40557
40443	40491		

Total 22

4-4-0 2P

Introduced 1928. Post-grouping development of Midland design, with modified dimensions and reduced boiler mountings.
*Introduced 1928. Locos. built for S. & D.J.R. (taken into L.M.S. stock, 1930).

Weight: Loco. 54 tons 1 cwt.
Pressure: 180 lb. Su.
Cyls.: 19" × 26".
Driving Wheels: 6′ 9".
T.E.: 17,730 lb.
P.V.

40563	40578	40593	40614
40564	40579	40595	40615
40566	40580	40596	40618
40569	40581	40597	40619
40570	40583	40602	40620
40571	40584	40603	40621
40572	40585	40604	40622
40574	40586	40609	40623
40575	40588	40612	40624
40577	40592	40613	40625

40626	40642	40664	40686
40627	40643	40665	40687
40628	40645	40668	40689
40629	40646	40669	40690
40630	40647	40670	40691
40631	40648	40671	40692
40632	40650	40672	40694
40634*	40651	40678	40695
40635*	40652	40681	40696
40637	40657	40682	40697
40638	40659	40683	40698
40640	40661	40684	40700
40641	40663	40685	

Total 91

4-4-0 (3-Cyl. Compd.) 4P

Introduced 1924. Post-grouping development of Johnson Midland compound with modified dimensions and reduced boiler mountings.

Weight: Loco. 61 tons 14 cwt.

Pressure: 200 lb. Su.

Cyls.: { L.P. (2) 21" × 26". H.P. (1) 19" × 26".

Driving Wheels: 6′ 9".

T.E. (of L.P. cyls. at 80% boiler pressure): 22,650 lb.

P.V. (H.P. cyl. only).

40907	41063	41162	41168
40936	41157		

Total 6

2-6-2T — 2

Introduced 1946. Ivatt L.M.S. taper boiler design.

Weight: 63 tons 5 cwt.

Pressure: 200 lb. Su.

Cyls.: (O) 16" × 24". / (O) 16½" × 24".*

Driving Wheels: 5' 0".

T.E.: 17,410 lb. / 18,510 lb.*

Walschaerts valve gear. P.V.

41200	41233	41266	41298*
41201	41234	41267	41299*
41202	41235	41268	41300*
41203	41236	41269	41301*
41204	41237	41270	41302*
41205	41238	41271	41303*
41206	41239	41272	41304*
41207	41240	41273	41305*
41208	41241	41274	41306*
41209	41242	41275	41307*
41210	41243	41276	41308*
41211	41244	41277	41309*
41212	41245	41278	41310*
41213	41246	41279	41311*
41214	41247	41280	41312*
41215	41248	41281	41313*
41216	41249	41282	41314*
41217	41250	41283	41315*
41218	41251	41284	41316*
41219	41252	41285	41317*
41220	41253	41286	41318*
41221	41254	41287	41319*
41222	41255	41288	41320*
41223	41256	41289	41321*
41224	41257	41290*	41322*
41225	41258	41291*	41323*
41226	41259	41292*	41324*
41227	41260	41293*	41325*
41228	41261	41294*	41326*
41229	41262	41295*	41327*
41230	41263	41296*	41328*
41231	41264	41297*	41329*
41232	41265		

Total 130

0-4-0T — 0F

Introduced 1907. Deeley Midland design.

Weight: 32 tons 16 cwt.

Pressure: 160 lb.

Cyls.: (O) 15" × 22".

Driving Wheels: 3' 9¾".

T.E.: 14,635 lb.

Walschaerts valve gear.

41528	41531	41533	41536
41529	41532	41535	41537

Total 8

0-6-0T — 1F

Introduced 1878. Johnson Midland design.

*Rebuilt with Belpaire firebox.

Weight: 39 tons 11 cwt.

Pressure: 150 lb. / 140 lb.*

Cyls.: 17" × 24".

Driving Wheels: 4' 7".

T.E.: 16,080 lb. / 15,005 lb.*

41702*	41739*	41804*	41855*
41708*	41763*	41835	41875*
41712*	41769*	41844*	41879*
41734*	41773*		

Total 14

0-4-4T — 2P

Introduced 1932. Stanier L.M.S. design. Push-and-pull fitted.

Weight: 58 tons 1 cwt.

Pressure: 160 lb.

Cyls.: 18" × 26".

Driving Wheels: 5' 7"

T.E.: 17,100 lb.

41900

Total 1

4-4-2T 3P

Introduced 1923. Midland and L.M.S. development of Whitelegg L.T. & S. "79" Class.
Weight: 71 tons 10 cwt.
Pressure: 170 lb.
Cyls.: (O) 19" × 26".
Driving Wheels: 6' 6".
T.E.: 17,390 lb.

41947 41949 41969

Total 3

0-6-2T 3F

Introduced 1903. Whitelegg L.T. & S. "69" Class.
Weight: 64 tons 13 cwt.
Pressure: 170 lb.
Cyls.: 18" × 26".
Driving Wheels: 5' 3".
T.E.: 19,320 lb.

41981

Total 1

2-6-4T 4

*Introduced 1927. Fowler L.M.S. parallel boiler design.
†Introduced 1933. As earlier engines, but with side-window cab and doors.
‡Introduced 1934. Stanier taper-boiler 3-cylinder design for L.T. & S.
§Introduced 1935. Stanier taper-boiler 2-cylinder design.
¶Introduced 1945. Fairburn development of Stanier design with shorter wheelbase and detail alterations.

Weight: 86 tons 5 cwt.*† / 92 tons 5 cwt.‡ / 87 tons 17 cwt.§ / 85 tons 5 cwt.¶
Pressure (all types): 200 lb. Su.
Cyls.: (O) 19" × 26".*† / (3) 16" × 26".‡ / (O) 19⅝" × 26".§¶
Driving Wheels (all types): 5' 9".
T.E.: 23,125 lb.*† / 24,600 lb.‡ / 24,670 lb.§¶
Walschaerts valve gear. P.V.

¶FAIRBURN LOCOS.

42050	42095	42140	42185
42051	42096	42141	42186
42052	42097	42142	42187
42053	42098	42143	42188
42054	42099	42144	42189
42055	42100	42145	42190
42056	42101	42146	42191
42057	42102	42147	42192
42058	42103	42148	42193
42059	42104	42149	42194
42060	42105	42150	42195
42061	42106	42151	42196
42062	42107	42152	42197
42063	42108	42153	42198
42064	42109	42154	42199
42065	42110	42155	42200
42066	42111	42156	42201
42067	42112	42157	42202
42068	42113	42158	42203
42069	42114	42159	42204
42070	42115	42160	42205
42071	42116	42161	42206
42072	42117	42162	42207
42073	42118	42163	42208
42074	42119	42164	42209
42075	42120	42165	42210
42076	42121	42166	42211
42077	42122	42167	42212
42078	42123	42168	42213
42079	42124	42169	42214
42080	42125	42170	42215
42081	42126	42171	42216
42082	42127	42172	42217
42083	42128	42173	42218
42084	42129	42174	42219
42085	42130	42175	42220
42086	42131	42176	42221
42087	42132	42177	42222
42088	42133	42178	42223
42089	42134	42179	42224
42090	42135	42180	42225
42091	42136	42181	42226
42092	42137	42182	42227
42093	42138	42183	42228
42094	42139	42184	42229

42230	42248	42266	42284
42231	42249	42267	42285
42232	42250	42268	42286
42233	42251	42269	42287
42234	42252	42270	42288
42235	42253	42271	42289
42236	42254	42272	42290
42237	42255	42273	42291
42238	42256	42274	42292
42239	42257	42275	42293
42240	42258	42276	42294
42241	42259	42277	42295
42242	42260	42278	42296
42243	42261	42279	42297
42244	42262	42280	42298
42245	42263	42281	42299
42246	42264	42282	
42247	42265	42283	

*FOWLER LOCOS.

42300	42326	42350	42374
42301	42327	42351	42375
42302	42328	42352	42376
42303	42329	42353	42377
42304	42330	42355	42378
42305	42331	42356	42379
42306	42332	42357	42380
42307	42333	42358	42381
42309	42334	42359	42382
42310	42335	42360	42383
42311	42336	42361	42384
42313	42337	42362	42385
42314	42338	42363	42386
42315	42339	42364	42387
42316	42340	42365	42388
42317	42342	42366	42389
42318	42343	42367	42390
42319	42344	42368	42391
42320	42345	42369	42392
42322	42346	42370	42393
42323	42347	42371	42394
42324	42348	42372	
42325	42349	42373	

†FOWLER LOCOS. WITH SIDE-WINDOW CAB

42395	42403	42411	42418
42396	42404	42412	42419
42397	42405	42413	42420
42398	42406	42414	42421
42399	42407	42415	42422
42400	42408	42416	42423
42401	42409	42417	42424
42402	42410		

§STANIER 2-CYL. LOCOS.

42425	42443	42461	42479
42426	42444	42462	42480
42427	42445	42463	42481
42428	42446	42464	42482
42429	42447	42465	42483
42430	42448	42466	42484
42431	42449	42467	42485
42432	42450	42468	42486
42433	42451	42469	42487
42434	42452	42470	42488
42435	42453	42471	42489
42436	42454	42472	42490
42437	42455	42473	42491
42438	42456	42474	42492
42439	42457	42475	42493
42440	42458	42476	42494
42441	42459	42477	
42442	42460	42478	

‡STANIER 3-CYL. LOCOS.

42500	42510	42519	42528
42501	42511	42520	42529
42502	42512	42521	42530
42503	42513	42522	42531
42504	42514	42523	42532
42505	42515	42524	42533
42506	42516	42525	42534
42507	42517	42526	42535
42508	42518	42527	42536
42509			

§STANIER 2-CYL. LOCOS.

42537	42571	42605	42639
42538	42572	42606	42640
42539	42573	42607	42641
42540	42574	42608	42642
42541	42575	42609	42643
42542	42576	42610	42644
42543	42577	42611	42645
42544	42578	42612	42646
42545	42579	42613	42647
42546	42580	42614	42648
42547	42581	42615	42649
42548	42582	42616	42650
42549	42583	42617	42651
42550	42584	42618	42652
42551	42585	42619	42653
42552	42586	42620	42654
42553	42587	42621	42655
42554	42588	42622	42656
42555	42589	42623	42657
42556	42590	42624	42658
42557	42591	42625	42659
42558	42592	42626	42660
42559	42593	42627	42661
42560	42594	42628	42662
42561	42595	42629	42663
42562	42596	42630	42664
42563	42597	42631	42665
42564	42598	42632	42666
42565	42599	42633	42667
42566	42600	42634	42668
42567	42601	42635	42669
42568	42602	42636	42670
42569	42603	42637	42671
42570	42604	42638	42672

¶FAIRBURN LOCOS.

42673	42680	42687	42694
42674	42681	42688	42695
42675	42682	42689	42696
42676	42683	42690	42697
42677	42684	42691	42698
42678	42685	42692	42699
42679	42686	42693	

Total 640

2-6-0 6P5F

Introduced 1926. Hughes L.M.S. design built under Fowler's direction. Walschaerts valve gear. P.V.

*Introduced 1953. Locos. rebuilt experimentally with Lentz R.C. poppet valves in 1931; rebuilt with Reidinger rotary poppet valve gear in 1953.

Weight: Loco. 66 tons 0 cwt.
Pressure: 180 lb. Su.
Cyls.: (O) 21″ × 26″.
Driving Wheels: 5′ 6″.
T.E.: 26,580 lb.

42700	42735	42770	42805
42701	42736	42771	42806
42702	42737	42772	42807
42703	42738	42773	42808
42704	42739	42774	42809
42705	42740	42775	42810
42706	42741	42776	42811
42707	42742	42777	42812
42708	42743	42778	42813
42709	42744	42779	42814
42710	42745	42780	42815
42711	42746	42781	42816
42712	42747	42782	42817
42713	42748	42783	42818*
42714	42749	42784	42819
42715	42750	42785	42820
42716	42751	42786	42821
42717	42752	42787	42822*
42718	42753	42788	42823
42719	42754	42789	42824*
42720	42755	42790	42825*
42721	42756	42791	42826
42722	42757	42792	42827
42723	42758	42793	42828
42724	42759	42794	42829*
42725	42760	42795	42830
42726	42761	42796	42831
42727	42762	42797	42832
42728	42763	42798	42833
42729	42764	42799	42834
42730	42765	42800	42835
42731	42766	42801	42836
42732	42767	42802	42837
42733	42768	42803	42838
42734	42769	42804	42839

42840	42867	42894	42920
42841	42868	42895	42921
42842	42869	42896	42922
42843	42870	42897	42923
42844	42871	42898	42924
42845	42872	42899	42925
42846	42873	42900	42926
42847	42874	42901	42927
42848	42875	42902	42928
42849	42876	42903	42929
42850	42877	42904	42930
42851	42878	42905	42931
42852	42879	42906	42932
42853	42880	42907	42933
42854	42881	42908	42934
42855	42882	42909	42935
42856	42883	42910	42936
42857	42884	42911	42937
42858	42885	42912	42938
42859	42886	42913	42939
42860	42887	42914	42940
42861	42888	42915	42941
42862	42889	42916	42942
42863	42890	42917	42943
42864	42891	42918	42944
42865	42892	42919	
42866	42893		

Total 245

2-6-0 6P5F

Introduced 1933. Stanier L.M.S. taper boiler design, some with safety valves mounted on the top feed.
Weight: Loco. 69 tons 2 cwt.
Pressure: 225 lb. Su.
Cyls.: (O) 18" × 28".
Driving Wheels: 5' 6".
T.E.: 26,290 lb.
Walschaerts valve gear. P.V.

42945	42955	42965	42975
42946	42956	42966	42976
42947	42957	42967	42977
42948	42958	42968	42978
42949	42959	42969	42979
42950	42960	42970	42980
42951	42961	42971	42981
42952	42962	42972	42982
42953	42963	42973	42983
42954	42964	42974	42984

Total 40

2-6-0 4

Introduced 1947. Ivatt L.M.S. taper boiler design with double chimney. Later engines introduced with single chimney, with which earlier engines are being rebuilt.
Weight: Loco. 59 tons 2 cwt.
Pressure: 225 lb. Su.
Cyls.: (O) 17½" × 26".
Driving Wheels: 5' 3".
T.E.: 24,170 lb.
Walschaerts valve gear. P.V.

43000	43036	43072	43108
43001	43037	43073	43109
43002	43038	43074	43110
43003	43039	43075	43111
43004	43040	43076	43112
43005	43041	43077	43113
43006	43042	43078	43114
43007	43043	43079	43115
43008	43044	43080	43116
43009	43045	43081	43117
43010	43046	43082	43118
43011	43047	43083	43119
43012	43048	43084	43120
43013	43049	43085	43121
43014	43050	43086	43122
43015	43051	43087	43123
43016	43052	43088	43124
43017	43053	43089	43125
43018	43054	43090	43126
43019	43055	43091	43127
43020	43056	43092	43128
43021	43057	43093	43129
43022	43058	43094	43130
43023	43059	43095	43131
43024	43060	43096	43132
43025	43061	43097	43133
43026	43062	43098	43134
43027	43063	43099	43135
43028	43064	43100	43136
43029	43065	43101	43137
43030	43066	43102	43138
43031	43067	43103	43139
43032	43068	43104	43140
43033	43069	43105	43141
43034	43070	43106	43142
43035	43071	43107	43143

43144	43149	43154	43158
43145	43150	43155	43159
43146	43151	43156	43160
43147	43152	43157	43161
43148	43153		

Total 162

0-6-0 3F

Introduced 1885. Johnson Midland locos., rebuilt from 1916 by Fowler with Belpaire firebox.

*Introduced 1885. Johnson Midland locos., rebuilt from 1920 by Fowler with Belpaire firebox.

†Introduced 1896. Locos. built for S. & D.J. (taken into L.M.S. stock 1930).

Weight: Loco. 43 tons 17 cwt.

Pressure: 175 lb.

Cyls.: 18" × 26".

Driving Wheels: { 5' 3". / 5' 3".† / 4' 11".* }

T.E.: { 19,890 lb. / 19,890 lb.† / 21,240 lb.* }

43185*	43242	43309	43389
43187*	43243	43314	43394
43188*	43245	43321	43395
43189*	43250	43325	43399
43194†	43254	43326	43400
43200	43257	43329	43405
43203	43261	43330	43410
43207	43263	43333	43411
43211†	43266	43340	43427
43212	43267	43342	43428
43213	43268	43344	43429
43214	43277	43359	43435
43216†	43282	43361	43436
43218†	43284	43368	43444
43225	43295	43371	43446
43234	43305	43373	43449
43235	43306	43374	43453
43240	43307	43386	43456

43457	43565	43624	43687
43459	43570	43627	43705
43464	43572	43634	43709
43468	43574	43637	43714
43474	43579	43639	43715
43482	43580	43644	43721
43484	43583	43645	43729
43496	43585	43650	43734
43499	43586	43652	43735
43507	43593	43657	43737
43510	43594	43658	43751
43514	43599	43668	43754
43515	43605	43669	43756
43521	43608	43673	43760
43523	43615	43679	43762
43529	43618	43680	43763
43548	43620	43681	43766
43562	43621	43682	43773

Total 144

0-6-0 3F

Introduced 1906. Deeley Midland design. Rebuilt by Fowler with Belpaire firebox.

Weight: Loco. 46 tons 3 cwt.

Pressure: 175 lb.

Cyls.: 18½" × 26".

Driving Wheels: 5' 3".

T.E.: 21,010 lb.

43778	43800	43812	43825
43784	43808	43814	43826
43789	43809	43822	43832
43793			

Total 13

0-6-0 4F

Introduced 1911. Fowler superheated Midland design.
Weight: Loco. 48 tons 15 cwt.
Pressure: 175 lb. Su.
Cyls.: 20" × 26".
Driving Wheels: 5' 3".
T.E.: 24,555 lb.
P.V.

43840	43897	43944	43985
43843	43899	43945	43986
43844	43900	43947	43987
43845	43902	43948	43988
43846	43903	43949	43989
43848	43905	43950	43991
43849	43906	43951	43994
43850	43908	43952	43995
43853	43911	43953	43996
43854	43913	43954	43999
43855	43914	43955	44001
43856	43915	43957	44002
43859	43917	43958	44003
43861	43918	43960	44004
43863	43920	43962	44007
43865	43921	43963	44008
43868	43922	43964	44009
43869	43923	43967	44010
43870	43924	43968	44011
43871	43925	43969	44012
43872	43928	43971	44013
43876	43929	43972	44015
43880	43931	43973	44016
43882	43932	43975	44019
43883	43933	43976	44020
43884	43935	43977	44022
43885	43937	43979	44023
43887	43938	43981	44025
43888	43940	43982	44026
43893	43942	43983	

Total 119

0-6-0 4F

Introduced 1924. Post-grouping development of Midland design with reduced boiler mountings.

*Introduced 1922. Locos. buil for S. & D.J.R. to M.R. design (taken into L.M.S. stock 1930).

Weight: Loco. 48 tons 15 cwt.
Pressure: 175 lb. Su.
Cyls.: 20" × 26".
Driving Wheels: 5' 3".
T.E.: 24,555 lb.
P.V.

44027	44070	44118	44164
44028	44071	44119	44165
44029	44074	44121	44166
44030	44075	44122	44167
44031	44076	44123	44168
44033	44078	44124	44169
44034	44079	44125	44170
44035	44080	44126	44171
44036	44081	44127	44172
44037	44082	44128	44174
44038	44083	44129	44176
44039	44085	44130	44177
44040	44086	44131	44178
44041	44087	44132	44179
44042	44088	44133	44180
44043	44089	44134	44181
44044	44090	44135	44182
44045	44091	44137	44183
44046	44092	44138	44184
44047	44094	44139	44185
44048	44096	44141	44186
44049	44097	44143	44187
44051	44098	44146	44188
44052	44099	44147	44189
44053	44100	44148	44190
44054	44101	44149	44191
44055	44102	44150	44192
44056	44104	44151	44193
44057	44105	44152	44194
44059	44106	44153	44195
44060	44107	44154	44196
44061	44109	44155	44197
44062	44110	44156	44198
44063	44111	44157	44199
44065	44112	44158	44200
44066	44113	44159	44202
44067	44114	44160	44203
44068	44115	44162	44205
44069	44117	44163	44206

44207
44208
44209
44210
44211
44212
44213
44214
44215
44216
44218
44219
44220
44221
44222
44223
44224
44226
44228
44229
44231
44232
44233
44234
44235
44236
44237
44238
44239
44240
44241
44242
44243
44244
44245
44246
44247
44248
44249
44250
44251
44252
44253
44254
44255
44256
44257
44258
44259
44260
44261
44262
44263
44264
44265
44266
44267
44268
44269
44270
44271
44272
44273
44274
44275
44276
44277
44278
44279
44280
44281
44282
44283
44284
44286
44287
44288
44289
44290
44292
44294
44295
44296
44297
44299
44300
44301
44302
44303
44304
44305
44307
44308
44309
44310
44311
44312
44314
44315
44318
44319
44320
44321
44322
44323
44324
44325
44327
44328
44329
44330
44331
44332
44333
44334
44335
44336
44337
44338
44339
44340
44341
44342
44344
44345
44346
44347
44348
44349
44350
44351
44352
44353
44354
44355
44356
44358
44359
44362
44363
44364
44367
44368
44370
44371
44373
44374
44375
44376
44377
44378
44379
44380
44381
44384
44386
44387
44388
44389
44390
44392
44393
44394
44395
44396
44397
44398
44399
44400
44401
44402
44403
44404
44405
44407
44408
44409
44411
44413
44414
44416
44417
44418
44419
44420
44421
44422
44424
44425
44426
44428
44429
44431
44432
44433
44434
44435
44436
44437
44439
44440
44441
44442
44443
44444
44445
44446
44447
44448
44449
44450
44451
44452
44454
44455
44456
44457
44458
44460
44461
44462
44463
44464
44465
44466
44467
44468
44469
44470
44472
44474
44475
44476
44477
44478
44479
44481
44482
44484
44485
44486
44487
44489
44490
44491
44492
44493
44494
44497
44499
44500
44501
44504
44505
44508
44509
44512
44514
44516
44517
44518
44519
44520
44521
44522
44523
44524
44525
44526
44527
44528
44529
44530
44531
44532
44533
44534
44535
44536
44537
44538
44539
44540
44541
44542
44543
44544
44545
44547
44548
44549
44550
44551
44552
44553
44554
44556
44557*
44558*
44559*
44560*
44561*
44562
44564
44565
44566
44567
44568
44569
44570
44571
44572
44573
44574
44575
44576
44577
44578
44579
44580
44581
44582
44583
44584
44585
44586
44587
44588
44589
44590
44591
44592
44593
44594
44595
44596
44597
44598
44599
44601
44602
44603
44604
44605
44606

Total 501

4-6-0 5

Introduced 1934. Stanier L.M.S. taper boiler design.

Experimental locomotives:—

1. Introduced 1947. Stephenson link motion (outside), Timken roller bearings.
2. Introduced 1948. Caprotti valve gear.
3. Introduced 1948. Caprotti valve gear, Timken roller bearings.
4. Introduced 1948. Caprotti valve gear, Timken roller bearings, double chimney.
5. Introduced 1947. Timken roller bearings.
6. Introduced 1947. Timken roller bearings, double chimney.
7. Introduced 1949. Fitted with steel firebox.
8. Introduced 1950. Skefko roller bearings.
9. Introduced 1950. Timken roller bearings on driving coupled axle only.
10. Introduced 1950. Skefko roller bearings on driving coupled axle only.
11. Introduced 1951. Caprotti valve gear, Skefko roller bearings.

Weight: Loco. { 72 tons 2 cwt. / 75 tons 6 cwt. (1, 5, 6, 8, 9, 10). / 74 tons 0 cwt. (2, 3, 4, 11). / 72 tons 2 cwt. (7).

Pressure: 225 lb. Su.
Cyls.: (O) $18\frac{1}{2}'' \times 28''$.
Driving Wheels: 6′ 0″.
T.E.: 25,455 lb.
Walschaerts valve gear and P.V. except where otherwise shown.

44658	44705	44752[3]	44799
44659	44706	44753[3]	44800
44660	44707	44754[3]	44801
44661	44708	44755[4]	44802
44662	44709	44756[4]	44803
44663	44710	44757[4]	44804
44664	44711	44758[5]	44805
44665	44712	44759[5]	44806
44666	44713	44760[5]	44807
44667	44714	44761[5]	44808
44668[10]	44715	44762[5]	44809
44669[10]	44716	44763[5]	44810
44670[10]	44717	44764[5]	44811
44671[10]	44718[7]	44765[6]	44812
44672[10]	44719[7]	44766[6]	44813
44673[10]	44720[7]	44767[1]	44814
44674[10]	44721[7]	44768	44815
44675[10]	44722[7]	44769	44816
44676[10]	44723[7]	44770	44817
44677[10]	44724[7]	44771	44818
44678[8]	44725[7]	44772	44819
44679[8]	44726[7]	44773	44820
44680[8]	44727[7]	44774	44821
44681[8]	44728	44775	44822
44682[8]	44729	44776	44823
44683[8]	44730	44777	44824
44684[8]	44731	44778	44825
44685[8]	44732	44779	44826
44686[11]	44733	44780	44827
44687[11]	44734	44781	44828
44688[9]	44735	44782	44829
44689[9]	44736	44783	44830
44690[9]	44737	44784	44831
44691[9]	44738[2]	44785	44832
44692[9]	44739[2]	44786	44833
44693[9]	44740[2]	44787	44834
44694[9]	44741[2]	44788	44835
44695[9]	44742[2]	44789	44836
44696[9]	44743[2]	44790	44837
44697[9]	44744[2]	44791	44838
44698	44745[2]	44792	44839
44699	44746[2]	44793	44840
44700	44747[2]	44794	44841
44701	44748[3]	44795	44842
44702	44749[3]	44796	44843
44703	44750[3]	44797	44844
44704	44751[3]	44798	44845

44846	44893	44940	44987
44847	44894	44941	44988
44848	44895	44942	44989
44849	44896	44943	44990
44850	44897	44944	44991
44851	44898	44945	44992
44852	44899	44946	44993
44853	44900	44947	44994
44854	44901	44948	44995
44855	44902	44949	44996
44856	44903	44950	44997
44857	44904	44951	44998
44858	44905	44952	44999
44859	44906	44953	45000
44860	44907	44954	45001
44861	44908	44955	45002
44862	44909	44956	45003
44863	44910	44957	45004
44864	44911	44958	45005
44865	44912	44959	45006
44866	44913	44960	45007
44867	44914	44961	45008
44868	44915	44962	45009
44869	44916	44963	45010
44870	44917	44964	45011
44871	44918	44965	45012
44872	44919	44966	45013
44873	44920	44967	45014
44874	44921	44968	45015
44875	44922	44969	45016
44876	44923	44970	45017
44877	44924	44971	45018
44878	44925	44972	45019
44879	44926	44973	45020
44880	44927	44974	45021
44881	44928	44975	45022
44882	44929	44976	45023
44883	44930	44977	45024
44884	44931	44978	45025
44885	44932	44979	45026
44886	44933	44980	45027
44887	44934	44981	45028
44888	44935	44982	45029
44889	44936	44983	45030
44890	44937	44984	45031
44891	44938	44985	45032
44892	44939	44986	45033

45034	45074	45114	45154*
45035	45075	45115	45155
45036	45076	45116	45156*
45037	45077	45117	45157*
45038	45078	45118	45158*
45039	45079	45119	45159
45040	45080	45120	45160
45041	45081	45121	45161
45042	45082	45122	45162
45043	45083	45123	45163
45044	45084	45124	45164
45045	45085	45125	45165
45046	45086	45126	45166
45047	45087	45127	45167
45048	45088	45128	45168
45049	45089	45129	45169
45050	45090	45130	45170
45051	45091	45131	45171
45052	45092	45132	45172
45053	45093	45133	45173
45054	45094	45134	45174
45055	45095	45135	45175
45056	45096	45136	45176
45057	45097	45137	45177
45058	45098	45138	45178
45059	45099	45139	45179
45060	45100	45140	45180
45061	45101	45141	45181
45062	45102	45142	45182
45063	45103	45143	45183
45064	45104	45144	45184
45065	45105	45145	45185
45066	45106	45146	45186
45067	45107	45147	45187
45068	45108	45148	45188
45069	45109	45149	45189
45070	45110	45150	45190
45071	45111	45151	45191
45072	45112	45152	45192
45073	45113	45153	45193

*** NAMES :**

45154 Lanarkshire Yeomanry
45156 Ayrshire Yeomanry
45157 The Glasgow Highlander
45158 Glasgow Yeomanry

45194	45241	45288	45335
45195	45242	45289	45336
45196	45243	45290	45337
45197	45244	45291	45338
45198	45245	45292	45339
45199	45246	45293	45340
45200	45247	45294	45341
45201	45248	45295	45342
45202	45249	45296	45343
45203	45250	45297	45344
45204	45251	45298	45345
45205	45252	45299	45346
45206	45253	45300	45347
45207	45254	45301	45348
45208	45255	45302	45349
45209	45256	45303	45350
45210	45257	45304	45351
45211	45258	45305	45352
45212	45259	45306	45353
45213	45260	45307	45354
45214	45261	45308	45355
45215	45262	45309	45356
45216	45263	45310	45357
45217	45264	45311	45358
45218	45265	45312	45359
45219	45266	45313	45360
45220	45267	45314	45361
45221	45268	45315	45362
45222	45269	45316	45363
45223	45270	45317	45364
45224	45271	45318	45365
45225	45272	45319	45366
45226	45273	45320	45367
45227	45274	45321	45368
45228	45275	45322	45369
45229	45276	45323	45370
45230	45277	45324	45371
45231	45278	45325	45372
45232	45279	45326	45373
45233	45280	45327	45374
45234	45281	45328	45375
45235	45282	45329	45376
45236	45283	45330	45377
45237	45284	45331	45378
45238	45285	45332	45379
45239	45286	45333	45380
45240	45287	45334	45381

45382	45412	45442	45472
45383	45413	45443	45473
45384	45414	45444	45474
45385	45415	45445	45475
45386	45416	45446	45476
45387	45417	45447	45477
45388	45418	45448	45478
45389	45419	45449	45479
45390	45420	45450	45480
45391	45421	45451	45481
45392	45422	45452	45482
45393	45423	45453	45483
45394	45424	45454	45484
45395	45425	45455	45485
45396	45426	45456	45486
45397	45427	45457	45487
45398	45428	45458	45488
45399	45429	45459	45489
45400	45430	45460	45490
45401	45431	45461	45491
45402	45432	45462	45492
45403	45433	45463	45493
45404	45434	45464	45494
45405	45435	45465	45495
45406	45436	45466	45496
45407	45437	45467	45497
45408	45438	45468	45498
45409	45439	45469	45499
45410	45440	45470	
45411	45441	45471	

Total 842

"Patriot" Class

4-6-0 6P5F & 7P

***6P5F.** Introduced 1930. Fowler 3-cyl. rebuild of L.N.W. "Claughton" Class (introduced 1912), retaining original wheels and other details.

Remainder. Introduced 1933. New locos. to Fowler design (45502–41 were officially considered as rebuilds).

†**7P.** Introduced 1946. Ivatt rebuild of Fowler locos. with larger taper boiler, new cylinders and double chimney.

Weight: Loco. { 80 tons 15 cwt. / 80 tons 15 cwt.* / 82 tons 0 cwt.† }
Pressure: { 200 lb. Su. / 200 lb. Su.* / 250 lb. Su.† }
Cyls: { (3) 18" × 26". / (3) 18" × 26".* / (3) 17" × 26".† }
Driving Wheels: 6' 9".
T.E.: { 26,520 lb. / 26,520 lb.* / 29,570 lb.† }
Walschaerts valve gear. P.V.

45500* Patriot
45501* St. Dunstan's
45502 Royal Naval Division
45503 The Royal Leicestershire Regiment
45504 Royal Signals
45505 The Royal Army Ordnance Corps
45506 The Royal Pioneer Corps
45507 Royal Tank Corps
45508
45509 The Derbyshire Yeomanry
45510
45511 Isle of Man
45512† Bunsen
45513
45514† Holyhead
45515 Caernarvon
45516 The Bedfordshire and Hertfordshire Regiment
45517
45518 Bradshaw
45519 Lady Godiva
45520 Llandudno
45521† Rhyl
45522† Prestatyn
45523† Bangor
45524 Blackpool
45525† Colwyn Bay
45526† Morecambe and Heysham
45527† Southport
45528† R.E.M.E.
45529† Stephenson
45530† Sir Frank Ree
45531† Sir Frederick Harrison
45532† Illustrious
45533 Lord Rathmore
45534† E. Tootal Broadhurst
45535† Sir Herbert Walker K.C.B.
45536† Private W. Wood, V.C.
45537 Private E. Sykes, V.C.
45538 Giggleswick
45539 E. C. Trench
45540† Sir Robert Turnbull
45541 Duke of Sutherland
45542
45543 Home Guard
45544
45545† Planet
45546 Fleetwood
45547
45548 Lytham St. Annes
45549
45550
45551

Total 52

"Jubilee" Class

4-6-0 6P5F & 7P

6P5F. Introduced 1934. Stanier **L.M.S.** taper boiler development of the "Patriot" class.

***7P.** Introduced 1942. Rebuilt with larger boiler and double chimney.

Weight: Loco. { 79 tons 11 cwt. / 82 tons 0 cwt.* }
Pressure: { 225 lb. Su. / 250 lb. Su.* }
Cyls.: (3) 17" × 26".
Driving Wheels: 6' 9".
T.E.: { 26,610 lb. / 29,570 lb.* }
Walschaerts valve gear. P.V.

45552 Silver Jubilee
45553 Canada
45554 Ontario
45555 Quebec

45556	Nova Scotia
45557	New Brunswick
45558	Manitoba
45559	British Columbia
45560	Prince Edward Island
45561	Saskatchewan
45562	Alberta
45563	Australia
45564	New South Wales
45565	Victoria
45566	Queensland
45567	South Australia
45568	Western Australia
45569	Tasmania
45570	New Zealand
45571	South Africa
45572	Eire
45573	Newfoundland
45574	India
45575	Madras
45576	Bombay
45577	Bengal
45578	United Provinces
45579	Punjab
45580	Burma
45581	Bihar and Orissa
45582	Central Provinces
45583	Assam
45584	North West Frontier
45585	Hyderabad
45586	Mysore
45587	Baroda
45588	Kashmir
45589	Gwalior
45590	Travancore
45591	Udaipur
45592	Indore
45593	Kolhapur
45594	Bhopal
45595	Southern Rhodesia
45596	Bahamas
45597	Barbados
45598	Basutoland
45599	Bechuanaland
45600	Bermuda
45601	British Guiana
45602	British Honduras
45603	Solomon Islands
45604	Ceylon
45605	Cyprus
45606	Falkland Islands
45607	Fiji
45608	Gibraltar
45609	Gilbert and Ellice Islands
45610	Ghana
45611	Hong Kong
45612	Jamaica
45613	Kenya
45614	Leeward Islands
45615	Malay States
45616	Malta G.C.
45617	Mauritius
45618	New Hebrides
45619	Nigeria
45620	North Borneo
45621	Northern Rhodesia
45622	Nyasaland
45623	Palestine
45624	St. Helena
45625	Sarawak
45626	Seychelles
45627	Sierra Leone
45628	Somaliland
45629	Straits Settlements
45630	Swaziland
45631	Tanganyika
45632	Tonga
45633	Aden
45634	Trinidad
45635	Tobago
45636	Uganda
45638	Zanzibar
45639	Raleigh
45640	Frobisher
45641	Sandwich
45642	Boscawen
45643	Rodney
45644	Howe
45645	Collingwood
45646	Napier
45647	Sturdee
45648	Wemyss
45649	Hawkins
45650	Blake

45651	Shovell
45652	Hawke
45653	Barham
45654	Hood
45655	Keith
45656	Cochrane
45657	Tyrwhitt
45658	Keyes
45659	Drake
45660	Rooke
45661	Vernon
45662	Kempenfelt
45663	Jervis
45664	Nelson
45665	Lord Rutherford of Nelson
45666	Cornwallis
45667	Jellicoe
45668	Madden
45669	Fisher
45670	Howard of Effingham
45671	Prince Rupert
45672	Anson
45673	Keppel
45674	Duncan
45675	Hardy
45676	Codrington
45677	Beatty
45678	De Robeck
45679	Armada
45680	Camperdown
45681	Aboukir
45682	Trafalgar
45683	Hogue
45684	Jutland
45685	Barfleur
45686	St. Vincent
45687	Neptune
45688	Polyphemus
45689	Ajax
45690	Leander
45691	Orion
45692	Cyclops
45693	Agamemnon
45694	Bellerophon
45695	Minotaur
45696	Arethusa
45697	Achilles
45698	Mars
45699	Galatea
45700	Amethyst
45701	Conqueror
45702	Colossus
45703	Thunderer
45704	Leviathan
45705	Seahorse
45706	Express
45707	Valiant
45708	Resolution
45709	Implacable
45710	Irresistible
45711	Courageous
45712	Victory
45713	Renown
45714	Revenge
45715	Invincible
45716	Swiftsure
45717	Dauntless
45718	Dreadnought
45719	Glorious
45720	Indomitable
45721	Impregnable
45722	Defence
45723	Fearless
45724	Warspite
45725	Repulse
45726	Vindictive
45727	Inflexible
45728	Defiance
45729	Furious
45730	Ocean
45731	Perseverance
45732	Sanspareil
45733	Novelty
45734	Meteor
45735*	Comet
45736*	Phoenix
45737	Atlas
45738	Samson
45739	Ulster
45740	Munster
45741	Leinster
45742	Connaught

Total 190

"Royal Scot" Class

4-6-0 7P

Introduced 1943. Stanier rebuild of Fowler **L.M.S.** locos. (introduced 1927) with taper boiler, new cylinders and double chimney.

*Introduced 1935. Stanier taper boiler rebuild with simple cylinders of experimental high pressure compound loco. No. 6399 *Fury*. (Introduced 1929.)

Weight: Loco. {83 tons. / 84 tons 1 cwt.*}

Pressure: 250 lb. Su.

Cyls.: (3) 18" × 26".

Driving Wheels: 6' 9".

T.E.: 33,150 lb.

Walschaerts valve gear. P.V.

46100 Royal Scot
46101 Royal Scots Grey
46102 Black Watch
46103 Royal Scots Fusilier
46104 Scottish Borderer
46105 Cameron Highlander
46106 Gordon Highlander
46107 Argyll and Sutherland Highlander
46108 Seaforth Highlander
46109 Royal Engineer
46110 Grenadier Guardsman
46111 Royal Fusilier
46112 Sherwood Forester
46113 Cameronian
46114 Coldstream Guardsman
46115 Scots Guardsman
46116 Irish Guardsman
46117 Welsh Guardsman
46118 Royal Welch Fusilier
46119 Lancashire Fusilier
46120 Royal Inniskilling Fusilier
46121 Highland Light Infantry, City of Glasgow Regiment
46122 Royal Ulster Rifleman
46123 Royal Irish Fusilier
46124 London Scottish
46125 3rd Carabinier
46126 Royal Army Service Corps
46127 Old Contemptibles
46128 The Lovat Scouts
46129 The Scottish Horse
46130 The West Yorkshire Regiment
46131 The Royal Warwickshire Regiment
46132 The King's Regiment Liverpool
46133 The Green Howards
46134 The Cheshire Regiment
46135 The East Lancashire Regiment
46136 The Border Regiment
46137 The Prince of Wales's Volunteers (South Lancashire)
46138 The London Irish Rifleman
46139 The Welch Regiment
46140 The King's Royal Rifle Corps
46141 The North Staffordshire Regiment
46142 The York & Lancaster Regiment
46143 The South Staffordshire Regiment
46144 Honourable Artillery Company
46145 The Duke of Wellington's Regt. (West Riding)
46146 The Rifle Brigade
46147 The Northamptonshire Regiment
46148 The Manchester Regiment
46149 The Middlesex Regiment
46150 The Life Guardsman
46151 The Royal Horse Guardsman
46152 The King's Dragoon Guardsman
46153 The Royal Dragoon
46154 The Hussar

46155 The Lancer
46156 The South Wales Borderer
46157 The Royal Artilleryman
46158 The Loyal Regiment
46159 The Royal Air Force
46160 Queen Victoria's Rifleman
46161 King's Own
46162 Queen's Westminster Rifleman
46163 Civil Service Rifleman
46164 The Artists' Rifleman
46165 The Ranger (12th London Regt.)
46166 London Rifle Brigade
46167 The Hertfordshire Regiment
46168 The Girl Guide
46169 The Boy Scout
46170* British Legion

Total 71

"Princess" Class

4-6-2 8P

*Introduced 1933. Stanier L.M.S. taper boiler design.

Remainder. Introduced 1935. Development of original design with alterations to valve gear, boiler and other details.

Weight: Loco. 104 tons 10 cwt.

Pressure: 250 lb. Su.

Cyls.: (4) 16¼" × 28".

Driving Wheels: 6' 6".

T.E.: 40,285 lb.

Walschaerts valve gear (inside valves operated by rocking shafts on No. 46205; remainder have four sets of valve gear). P.V.

46200* The Princess Royal
46201* Princess Elizabeth
46203 Princess Margaret Rose
46204 Princess Louise
46205 Princess Victoria
46206 Princess Marie Louise
46207 Princess Arthur of Connaught
46208 Princess Helena Victoria
46209 Princess Beatrice
46210 Lady Patricia
46211 Queen Maud
46212 Duchess of Kent

Total 12

"Coronation" Class

4-6-2 8P

Introduced 1937. Stanier L.M.S. enlargement of "Princess Royal" class. All except Nos. 46230–4/49–55 originally streamlined. (Streamlining removed from 1946.)

*Introduced 1947. Ivatt development with roller bearings and detail alterations.

Weight: Loco. { 105 tons 5 cwt. / 106 tons 8 cwt.* }

Pressure: 250 lb. Su.

Cyls.: (4) 16½" × 28".

Driving Wheels: 6' 9".

T.E.: 40,000 lb.

Walschaerts valve gear and rocking shafts. P.V.

46220 Coronation
46221 Queen Elizabeth
46222 Queen Mary
46223 Princess Alice
46224 Princess Alexandra
46225 Duchess of Gloucester
46226 Duchess of Norfolk
46227 Duchess of Devonshire
46228 Duchess of Rutland
46229 Duchess of Hamilton
46230 Duchess of Buccleuch
46231 Duchess of Atholl
46232 Duchess of Montrose
46233 Duchess of Sutherland
46234 Duchess of Abercorn
46235 City of Birmingham
46236 City of Bradford
46237 City of Bristol

4900 Class 4-6-0 No. 5979 *Cruckton Hall* [G. Wheeler

6959 Class 4-6-0 No. 7914 *Lleweni Hall* [P. H. Groom

1000 Class 4-6-0 No. 1002 *County of Berks.* [G. Wheeler

Standard Class 7P6F 4-6-2 No. 70016 *Ariel* [*A. W. Martin*

6800 Class 4-6-0 No. 6860 *Aberporth Grange* [*G. Wheeler*

7800 Class 4-6-0 No. 7810 *Draycott Manor* [*G. Wheeler*

Standard Class 2 2-6-0 No. 78000 [*A. W. Martin*

9000 Class 4-4-0 No. 9014 [*S. D. Wainwright*

City Class 4-4-0 No. 3440 *City of Truro* [*O. S. Nock*

4200 Class 2-8-0T No. 5202 [R. Goult

Vale of Rheidol 2-6-2T No. 9 *Prince of Wales* [P. J. Sharpe

6100 Class 2-6-2T No. 6157 [G. Wheeler

Class MN 4-6-2 No. 35028 *Clan Line* *G. Wheeler*

Rebuilt Class WC 4-6-2 No. 34048 *Crediton* [*C. P. Boocock*

Class BB 4-6-2 No. 34076 *41 Squadron* [*R. A. Panting*

Class LN 4-6-0 No. 30863 *Lord Rodney* [K. L. Cook

Class V 4-4-0 No. 30935 *Sevenoaks* P. H. Groom

Class V 4-4-0 No. 30907 *Dulwich* (with multiple-jet blastpipe and chimney) [G. Wheeler]

Class T9 4-4-0 No. 30707 [*P. H. Wells*

Class N15 4-6-0 No. 30806 *Sir Galleron* [*C. P. Boocock*

Class N15 4-6-0 No. 30448 *Sir Tristram* [*K. R. Pirt*

Class D1 4-4-0 No. 31749 [R. C. Riley

Class E1 4-4-0 No. 31019 [L. Marshall

Class L1 4-4-0 No. 31786 [J. B. Bucknall

Class 700 0-6-0 No. 30306 [L. King

Class O1 0-6-0 No. 31048 [B. K. B. Green

Class C 0-6-0 No. 31061 [P. H. Groom

Class Q 0-6-0 No. 30545 [*C. P. Boocock*

Class C2X 0-6-0 No. 32527 (with double dome) [*P. H. Groom*

Class C2X 0-6-0 No. 32529 [*P. H. Groom*

Class K 2-6-0 No. 32342 [L. King

Class E6 0-6-2T No. 32408 [L. Marshall

Class E4 0-6-2T No. 32470 [G. Wheeler

Class Q1 0-6-0 No. 33018 [P. H. Groom

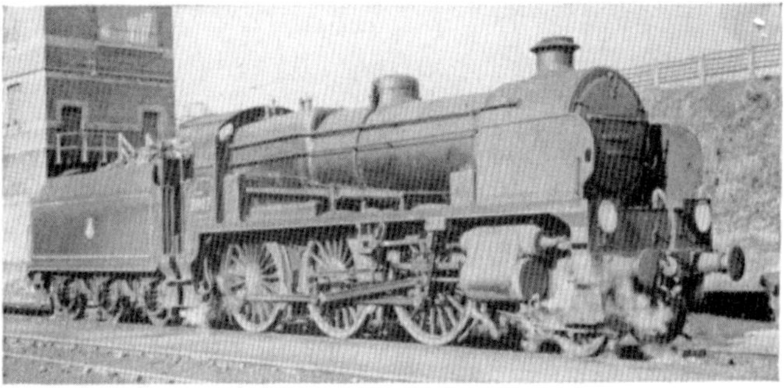

Class U1 2-6-0 No. 31907 [D. Penney

Class U 2-6-0 No. 31622 [P. H. Groom

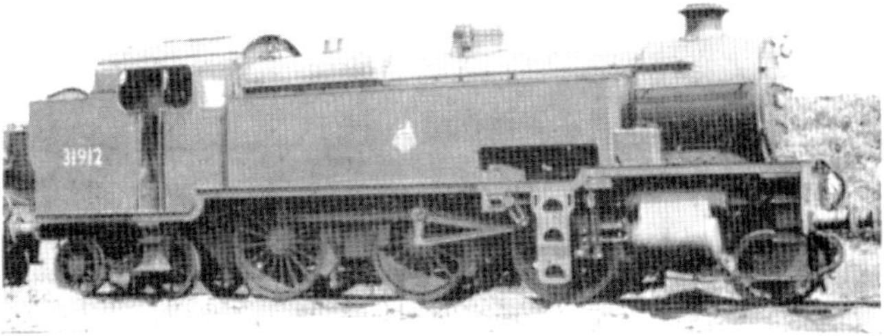

Class W 2-6-4T No. 31912 [*R. C. Riley*

Class G16 4-8-0T No. 30495 [*P. H. Groom*

Class H16 4-6-2T No. 30516 [*P. H. Groom*

Top: Class H 0-4-4T
No. 31305
[*J. B. Bucknall*

Centre: Class R1 0-6-0T
No. 31337
[*P. H. Groom*

Left: Class P 0-6-0T
No. 31556
[*A. A. Cameron*

Top: Class M7 0-4-4T No. 30377
[*P. H. Groom*

Centre: Class O2 0-4-4T No. 30199
[*C. P. Boocock*

Right: Class O2 0-4-4T No. 27 *Merstone*
[*P. H. Groom*

Class G6 0-6-0T No. 30274 [*C. P. Boocock*

Class 0415 4-4-2T No. 30583 [*R. C. Riley*

Class 0298 2-4-0WT No. 30585 [*R. E. Vincent*

46238	City of Carlisle
46239	City of Chester
46240	City of Coventry
46241	City of Edinburgh
46242	City of Glasgow
46243	City of Lancaster
46244	King George VI
46245	City of London
46246	City of Manchester
46247	City of Liverpool
46248	City of Leeds
46249	City of Sheffield
46250	City of Lichfield
46251	City of Nottingham
46252	City of Leicester
46253	City of St. Albans
46254	City of Stoke-on-Trent
46255	City of Hereford
46256*	Sir William A. Stanier, F.R.S.
46257*	City of Salford

Total 38

2-6-0 2

Introduced 1946. Ivatt L.M.S. taper boiler design.

Weight: Loco. 47 tons 2 cwt.

Pressure: 200 lb. Su.

Cyls.: { (O) 16" × 24". (O) 16½" × 24".*

Driving Wheels: 5' 0".

T.E.: { 17,410 lb. 18,510 lb.*

Walschaerts valve gear. P.V.

46400	46410	46420	46430
46401	46411	46421	46431
46402	46412	46422	46432
46403	46413	46423	46433
46404	46414	46424	46434
46405	46415	46425	46435
46406	46416	46426	46436
46407	46417	46427	46437
46408	46418	46428	46438
46409	46419	46429	46439

46440	46462	46484*	46506*
46441	46463	46485*	46507*
46442	46464	46486*	46508*
46443	46465*	46487*	46509*
46444	46466*	46488*	46510*
46445	46467*	46489*	46511*
46446	46468*	46490*	46512*
46447	46469*	46491*	46513*
46448	46470*	46492*	46514*
46449	46471*	46493*	46515*
46450	46472*	46494*	46516*
46451	46473*	46495*	46517*
46452	46474*	46496*	46518*
46453	46475*	46497*	46519*
46454	46476*	46498*	46520*
46455	46477*	46499*	46521*
46456	46478*	46500*	46522*
46457	46479*	46501*	46523*
46458	46480*	46502*	46524*
46459	46481*	46503*	46525*
46460	46482*	46504*	46526*
46461	46483*	46505*	46527*

Total 128

0-4-0ST 0F

Introduced 1932. Kitson design prepared to Stanier's requirements for L.M.S.

*Introduced 1953. Extended side tanks and coal space.

Weight: { 33 tons 0 cwt. 34 tons 0 cwt.*

Pressure: 160 lb.

Cyls.: (O) 15½" × 20".

Driving Wheels: 3' 10".

T.E.: 14,205 lb.

47000	47003	47006*	47008*
47001	47004	47007*	47009*
47002	47005*		

Total 10

0-6-0T 2F

Introduced 1928. Fowler L.M.S. short-wheelbase dock tanks.
Weight: 43 tons 12 cwt.
Pressure: 160 lb.
Cyls.: (O) 17″ × 22″.
Driving Wheels: 3′ 11″.
T.E.: 18,400 lb.
Walschaerts valve gear.

47160	47163	47165	47167
47161	47164	47166	47168

Total 8

0-4-0T Sentinel

Geared Sentinel locos.

Introduced 1929. Single-speed locos. for S. & D.J. (taken into L.M.S. stock 1930).

Weight: 27 tons 15 cwt.
Pressure: 275 lb. Su.
Cyls.: (4) $6\frac{3}{4}''$ × 9″.
Driving Wheels: 3′ $1\frac{1}{2}''$.
T.E.: 15,500 lb.
Poppet valves.

47190

Total 1

0-6-0T 3F

Introduced 1899. Johnson large Midland design, rebuilt with Belpaire firebox from 1919; fitted with condensing apparatus for London area.

*Introduced 1899. Non-condensing locos.
Weight: 48 tons 15 cwt.
Pressure: 160 lb.
Cyls.: 18″ × 26″.
Driving Wheels: 4′ 7″.
T.E.: 20,835 lb.

47200	47212	47225	47241
47201*	47213	47228	47248*
47202	47217	47230*	47250*
47203	47218	47231*	47254*
47204	47221	47235*	47255*
47207	47223	47236*	47257*
47209	47224	47239*	47259*
47211			

Total 29

0-6-0T 3F

Introduced 1924. Post-grouping development of Midland design with detail alterations.

*Introduced 1929. Locos. built for S. & D.J. (taken into L.M.S. stock 1930).

†Push-and-pull fitted.

Weight: 49 tons 10 cwt.
Pressure: 160 lb.
Cyls.: 18″ × 26″.
Driving Wheels: 4′ 7″.
T.E.: 20,835 lb.

47260	47297	47340	47380
47261	47298	47341	47381
47262	47300	47342	47383
47263	47302	47343	47384
47264	47303	47344	47385
47265	47304	47345	47386
47266	47305	47347	47388
47267	47306	47348	47389
47268	47307	47349	47390
47269	47308	47350	47391
47270	47310*	47351	47392
47271	47311*	47353	47393
47272	47312*	47354	47395
47273	47313*	47355	47396
47275	47314*	47356	47397
47276	47316*	47357	47398
47277	47317	47358	47399
47278	47318	47359	47400
47279	47319	47360	47401
47280	47320	47361	47402
47281	47321	47362	47403
47282	47322	47365	47404
47283	47324	47366	47405
47284	47325	47367	47406
47285	47326	47368	47408
47286	47327	47369	47410
47287	47328	47371	47412
47288	47330	47372	47413
47289	47332	47373	47414
47290	47333	47375	47415
47292	47334	47376	47416
47293	47335	47377	47417
47294	47336	47378	47418
47295	47338	47379	47419

47420	47469	47520	47569
47421	47470	47521	47570
47422	47471	47522	47571
47423	47472	47523	47572
47424	47473	47524	47573
47425	47474	47525	47574
47426	47475	47526	47575
47427	47476	47527	47576
47428	47478†	47528	47577
47429	47479†	47529	47578
47430	47480†	47530	47579
47431	47481†	47531	47580
47432	47482	47532	47581
47433	47483	47533	47582
47434	47484	47534	47583
47435	47485	47535	47584
47436	47487	47536	47585
47437	47488	47537	47586
47438	47490	47539	47587
47439	47491	47540	47588
47441	47492	47541	47589
47442	47493	47542	47590
47443	47494	47543	47591
47444	47495	47544	47592S
47445	47496	47545	47593
47446	47497	47546	47594
47447	47499	47547	47595
47448	47500	47548	47596
47449	47501	47549	47597
47450	47502	47550	47598
47451	47503	47551	47599
47452	47504	47552	47600
47453	47505	47554	47601
47454	47506	47555	47602
47455	47507	47556	47603
47457	47508	47557	47604
47458	47509	47558	47605
47459	47510	47559	47606
47460	47511	47560	47607
47461	47512	47561	47608
47462	47513	47562	47609
47463	47514	47563	47610
47464	47515	47564	47611
47465	47516	47565	47612
47466	47517	47566	47614
47467	47518	47567	47615
47468	47519	47568	47616

47618	47634	47651	47667
47619	47635	47652	47668
47620	47637	47653	47669
47621	47638	47654	47670
47622	47639	47655†	47671
47623	47640	47656	47672
47624	47641	47657	47673
47625	47642	47658	47674
47626	47643	47659	47675
47627	47644	47660	47676
47628	47645	47661	47677
47629	47646	47662	47678
47630	47647	47664	47679
47631	47648	47665	47680
47632	47649	47666	47681†
47633	47650		

Total 386

2-8-0 8F

Introduced 1935. Stanier L.M.S. taper boiler design.

Weight: Loco. 72 tons 2 cwt.

Pressure: 225 lb. Su.

Cyls.: (O) $18\frac{1}{2}'' \times 28''$.

Driving Wheels: $4'\ 8\frac{1}{2}''$.

T.E.: 32,440 lb.

Walschaerts valve gear. P.V.

48000	48011	48035	48057
48001	48012	48036	48060
48002	48016	48037	48061
48003	48017	48039	48062
48004	48018	48045	48063
48005	48020	48046	48064
48006	48024	48050	48065
48007	48026	48053	48067
48008	48027	48054	48069
48009	48029	48055	48070
48010	48033	48056	48073

48074	48124	48171	48218	48285	48335	48382	48429
48075	48125	48172	48219	48286	48336	48383	48430
48076	48126	48173	48220	48287	48337	48384	48431
48077	48127	48174	48221	48288	48338	48385	48432
48078	48128	48175	48222	48289	48339	48386	48433
48089	48129	48176	48223	48290	48340	48387	48434
48080	48130	48177	48224	48291	48341	48388	48435
48081	48131	48178	48225	48292	48342	48389	48436
48082	48132	48179	48246	48293	48343	48390	48437
48083	48133	48180	48247	48294	48344	48391	48438
48084	48134	48181	48248	48295	48345	48392	48439
48085	48135	48182	48249	48296	48346	48393	48440
48088	48136	48183	48250	48297	48347	48394	48441
48089	48137	48184	48251	48301	48348	48395	48442
48090	48138	48185	48252	48302	48349	48396	48443
48092	48139	48186	48253	48303	48350	48397	48444
48093	48140	48187	48254	48304	48351	48398	48445
48094	48141	48188	48255	48305	48352	48399	48446
48095	48142	48189	48256	48306	48353	48400	48447
48096	48143	48190	48257	48307	48354	48401	48448
48097	48144	48191	48258	48308	48355	48402	48449
48098	48145	48192	48259	48309	48356	48403	48450
48099	48146	48193	48260	48310	48357	48404	48451
48100	48147	48194	48261	48311	48358	48405	48452
48101	48148	48195	48262	48312	48359	48406	48453
48102	48149	48196	48263	48313	48360	48407	48454
48103	48150	48197	48264	48314	48361	48408	48455
48104	48151	48198	48265	48315	48362	48409	48456
48105	48152	48199	48266	48316	48363	48410	48457
48106	48153	48200	48267	48317	48364	48411	48458
48107	48154	48201	48268	48318	48365	48412	48459
48108	48155	48202	48269	48319	48366	48413	48460
48109	48156	48203	48270	48320	48367	48414	48461
48110	48157	48204	48271	48321	48368	48415	48462
48111	48158	48205	48272	48322	48369	48416	48463
48112	48159	48206	48273	48323	48370	48417	48464
48113	48160	48207	48274	48324	48371	48418	48465
48114	48161	48208	48275	48325	48372	48419	48466
48115	48162	48209	48276	48326	48373	48420	48467
48116	48163	48210	48277	48327	48374	48421	48468
48117	48164	48211	48278	48328	48375	48422	48469
48118	48165	48212	48279	48329	48376	48423	48470
48119	48166	48213	48280	48330	48377	48424	48471
48120	48167	48214	48281	48331	48378	48425	48472
48121	48168	48215	48282	48332	48379	48426	48473
48122	48169	48216	48283	48333	48380	48427	48474
48123	48170	48217	48284	48334	48381	48428	48475

48476	48537	48624	48671
48477	48538	48625	48672
48478	48539	48626	48673
48479	48540	48627	48674
48490	48541	48628	48675
48491	48542	48629	48676
48492	48543	48630	48677
48493	48544	48631	48678
48494	48545	48632	48679
48495	48546	48633	48680
48500	48547	48634	48681
48501	48548	48635	48682
48502	48549	48636	48683
48503	48550	48637	48684
48504	48551	48638	48685
48505	48552	48639	48686
48506	48553	48640	48687
48507	48554	48641	48688
48508	48555	48642	48689
48509	48556	48643	48690
48510	48557	48644	48691
48511	48558	48645	48692
48512	48559	48646	48693
48513	48600	48647	48694
48514	48601	48648	48695
48515	48602	48649	48696
48516	48603	48650	48697
48517	48604	48651	48698
48518	48605	48652	48699
48519	48606	48653	48700
48520	48607	48654	48701
48521	48608	48655	48702
48522	48609	48656	48703
48523	48610	48657	48704
48524	48611	48658	48705
48525	48612	48659	48706
48526	48613	48660	48707
48527	48614	48661	48708
48528	48615	48662	48709
48529	48616	48663	48710
48530	48617	48664	48711
48531	48618	48665	48712
48532	48619	48666	48713
48533	48620	48667	48714
48534	48621	48668	48715
48535	48622	48669	48716
48536	48623	48670	48717

48718	48733	48748	48763
48719	48734	48749	48764
48720	48735	48750	48765
48721	48736	48751	48766
48722	48737	48752	48767
48723	48738	48753	48768
48724	48739	48754	48769
48725	48740	48755	48770
48726	48741	48756	48771
48727	48742	48757	48772
48728	48743	48758	48773
48729	48744	48759	48774
48730	48745	48760	48775
48731	48746	48761	
48732	48747	48762	

Total 666

0-8-0 7F

Introduced 1936. L.N.W. G2a Class. Bowen-Cooke G1 superheated design of 1912, rebuilt with G2 boiler and Belpaire firebox.
Weight: Loco. 62 tons 0 cwt.
Pressure: 175 lb. Su.
Cyls.: 20½" × 24".
Driving Wheels: 4' 5½".
T.E.: 28,045 lb.
Joy valve gear. P.V

48895	49034	49114	49173
48898	49037	49119	49191
48915	49045	49122	49196
48927	49049	49125	49199
48930	49061	49126	49209
48932	49064	49129	49210
48942	49070	49130	49216
48950	49077	49134	49224
48951	49078	49137	49229
48953	49079	49139	49234
48964	49081	49141	49240
49002	49082	49142	49243
49007	49087	49144	49246
49008	49093	49147	49262
49020	49094	49154	49267
49021	49099	49155	49275
49023	49104	49158	49277
49025	49106	49164	49281

49287	49323	49350	49377
49288	49328	49352	49381
49293	49335	49357	49382
49310	49342	49361	49391
49313	49343	49373	49392
49314	49344	49375	49394
49321			

Total 97

0-8-0 7F

Introduced 1921. Development of L.N.W. G2 Class. Bowen-Cooke G1 superheated design of 1912 with higher pressure boiler. Many later rebuilt with Belpaire firebox.

Weight: Loco. 62 tons 0 cwt.
Pressure: 175 lb. Su.
Cyls.: 20½" × 24".
Driving Wheels: 4' 5½".
T.E.: 28,045 lb.
Joy valve gear. P.V.

49399	49413	49430	49443
49401	49414	49431	49444
49402	49415	49432	49446
49403	49416	49433	49447
49404	49421	49434	49448
49405	49422	49437	49449
49406	49423	49438	49451
49407	49425	49439	49452
49408	49426	49440	49453
49411	49428	49441	49454
49412			

Total 41

0-8-0 7F

Introduced 1929. Fowler L.M.S. design, developed from L.N.W. G2.

Weight: Loco. 60 tons 15 cwt.
Pressure: 200 lb. Su.
Cyls.: 19½" × 26".
Driving Wheels: 4' 8½".
T.E.: 29,745 lb.
Walschaerts valve gear. P.V.

49505	49618	49637	49668
49508	49627		

Total 6

2-4-2T 2P

Introduced 1889. Aspinall L. & Y. Class 5 with 2 tons coal capacity.
*Introduced 1898. Locos. with longer tanks and 4 tons coal capacity. Rebuilt 1910 with Belpaire firebox and extended smokebox.

Weight: { 55 tons 19 cwt. / 59 tons 3 cwt.* }
Pressure: 180 lb.
Cyls.: 18" × 26".
Driving Wheels: 5' 8".
T.E.: 18,955 lb.
Joy valve gear.

50721 50746 50850*

Total 3

0-4-0ST 0F

Introduced 1891. Aspinall L. & Y. Class 21.

Weight: 21 tons 5 cwt.
Pressure: 160 lb.
Cyls.: (O) 13" × 18".
Driving Wheels: 3' 0⅜".
T.E.: 11,335 lb.

51204	51218	51232	51244
51206	51222	51237	51246
51207	51227	51241	51253
51217	51229		

Total 14

0-6-0ST 2F

Introduced 1891. Aspinall rebuild of L. & Y. Barton Wright Class 23 0-6-0. Originally introduced 1877.

Weight: 43 tons 17 cwt.
Pressure: 140 lb.
Cyls.: 17½" × 26".
Driving Wheels: 4' 6".
T.E.: 17,545 lb.

See also Service locomotives.

51336	51413	51444S	51496
51371	51419	51445	51498
51408	51429S	51446S	51524
51412S	51441	51486	

Total 20

0-6-0T 1F

Introduced 1897. Aspinall L. & Y. Class 24 dock tanks.
Weight: 50 tons 0 cwt.
Pressure: 140 lb.
Cyls.: (O) 17" × 24".
Driving Wheels: 4' 0".
T.E.: 15,285 lb.
Allan straight link valve gear.

51537

Total 1

0-6-0 3F

Introduced 1889. Aspinall L. & Y. Class 27. Nos. 52515–26 built superheated with roundtop firebox and extended smokebox, later rebuilt with saturated boiler and short smokebox.

*Introduced 1911. Rebuilt with Belpaire firebox and extended smokebox.

Weight: Loco. 42 tons 3 cwt.
Pressure: 180 lb.
Cyls.: 18" × 26".
Driving Wheels: 5' 1".
T.E.: 21,130 lb.
Joy valve gear.

52089	52201*	52305	52415
52093S	52207	52311	52429
52119	52218S	52312*S	52438*
52121	52225S	52319	52441S
52129	52230	52322	52445*
52133	52240	52341	52452
52140*	52244	52345S	52456
52141	52248	52351	52459S
52154*	52252	52355	52461
52161*	52260	52378	52464S
52162*	52270	52393	52466
52171	52271	52400*	52515
52179	52275	52411	52523
52182	52290	52413*	52526

Total 56

2-8-0 7F

Introduced 1914. Fowler design for S. & D.J.
(All taken into L.M.S. stock, 1930.)
Weight: Loco. 64 tons 15 cwt.
Pressure: 190 lb. Su.
Cyls.: (O) 21" × 28".
Driving Wheels: 4' 8½".
T.E.: 35,295 lb.
Walschaerts valve gear. P.V.

53801	53804	53807	53809
53802	53805	53808	53810
53803	53806		

Total 10

4-4-0 3P

Introduced 1916. Pickersgill Caledonian "113" and "928" classes.
Weight: Loco. 61 tons 5 cwt.
Pressure: 180 lb. Su.
Cyls.: 20" × 26".
Driving Wheels: 6' 6".
T.E.: 20,400 lb.
P.V.

54462	54464	54466	54476
54463	54465	54475	

Total 7

4-4-0 3P

Introduced 1920. Pickersgill Caledonian "72" class.
Weight: Loco. 61 tons 5 cwt.
Pressure: 180 lb. Su.
Cyls.: 20½" × 26".
Driving Wheels: 6' 6".
T.E.: 21,435 lb.
P.V.

54477	54486	54492	54500
54478	54487	54493	54501
54480	54488	54494	54502
54482	54489	54495	54505
54483	54490	54498	54506
54485	54491	54499	54507

Total 24

0-4-4T 2P

*Introduced 1895. McIntosh Caledonian "19" class, with railed coal bunker.
†Introduced 1897. McIntosh "92" class, developed from "29" class with larger tanks and highsided coal bunker (both classes originally fitted for condensing on Glasgow Central Low Level lines).
Weight: 53 tons 16 cwt.* / 53 tons 19 cwt.†
Pressure: 180 lb.
Cyls.: 18" × 26".
Driving Wheels: 5' 9"
T.E.: 18,680 lb.

55124* 55126†

Total 2

0-4-4T 2P

Introduced 1900. McIntosh Caledonian "439" or "Standard Passenger" class.
*Introduced 1915. Pickersgill locos. with detail alterations.
Weight: 53 tons 19 cwt. / 57 tons 12 cwt.*
Pressure: 180 lb.
Cyls.: 18" × 26".
Driving Wheels: 5' 9".
T.E.: 18,680 lb.

55165	55202	55216	55227*
55167	55203	55217	55228*
55169	55204	55219	55229*
55173	55206	55220	55230*
55185	55207	55221	55231*
55189	55208	55222	55232*
55195	55209	55223	55233*
55198	55210	55224	55234*
55199	55211	55225	55235*
55200	55214	55226	55236*
55201	55215		

Total 42

0-4-4T 2P

Introduced 1922. Pickersgill Caledonian "431" class (developed from "439" class) with cast-iron front buffer beam for banking.
Weight: 57 tons 17 cwt.
Pressure: 180 lb.
Cyls.: 18¼" × 26".
Driving Wheels: 5' 9".
T.E.: 19,200 lb.

55237 55238 55239 55240

Total 4

0-4-4T 2P

Introduced 1925. Post-Grouping development of Caledonian "439" class.
Weight: 59 tons 12 cwt.
Pressure: 180 lb.
Cyls.: 18¼" × 26".
Driving Wheels: 5' 9".
T.E.: 19,200 lb.

55260	55263	55266	55268
55261	55264	55267	55269
55262	55265		

Total 10

0-4-0ST 0F

Introduced 1885. Drummond and McIntosh Caledonian "Pugs."
Weight: 27 tons 7 cwt.
Pressure: 160 lb.
Cyls.: (O) 14" × 20".
Driving Wheels: 3' 8".
T.E.: 12,115 lb.

56025S	56029	56032S	56039
56027S	56031	56035	

Total 7

0-6-0T 2F

Introduced 1911. McIntosh Caledonian dock shunters, "498" class.
Weight: 47 tons 15 cwt.
Pressure: 160 lb.
Cyls.: (O) 17" × 22".
Driving Wheels: 4' 0".
T.E.: 18,015 lb.

56151	56167	56169	56172
56158	56168	56171	56173
56159			

Total 9

0-6-0T 3F

Introduced 1895. McIntosh Caledonian "29" and "782" classes (56232–9 originally condensing).
Weight: 47 tons 15 cwt.
Pressure: 160 lb.
Cyls.: 18" × 26".
Driving Wheels: 4' 6"
T.E.: 21,215 lb.

56232	56292	56325	56349
56239	56298	56326	56356
56240	56300	56331	56360
56242	56302	56335	56361
56246	56304	56336	56362
56256	56305	56337	56363
56259	56308	56338	56364
56260	56309	56341	56368
56278	56310	56343	56370
56279	56312	56347	56372
56286	56313	56348	56376
56289	56324		

Total 46

0-6-0 2F

Introduced 1883. Drummond Caledonian "Standard Goods"; later additions by Lambie and McIntosh.

*Some rebuilt with L.M.S. boiler.

Weight: Loco. { 41 tons 6 cwt. / 42 tons 4 cwt.*

Pressure: 180 lb.

Cyls.: 18" × 26".

Driving Wheels: 5' 0".

T.E.: 21,480 lb.

57232	57269	57331	57383
57233	57270	57335	57384
57236	57271	57336	57385
57237	57274	57338	57386
57238	57275	57340	57389
57239	57278	57341	57392
57240	57284	57345	57398
57242	57285	57347	57404
57244	57287	57348	57411
57245	57288	57349	57416
57246	57291	57350	57417
57249	57292	57353	57418
57250	57295	57355	57426
57251	57296	57356	57429
57252	57299	57357	57431
57253	57300	57359	57432
57254	57302	57360	57434
57256	57303	57362	57436
57257	57309	57363	57441
57258	57311	57364	57445
57259	57314	57365	57446
57261	57317	57366	57447
57262	57319	57367	57448
57263	57321	57369	57451
57264	57324	57370	57461
57265	57325	57373	57463
57266	57326	57375	57470
57267	57328	57377	57472
57268	57329	57378	57473

Total 116

0-6-0 3F

Introduced 1899. McIntosh Caledonian "812" (Nos. 57550–57623) and "652" (remainder) classes.
Weight: Loco. 45 tons 14 cwt.
Pressure: 180 lb.
Cyls.: $18\frac{1}{2}'' \times 26''$.
Driving Wheels: 5′ 0″.
T.E.: 22,690 lb.

57550	57577	57602	57622
57554	57579	57603	57623
57555	57580	57604	57625
57557	57581	57605	57626
57558	57583	57607	57627
57559	57585	57608	57630
57560	57586	57609	57631
57562	57587	57611	57632
57563	57590	57612	57633
57564	57591	57613	57634
57565	57592	57614	57635
57566	57593	57615	57637
57568	57594	57617	57640
57569	57596	57618	57642
57570	57597	57619	57643
57571	57600	57620	57644
57572	57601	57621	57645
57576			

Total 69

0-6-0 3F

Introduced 1918. Pickersgill Caledonian "294" class (superheated) and "670" classes.
Weight: Loco. 50 tons 13 cwt.
Pressure: 180 lb. Su.
Cyls.: $18\frac{1}{2}'' \times 26''$.
Driving Wheels: 5′ 0″.
T.E.: 22,690 lb.
P.V.

57650	57661	57670	57682
57651	57663	57671	57684
57652	57665	57672	57686
57653	57666	57673	57688
57654	57667	57674	57689
57655	57668	57679	57690
57658	57669	57681	57691
57659			

Total 29

0-4-4T 1P

Introduced 1895. Final Johnson 0-4-4T design, with higher-pitched boiler and larger tanks, later rebuilt with Belpaire firebox.
Push-and-pull fitted.
Weight: 53 tons 4 cwt.
Pressure: 150 lb.
Cyls.: 17″ × 24″.
Driving Wheels: 5′ 4″.
T.E.: 16,255 lb.

58086

Total 1

0-6-0 2F

†Introduced 1917. Johnson Midland 4′ 11″ design of 1875 rebuilt with Belpaire firebox.
§Introduced 1917. Johnson Midland 5′ 3″ design rebuilt with Belpaire firebox.
Weight: Loco. Various—
37 tons 12 cwt. to 40 tons 3 cwt.
Pressure: 160 lb.
Cyls.: 18″ × 26″.
Driving Wheels: { 4′ 11″.† / 5′ 3″.§ }
T.E.: { 19,420 lb.† / 18,185 lb.§ }

58115†	58148†	58175†	58221§
58120†	58153†	58177†	58228§
58122†	58158†	58181†	58260§
58123†	58160†	58182†	58271§
58124†	58163†	58185†	58283§
58128†	58165†	58186†	58287§
58131†	58166†	58197§	58291§
58135†	58168†	58209§	58293§
58137†	58169†	58214§	58295§
58138†	58170†	58215§	58298§
58143†	58173†	58218§	58305§
58144†	58174†	58220§	

Total 47

0-6-0T 2F

Introduced 1879. Park North London design.
Weight: 45 tons 10 cwt.
Pressure: 160 lb.
Cyls.: (O) 17" × 24".
Driving Wheels: 4' 4".
T.E.: 18,140 lb.

58850 Total 1

PRESERVED LOCOS IN WORKING ORDER

4-4-0 (3-Cyl. Compd.) 4P

Introduced 1902. Johnson Midland design, rebuilt by Deeley in 1914. Withdrawn 1951 for preservation. Restored to 1914 condition and returned to service for special use 1959.
Weight: Loco. 61 tons 14 cwt.
Pressure: 200 lb.
Cyls.: L.P. (2) 21" × 26". H.P. (1) 19" × 26".
Driving Wheels: 7' 0".
T.E. (of L.P. cyls. at 80% boiler pressure): 21,840 lb.

1000

4-2-2

Introduced 1886. Neilson & Co. design for the Caledonian Railway incorporating Drummond details. Withdrawn as L.M.S. No. 14010 in 1935. Restored to Caledonian livery and returned to service for special use 1958.
Weight: Engine and Tender: 75 tons.
Pressure: 150 lb.
Cyls.: 18" × 26".
Driving Wheels: 7' 0".
T.E.: 12,785 lb.

123

4-6-0

Introduced 1894. Jones Highland goods design. Withdrawn 1934 as L.M.S. No. 17916 for preservation. Restored to original condition and returned to service for special use 1959.
Weight: Loco. 56 tons.
Pressure: 175 lb.
Cyls.: 20" × 26".
Driving Wheels: 5' 3".
T.E.: 24,555 lb.

103

SERVICE LOCOS.

Details of Diesel Service Locomotives are shown in ABC of British Railways Diesels and the Diesel section of the Combined Volume of ABC of British Railways Locomotives.

0-4-0 Diesel

E.D.1	E.D.4	E.D.6
E.D.2	E.D.5	E.D.7
E.D.3		

0-4-0 (3'0" gauge) Diesel

E.D.10

0-4-0 (1' 6" gauge) Diesel

ZM 32

0-6-0ST 2F

For details see Nos. 51336-51524.

11304	11324	11368	11394
11305			

CHIEF MECHANICAL ENGINEERS

BRITISH RAILWAYS (L.M. Region)

H. G. Ivatt ... 1948–1951

L.M.S.

George Hughes	1923–1925
Sir Henry Fowler	1925–1931
E. H. J. Lemon (Sir Ernest Lemon)	1931–1932
Sir William Stanier ...	1932–1944
Charles E. Fairburn ...	1944–1945
H. G. Ivatt	1945–1947

LOCOMOTIVE SUPERINTENDENTS AND C.M.E.'S—L.M.S. CONSTITUENT COMPANIES

CALEDONIAN RAILWAY

Robert Sinclair (First loco. engineer)*	1847–1856
Benjamin Connor	1856–1876
George Brittain	1876–1882
Dugald Drummond ...	1882–1890
Hugh Smellie	1890
J. Lambie	1890–1895
J. F. McIntosh	1895–1914
William Pickersgill ...	1914–1923

FURNESS RAILWAY

R. Mason	1890–1897
W. F. Pettigrew	1897–1918
D. J. Rutherford	1918–1923

GLASGOW AND SOUTH WESTERN RAILWAY

Patrick Stirling	1853–1866
James Stirling	1866–1878
Hugh Smellie	1878–1890
James Manson	1890–1912
Peter Drummond	1912–1918
R. H. Whitelegg	1918–1923

HIGHLAND RAILWAY

William Stroudley (First loco. engineer) ...	1866–1869
David Jones	1869–1896
Peter Drummond	1896–1911
F. G. Smith...	1912–1915
C. Cumming	1915–1923

L. & Y.R.

Sir John Hawkshaw (Consultant),* Hurst and Jenkins successively to 1868

W. Hurst	1868–1876
W. Barton Wright ...	1876–1886
John A. F. Aspinall ...	1886–1899
H. A. Hoy	1899–1904
George Hughes	1904–1921

The L. & Y. amalgamated with L.N.W.R. as from January 1st, 1922.

L.N.W.R.

Francis Trevithick and J. E. McConnell, first loco. engineers, 1846, with Alexander Allan largely responsible for design at Crewe.*

John Ramsbottom... ...	1857–1871
Francis William Webb ...	1871–1903
George Whale	1903–1909
Charles John Bowen-Cooke	1909–1920
Capt. Hewitt Pearson Montague Beames ...	1920–1921
George Hughes	1922

L.T. & S.R.

Thomas Whitelegg ...	1880–1910
Robert Harben Whitelegg	1910–1912

(L.T. & S.R. absorbed by M.R., control of locos. transferred to Derby as from August, 1912.)

* Exclusive of previous service with constituent company.

LOCOMOTIVE SUPERINTENDENTS AND C.M.E.'S *(continued)*

MARYPORT & CARLISLE

Hugh Smellie 1870–1878
J. Campbell 1878–
William Coulthard ... * –1904
J. B. Adamson 1904–1923

MIDLAND RAILWAY

Matthew Kirtley
(First loco. engineer) ... 1844–1873
Samuel Waite Johnson ... 1873–1903
Richard Mountford Deeley 1903–1909
Henry Fowler 1909–1923

SOMERSET AND DORSET JOINT RAILWAY

Until leased by Mid. and L. & S. W. (as from 1st November, 1875) locomotives were bought from outside builders, principally George England of Hatcham Iron Works, S.E. After the above date, Derby and its various Loco. Supts. and C.M.E.'s have acted for S. & D.J. aided by a resident Loco. Supt. stationed at Highbridge Works.

NORTH STAFFORDSHIRE RAILWAY

L. Clare 1876–1882
L. Longbottom 1882–1902
J. H. Adams 1902–1915
J. A. Hookham 1915–1923

W. Angus was Loco. Supt. at Stoke prior to 1876. No earlier records can be traced.

WIRRAL

Eric G. Barker 1892–1902
T. B. Hunter 1903–1923

Barker of the Wirral Railway is noteworthy for originating the 4-4-4 tank type in this country (1896).

NORTH LONDON RAILWAY

(Worked by L. & N.W. by agreement dated December, 1908.)

William Adams 1853–1873
J. C. Park 1873–1893
Henry J. Pryce 1893–1903

* Date of actual entry into office not known.

HISTORIC LOCOMOTIVES PRESERVED IN STORE

Type	*Originating Company*	*Pre-Grouping No.*	*L.M.S. No.*	*Name*	*Place of Preservation*
4-2-2	M.R.	118	(673)	—	Derby
2-4-0	M.R.	158A	—	—	Derby
4-4-2T	L.T. & S.	80	(2148)	Thundersley	Derby
2-2-2	L.N.W.	(49)	—	Columbine	York Museum
2-2-2	L.N.W.	3020	—	Cornwall	Crewe
2-4-0	L.N.W.	790	(5031)	Hardwicke	Crewe
0-4-0ST	L.N.W.	1439	—	—	Crewe
†0-4-0T	L.N.W.	—	—	Pet	Crewe
2-4-2T	L. & Y.	1008	(10621)	—	Horwich
0-4-0	F.R.	3	—	Coppernob	Horwich
0-4-2	Liverpool & Manchester	—	—	Lion	Crewe
‡4-4-0	H.R.	(2)	(14398)	Ben Alder	Boat of Garten

The unbracketed numbers are the ones at present carried by the locos.
† 18 in. gauge works shunter.
‡ Present number 54398.

NUMERICAL LIST OF ENGINES

The code given in smaller bold type at the head of each class, e.g. " 4MT ", denotes its British Railways power classification.

The numbers of locomotives in service have been checked to March 19th, 1960.

4-6-2 8P6F Class A4

Introduced 1935. Gresley streamlined design with corridor tender (except those marked †). All fitted with double blastpipe and chimney.
*Inside cylinder reduced to 17".
Weight: Loco. 102 tons 19 cwt.
Tender { 64 tons 19 cwt. / 60 tons 7 cwt.†
Pressure: 250 lb. Su.
Cyls.: { (3) 18½" × 26". / (2) 18½" × 26" (1) 17" × 26".*
Driving Wheels: 6' 8".
T.E.: { 35,455 lb. / 33,616 lb.*
Walschaerts valve gear and derived motion. P.V.

60001† Sir Ronald Matthews
60002† Sir Murrough Wilson
60003† Andrew K. McCosh
60004 William Whitelaw
60005† Sir Charles Newton
60006† Sir Ralph Wedgwood
60007 Sir Nigel Gresley
60008† Dwight D. Eisenhower
60009 Union of South Africa
60010 Dominion of Canada
60011 Empire of India
60012* Commonwealth of Australia
60013 Dominion of New Zealand
60014 Silver Link
60015 Quicksilver
60016† Silver King
60017 Silver Fox
60018† Sparrow Hawk
60019† Bittern
60020*† Guillemot
60021 Wild Swan
60022 Mallard
60023† Golden Eagle
60024 Kingfisher
60025 Falcon
60026† Miles Beevor
60027 Merlin
60028 Walter K. Whigham
60029 Woodcock
60030 Golden Fleece
60031 Golden Plover
60032 Gannet
60033 Seagull
60034 Lord Faringdon

Total 34

4-6-2 7P6F Class A3

Introduced 1927. Development of Gresley G.N. 180 lb. Pacific (introduced 1922, L.N.E.R. A1, later A10) with 220 lb. pressure (prototype and others rebuilt from A10). Some have G.N.-type tender with coal rails†, remainder L.N.E.R. pattern. All fitted with double blastpipe and chimney.
Weight: Loco. 96 tons 5 cwt.
Tender { 56 tons 6 cwt.† / 57 tons 18 cwt.
Pressure: 220 lb. Su.
Cyls.: (3) 19" × 26".
Driving Wheels: 6' 8".
T.E.: 32,910 lb.
Walschaerts valve gear and derived motion. P.V.

60035 Windsor Lad
60036 Colombo
60037 Hyperion
60038 Firdaussi
60039 Sandwich
60040 Cameronian
60041 Salmon Trout
60042 Singapore
60043 Brown Jack
60044 Melton
60045 Lemberg
60046 Diamond Jubilee
60047 Donovan
60048 Doncaster
60049 Galtee More
60050 Persimmon

60051 Blink Bonny
60052 Prince Palatine
60053 Sansovino
60054 Prince of Wales
60055 Woolwinder
60056 Centenary
60057 Ormonde
60058 Blair Athol
60059 Tracery
60060 The Tetrarch
60061 Pretty Polly
60062 Minoru
60063 Isinglass
60064 Tagalie
60065 Knight of Thistle
60066 Merry Hampton
60067 Ladas
60068 Sir Visto
60069 Sceptre
60070 Gladiateur
60071 Tranquil
60072 Sunstar
60073 St. Gatien
60074 Harvester
60075 St. Frusquin
60076 Galopin
60077 The White Knight
60078 Night Hawk
60079 Bayardo
60080 Dick Turpin
60081 Shotover
60082 Neil Gow
60083 Sir Hugo
60084 Trigo
60085 Manna
60086 Gainsborough
60087 Blenheim
60088 Book Law
60089 Felstead
60090 Grand Parade
60091 Captain Cuttle
60092 Fairway
60093 Coronach
60094 Colorado
60095 Flamingo
60096 Papyrus
60097 Humorist
60098 Spion Kop
60099 Call Boy
60100 Spearmint
60101 Cicero
60102 Sir Frederick Banbury
60103 Flying Scotsman
60105 Victor Wild
60106 Flying Fox
60107 Royal Lancer
60108 Gay Crusader
60109 Hermit
60110 Robert the Devil
60111 Enterprise
60112 St. Simon

Total **77**

4-6-2 8P6F Class A1

A1/1* Introduced 1945. Thompson rebuild of A10.
A1 Peppercorn development of A1/1 for new construction.
A1† Fitted with roller bearings.
Weight: Loco. { 101 tons.* / 104 tons 2 cwt.
Tender 60 tons 7 cwt.
Pressure: 250 lb. Su.
Cyls.: (3) 19" × 26".
Driving Wheels: 6' 8".
T.E.: 37,400 lb.
Walschaerts valve gear. P.V.

60113* Great Northern
60114 W. P. Allen
60115 Meg Merrilies
60116 Hal o' the Wynd
60117 Bois Roussel
60118 Archibald Sturrock
60119 Patrick Stirling
60120 Kittiwake
60121 Silurian
60122 Curlew
60123 H. A. Ivatt
60124 Kenilworth
60125 Scottish Union
60126 Sir Vincent Raven
60127 Wilson Worsdell
60128 Bongrace
60129 Guy Mannering
60130 Kestrel

60131 Osprey
60132 Marmion
60133 Pommern
60134 Foxhunter
60135 Madge Wildfire
60136 Alcazar
60137 Redgauntlet
60138 Boswell
60139 Sea Eagle
60140 Balmoral
60141 Abbotsford
60142 Edward Fletcher
60143 Sir Walter Scott
60144 King's Courier
60145 Saint Mungo
60146 Peregrine
60147 North Eastern
60148 Aboyeur
60149 Amadis
60150 Willbrook
60151 Midlothian
60152 Holyrood
60153† Flamboyant
60154† Bon Accord
60155† Borderer
60156† Great Central
60157† Great Eastern
60158 Aberdonian
60159 Bonnie Dundee
60160 Auld Reekie
60161 North British
60162 Saint Johnstoun

Total 50

4-6-2 8P7F (A2/1: 7P6F) Class A2

A2/2* Introduced 1943. Thompson rebuild of Gresley Class P2 2-8-2 (introduced 1934).
Weight: Loco. 101 tons 10 cwt.
Pressure: 225 lb. Su.
Cyls.: (3) 20″ × 26″.
Driving Wheels: 6′ 2″.
T.E.: 40,320 lb.

A2/1† Introduced 1944. Development of Class A2/2, incorporating Class V2 2-6-2 boiler.
Weight: Loco. 98 tons.
Pressure: 225 lb. Su.
Cyls.: (3) 19″ × 26″.
Driving Wheels: 6′ 2″. T.E.: 36,385 lb.

A2/3‡ Introduced 1946. Development of Class A2/2 for new construction.
Weight: Loco. 101 tons 10 cwt.
Pressure: 250 lb. Su.
Cyls.: (3) 19″ × 26″.
Driving Wheels: 6′ 2″.
T.E.: 40,430 lb.

A2§ Introduced 1947. Peppercorn development of Class A2/2 with shorter wheelbase. (No. 60539 built with double blast pipe.)

A2** Rebuilt with double blast pipe and multiple valve regulator.
Weight: Loco. 101 tons.
Pressure: 250 lb. Su.
Cyls.: (3) 19″ × 26″.
Driving Wheels: 6′ 2″.
T.E.: 40,430 lb.
Tender weight (all parts): 60 tons 7 cwt.
Walschaerts valve gear. P.V.

60500‡ Edward Thompson
60501* Cock o' the North
60502* Earl Marischal
60504* Mons Meg
60506* Wolf of Badenoch
60507† Highland Chieftain
60508† Duke of Rothesay
60509† Waverley
60510† Robert the Bruce
60511‡ Airborne
60512‡ Steady Aim
60513‡ Dante
60514‡ Chamossaire
60515‡ Sun Stream
60516‡ Hycilla
60517‡ Ocean Swell
60518‡ Tehran
60519‡ Honeyway
60520‡ Owen Tudor
60521‡ Watling Street
60522‡ Straight Deal
60523‡ Sun Castle
60524‡ Herringbone
60525§ A. H. Peppercorn
60526** Sugar Palm

60527§ Sun Charlot
60528§ Tudor Minstrel
60529**Pearl Diver
60530§ Sayajirao
60531§ Bahram
60532**Blue Peter
60533**Happy Knight
60534§ Irish Elegance
60535§ Hornet's Beauty
60536§ Trimbush
60537§ Bachelor's Button
60538**Velocity
60539§ Bronzino

Total

Class A2 15 Class A2/2 4
Class A2/1 4 Class A2/3 15

2-6-2 7P6F Class V2

Introduced 1936. Gresley design.
Weight: Loco. 93 tons 2 cwt.
Tender 52 tons.
Pressure: 220 lb. Su.
Cyls.: (3) $18\frac{1}{2}''$ × 26″.
Driving Wheels: 6′ 2″.
T.E.: 33,730 lb.
Walschaerts valve gear and derived motion. P.V.

60800 Green Arrow
60801
60802
60803
60804
60805
60806
60807
60808
60809 The Snapper, The East Yorkshire Regiment, The Duke of York's Own
60810
60811
60812
60813
60814
60815
60816
60817
60818
60819
60820
60821
60822
60823
60824
60825
60826
60827
60828
60829
60830
60831
60832
60833
60834
60835 The Green Howard Alexandra, Princess of Wales's Own Yorkshire Regiment
60836
60837
60838
60839
60840
60841
60842
60843
60844
60845
60846
60847 St. Peter's School York, A.D. 627
60848
60849
60850
60851
60852
60853
60854

60855
60856
60857
60858
60859
60860 Durham School
60861
60862
60863
60864
60865
60866
60867
60868
60869
60870
60871
60872 King's Own Yorkshire Light Infantry
60873 Coldstreamer
60874

60875	60897	60919	60941
60576	60898	60920	60942
60877	60899	60921	60943
60878	60900	60922	60944
60879	60901	60923	60945
60880	60902	60924	60946
60881	60903	60925	60947
60882	60904	60926	60948
60883	60905	60927	60949
60884	60906	60928	60950
60885	60907	60929	60951
60886	60908	60930	60952
60887	60909	60931	60953
60888	60910	60932	60954
60889	60911	60933	60955
60890	60912	60934	60956
60891	60913	60935	60957
60892	60914	60936	60958
60893	60915	60937	60959
60894	60916	60938	60960
60895	60917	60939	60961
60896	60918	60940	60962

60963
60964 The Durham Light Infantry

60965	60967	60969
60966	60968	60970

60971	60975	60979	60983
60972	60976	60980	
60973	60977	60981	
60974	60978	60982	

Total 184

4-6-0 5MT Class B1

Introduced 1942. Thompson design.
Weight: Loco. 71 tons 3 cwt.
Tender 52 tons.
Pressure: 225 lb. Su.
Cyls.: (O) 20" × 26".
Driving Wheels: 6' 2".
T.E.: 26,880 lb.
Walschaerts valve gear. P.V.

61000 Springbok
61001 Eland
61002 Impala
61003 Gazelle
61004 Oryx
61005 Bongo
61006 Blackbuck
61007 Klipspringer
61008 Kudu
61009 Hartebeeste
61010 Wildebeeste
61011 Waterbuck
61012 Puku
61013 Topi
61014 Oribi
61015 Duiker
61016 Inyala
61017 Bushbuck
61018 Gnu
61019 Nilghai
61020 Gemsbok
61021 Reitbok
61022 Sassaby
61023 Hirola
61024 Addax
61025 Pallah
61026 Ourebi
61027 Madoqua
61028 Umseke
61029 Chamois
61030 Nyala
61031 Reedbuck

61032 Steinbok
61033 Dibatag
61034 Chiru
61035 Pronghorn
61036 Ralph Assheton
61037 Jairou
61038 Blacktail
61039 Steinbok
61040 Roedeer
61041
61042
61043
61044
61045
61046
61047
61048
61049
61050
61051
61052
61053
61054
61055
61056
61058
61059
61060
61061
61062
61063
61064
61065
61066
61067
61068
61069
61070
61071
61072
61073
61074
61075
61076
61077
61078
61079
61080
61081
61082
61083
61084
61085
61086
61087
61088
61089
61090
61091
61092
61093
61094
61095
61096
61097
61098
61099
61100
61101
61102
61103
61104
61105
61106
61107
61108
61109
61110
61111
61112
61113
61114
61115
61116
61117
61118
61119
61120
61121
61122
61123
61124
61125
61126
61127
61128
61129
61130
61131
61132
61133
61134
61135
61136
61137
61138
61139
61140
61141
61142
61143
61144
61145
61146
61147
61148
61149
61150
61151
61152
61153
61154
61155
61156
61157
61158
61159
61160
61161
61162
61163
61164
61165
61166
61167
61168
61169
61170
61171
61172
61173
61174
61175
61176
61177
61178
61179
61180
61181
61182
61183
61184
61185
61186
61187
61188
61189 Sir William Gray
61190
61191
61192
61193
61194
61195
61196
61197
61198
61199
61200
61201
61202
61203
61204
61205
61206
61207
61208
61209
61210
61211
61212
61213
61214
61215 William Henton Carver
61216
61217
61218
61219
61220
61221 Sir Alexander Erskine-Hill
61222
61223
61224
61225
61226
61227
61228
61229
61230
61231
61232
61233
61234
61235

61236	
61237	Geoffrey H. Kitson
61238	Leslie Runciman
61239	
61240	Harry Hinchcliffe
61241	Viscount Ridley
61242	Alexander Reith Gray
61243	Sir Harold Mitchell
61244	Strang Steel
61245	Murray of Elibank
61246	Lord Balfour of Burleigh
61247	Lord Burghley
61248	Geoffrey Gibbs
61249	FitzHerbert Wright
61250	A. Harold Bibby
61251	Oliver Bury

61252	61283	61314	61345
61253	61284	61315	61346
61254	61285	61316	61347
61255	61286	61317	61348
61256	61287	61318	61349
61257	61288	61319	61350
61258	61289	61320	61351
61259	61290	61321	61352
61260	61291	61322	61353
61261	61292	61323	61354
61262	61293	61324	61355
61263	61294	61325	61356
61264	61295	61326	61357
61265	61296	61327	61358
61266	61297	61328	61359
61267	61298	61329	61360
61268	61299	61330	61361
61269	61300	61331	61362
61270	61301	61332	61363
61271	61302	61333	61364
61272	61303	61334	61365
61273	61304	61335	61366
61274	61305	61336	61367
61275	61306	61337	61368
61276	61307	61338	61369
61277	61308	61339	61370
61278	61309	61340	61371
61279	61310	61341	61372
61280	61311	61342	61373
61281	61312	61343	61374
61282	61313	61344	61375

61376 61377 61378

61379 Mayflower

61380	61388	61396	61404
61381	61389	61397	61405
61382	61390	61398	61406
61383	61391	61399	61407
61384	61392	61400	61408
61385	61393	61401	61409
61386	61394	61402	
61387	61395	61403	

Total 409

4-6-0 5MT Class B16

B16/1 Introduced 1920. Raven N.E. design with Stephenson valve gear.

B16/2* Introduced 1937. Gresley rebuild of B16/1 with Walschaerts valve gear and derived motion for inside cylinder.

B16/3† Introduced 1944. Thompson rebuild of B16/1 with individual sets of Walschaerts valve gear for each cylinder.

Weight: Loco. 77 tons 14 cwt. / 79 tons 4 cwt.* / 78 tons 19 cwt.†
Tender 46 tons 12 cwt.
Pressure: 180 lb. Su.
Cyls.: (3) $18\frac{1}{2}'' \times 26''$.
Driving Wheels: 5′ 8″.
T.E.: 30,030 lb. P.V.

61410	61425	61446	61461†
61411	61428	61447	61462
61412	61429	61448†	61463†
61413	61431	61449†	61464†
61414	61432	61450	61466
61415	61434†	61451	61467†
61416	61435*	61452	61468†
61417†	61436	61453†	61469
61418†	61437*	61454†	61471
61419	61438*	61455*	61472†
61420†	61439†	61456	61473
61421*	61440	61457*	61475*
61422	61443	61459	61476†
61423	61444†	61460	61478
61424	61445		

Total: Class B16/1 34
Class B16/3 17 Class B16/2 7

4-6-0 4P3F Class B12

B12/3 introduced 1932. Gresley rebuild of Holden G.E. design of 1911 with large boiler, round-topped firebox and long-travel valves.
(B12/2 was a development of B12/1 with Lentz valves, since rebuilt to B12/3.)
Weight: Loco. 69 tons 10 cwt.
Tender 39 tons 6 cwt.
Pressure: 180 lb. Su.
Cyls.: 20" × 28".
Driving Wheels: 6' 6".
T.E.: 21,970 lb.
P.V.

61564 61572

Total 2

4-6-0 5P4F Class B17

B17/4[1] Introduced 1936. Locos. with R. 4,200-gallon tender.
B17/6[2] Introduced 1943. B17/4 fitted 100A (B1-type) boiler.
B17/6[3] Rebuild of streamlined B17/5 introduced in 1937. Rebuilt with 100A boiler and de-streamlined in 1951.
Weight: Loco. 77 tons 5 cwt.
Tender 52 tons.[123]
Pressure: 180 lb.[1] / 225 lb.[23] Su.
Cyls.: (3) 17½" × 26".
Driving Wheels: 6' 8".
T.E.: 22,485 lb.[1] / 28,555 lb.[23]
Walschaerts valve gear and derived motion. P.V.

61657[2] Doncaster Rovers
61660[1] Hull City
61664[2] Liverpool
61668[2] Bradford City
61670[3] City of London

Total

Class B17/4 1 Class B17/6 4

2-6-0 4MT Class K2

K2/2 Introduced 1914. Gresley G.N. design.
K2/1* Introduced 1931. Rebuilt from small-boilered K1 (introduced 1912).
†K2/2 with side-window cab.
Weight: Loco. 64 tons 8 cwt.
Tender 43 tons 2 cwt.
Pressure: 180 lb. Su.
Cyls.: (O) 20" × 26".
Driving Wheels: 5' 8".
T.E.: 23,400 lb.
Walschaerts valve gear. P.V.

61728*	61741†	61747	61761
61730	61742	61756	61763
61740	61745	61760	

61764† Loch Arkaig
61766
61767
61769†
61771
61773
61779†
61782† Loch Eil
61784†
61788† Loch Rannoch
61791† Loch Laggan
61792†
61794† Loch Oich

Total

Class K2/1 1 Class K2/2 23

2-6-0 5P6F Classes K3 & K5

K3/2 Introduced 1924. Development of Gresley G.N. design, built to L.N.E.R. loading gauge.

K3/3* Introduced 1929. Differ in details only, such as springs, from K3/2.

‡K3/2 fitted with G.N. tender.

(K3/1 were G.N. locos. (introduced 1920), with G.N. cabs, and K3/4, K3/5 and K3/6 were variations of K3/2 differing in weight and details. These locos. have now been modified to K3/2.)

Weight: Loco. 72 tons 12 cwt.
Tender { 52 tons. / 43 tons 2 cwt.‡

Pressure: 180 lb. Su.

Cyls.: (3) $18\frac{1}{2}'' \times 26''$.

Driving Wheels: 5′ 8″.

T.E.: 30,030 lb.

Walschaerts valve gear and derived motion. P.V.

K5† Introduced 1945. Thompson 2-cyl. rebuild of K3.

Weight: Loco. 71 tons 5 cwt.
Tender 52 tons.

Pressure: 225 lb. Su.

Cyls.: (O) $20'' \times 26''$.

Driving Wheels: 5′ 8″.

T.E.: 29,250 lb.

Walschaerts valve gear. P.V.

61800	61820	61839	61858‡	61877*	61908	61938	61964
61801	61821	61840	61859‡	61880*	61909	61939	61965
61803	61822	61841‡	61860	61881*	61910	61940	61966
61804	61824	61842	61861	61882*	61912	61941	61967
61805	61825	61843	61862	61883*	61913	61942	61968
61807	61826	61844	61863†	61884*	61914	61943	61969
61808	61827	61845	61864	61886*	61915	61944	61970
61809	61828	61846	61865	61887*	61916	61945	61971
61810	61829	61847	61866	61888*	61917	61946	61972
61811	61830	61848	61867	61889*	61918	61947	61973
61812‡	61831	61849	61868	61890	61919	61948	61974
61813	61832	61850	61869	61891	61920	61949	61975
61814	61833	61851	61870*	61892	61921	61950	61976
61815	61834	61852	61871*	61893	61922	61951	61977
61816	61835	61853	61872*	61894	61923	61952	61978
61817	61836	61854‡	61873*	61895	61924	61953	61979
61818	61837	61856‡	61874*	61896	61925	61954	61980
61819	61838	61857‡	61875*	61897	61926	61955	61981
				61899	61927	61956	61982
				61900	61929	61957	61984
				61901	61930	61958	61985
				61902	61932	61959	61986
				61903	61933	61960	61987
				61904	61934	61961	61989
				61905	61935	61962	61990
				61906	61936	61963	61992
				61907			

Total
Class K3/2 **160** Class K5 **1**
Class K3/3 **16**

2-6-0 5P6F Classes K1 & K4

K4* Introduced 1937. Gresley locos. for West Highland line.

Weight: Loco. 68 tons 8 cwt.
Tender 44 tons 4 cwt.

Pressure: 200 lb. Su.

Cyls.: (3) $18\frac{1}{2}'' \times 26''$.

Driving Wheels: 5′ 2″.

T.E.: 36,600 lb.

Walschaerts valve gear and derived motion. P.V.

K1/1† Introduced 1945. Thompson 2-cyl. loco. Rebuilt from K4.

K1 Introduced 1949. Peppercorn development of Thompson K1/1 (No. 61997) for new construction, with increased length.

Weight: Loco. 66 tons 17 cwt.
Tender 44 tons 4 cwt.

Pressure: 225 lb. Su.

Cyls.: (O) 20" × 26".

Driving Wheels: 5' 2".

T.E.: 32,080 lb.

Walschaerts valve gear. P.V.

61993* Loch Long
61994* The Great Marquess
61995* Cameron of Lochiel
61996* Lord of the Isles
61997† MacCailin Mor
61998* Macleod of Macleod

62001	62019	62037	62054
62002	62020	62038	62055
62003	62021	62039	62056
62004	62022	62040	62057
62005	62023	62041	62058
62006	62024	62042	62059
62007	62025	62043	62060
62008	62026	62044	62061
62009	62027	62045	62062
62010	62028	62046	62063
62011	62029	62047	62064
62012	62030	62048	62065
62013	62031	62049	62066
62014	62032	62050	62067
62015	62033	62051	62068
62016	62034	62052	62069
62017	62035	62053	62070
62018	62036		

Total

Class K1 70 **Class K4 5**

Class K1/1 1

4-4-0 3P Class D30

D30/2 Introduced 1914. Development of D30/1, introduced 1912 (Reid N.B. "Scott" class) with detail differences.

Weight: Loco. 57 tons 16 cwt.
Tender 46 tons 13 cwt.

Pressure: 165 lb. Su.

Cyls.: 20" × 26".

Driving Wheels: 6' 6".

T.E.: 18,700 lb.

P.V.

62421 Laird o' Monkbarns
62426 Cuddie Headrigg

Total 2

4-4-0 3P Class D34

Introduced 1913. Reid N.B. "Glen" class.

Weight: Loco. 57 tons 4 cwt.
Tender 46 tons 13 cwt.

Pressure: 165 lb. Su.

Cyls.: 20" × 26".

Driving Wheels: 6' 0".

T.E.: 20,260 lb.

P.V.

62467 Glenfinnan
62471 Glen Falloch
62474 Glen Croe
62479 Glen Sheil
62482 Glen Mamie
62484 Glen Lyon
62485 Glen Murran
62488 Glen Aladale
62493 Glen Gloy
62495 Glen Luss
62496 Glen Loy
62497 Glen Mallie
62498 Glen Moidart

Total 13

4-4-0 3P1F Class D16

D16/3 Introduced 1938. Rebuild of D16/2 with round-topped firebox, but retaining original footplating and slide valves.

Weight: Loco. 55 tons 18 cwt.
Tender 39 tons 5 cwt.
Pressure: 180 lb. Su.
Cyls.: 19" × 26".
Driving Wheels: 7' 0".
T.E.: 17,095 lb.

62613

Total 1

4-4-0 3P2F Class D11

D11/1* Introduced 1920. Robinson G.C. "Large Director" development of D10 (introduced 1913).

D11/2 Introduced 1924. Post-grouping locos. built to Scottish loading gauge. From 1938 the class has been rebuilt with long-travel valves.

Weight: Loco. 61 tons 3 cwt.
Tender 48 tons 6 cwt.
Pressure: 180 lb. Su.
Cyls.: 20" × 26".
Driving Wheels: 6' 9".
T.E.: 19,645 lb.
P.V.

62660* Butler-Henderson
62661* Gerard Powys Dewhurst
62662* Prince of Wales
62663* Prince Albert
62664* Princess Mary
62666* Zeebrugge
62667* Somme
62668* Jutland
62669* Ypres
62670* Marne
62671 Bailie MacWheeble
62672 Baron of Bradwardine
62674 Flora MacIvor
62680 Lucy Ashton
62681 Captain Craigengelt
62682 Haystoun of Bucklaw
62685 Malcolm Graeme
62686 The Fiery Cross
62687 Lord James of Douglas
62688 Ellen Douglas
62689 Maid of Lorn
62690 The Lady of the Lake
62691 Laird of Balmawhapple
62693 Roderick Dhu

Total
Class D11/1 10 Class D11/2 14

4-4-0 4P Class D49

D49/1* Introduced 1927. Gresley design with piston valves. Walschaerts valve gear and derived motion.

D49/2† Introduced 1928. Development of D49/1 with Lentz Rotary Cam poppet valves.

D49/2‡ Introduced 1949. Fitted with Reidinger R.R. Rotary valve gear.

(D49/3 comprised locos. 62720–5 as built with Lentz Oscillating Cam poppet valves. From 1938 these locos. were converted to D49/1. 62751–75 have larger valves than the earlier D49/2, and were at first classified D49/4).

[1]Fitted with G.C. tender.
[2]Fitted with N.E. tender.
[3]The remainder have L.N.E.R. tenders.

Weight: Loco. { 66 tons.*† / 64 tons 10 cwt.‡ }
Tender { 48 tons 6 cwt.[1] / 44 tons 2 cwt.[2] / 52 tons.[3] }
Pressure: 180 lb. Su.
Cyls.: (3) 17" × 26".
Driving Wheels: 6' 8".
T.E.: 21,555 lb.

62710*[1] Lincolnshire
62711*[1] Dumbartonshire
62712*[1] Morayshire
62716*[1] Kincardineshire
62717*[1] Banffshire
62718*[1] Kinross-shire
62723*[2] Nottinghamshire
62727†[2] The Quorn

62729*[1] Rutlandshire
62733*[1] Northumberland
62734*[2] Cumberland
62739†[3] The Badsworth
62740†[3] The Bedale
62743†[3] The Cleveland
62744†[3] The Holderness
62747†[3] The Percy
62759†[3] The Craven
62762†[3] The Fernie
62763‡[3] The Fitzwilliam
62765†[3] The Goathland

Total
Class D49/1 10 Class D49/2 10

0-8-0 6F Class Q6

Introduced 1913. Raven N.E. design.
*Some locos. are fitted with tender from withdrawn B15 locos.
Weight: Loco. 65 tons 18 cwt.
Tender { 44 tons 2 cwt. / 44 tons.*
Pressure: 180 lb. Su.
Cyls.: (O) 20" × 26".
Driving Wheels: 4' 7½".
T.E.: 28,800 lb.
P.V.

63340	63354	63368	63382
63341	63355	63369	63383
63342	63356	63370	63384
63343	63357	63371	63385
63344	63358	63372	63386
63345	63359	63373	63387
63346	63360	63374	63388
63347	63361	63375	63389
63348	63362	63376	63390
63349	63363	63377	63391
63350	63364	63378	63392
63351	63365	63379	63393
63352	63366	63380	63394
63353	63367	63381	63395
63396	63412	63428	63444
63397	63413	63429	63445
63398	63414	63430	63446
63399	63415	63431	63447
63400	63416	63432	63448
63401	63417	63433	63449
63402	63418	63434	63450
63403	63419	63435	63451
63404	63420	63436	63452
63405	63421	63437	63453
63406	63422	63438	63454
63407	63423	63439	63455
63408	63424	63440	63456
63409	63425	63441	63457
63410	63426	63442	63458
63411	63427	63443	63459

Total 120

0-8-0 8F Class Q7

Introduced 1919. Raven N.E. design.
Weight: Loco. 71 tons 12 cwt.
Tender 44 tons 2 cwt.
Pressure: 180 lb. Su.
Cyls.: (3) 18½" × 26".
Driving Wheels: 4' 7¼".
T.E.: 36,965 lb.
P.V.

63460	63464	63468	63472
63461	63465	63469	63473
63462	63466	63470	63474
63463	63467	63471	

Total 15

2-8-0 8F (O1) 7F (O4) Classes O1 & O4

O4/1[1] Introduced 1911. Robinson G.C. design with small boiler, Belpaire firebox, steam and vacuum brakes and water scoop.

O4/3[2] Introduced 1917. R.O.D. locos. with steam brake only and no scoop.

O4/2[3] Introduced 1925. O4/3 with cabs and boiler mountings reduced.

O4/6[4] Introduced 1924. Rebuilt from O5 retaining higher cab (63914–20 with side windows).

O4/7[5] Introduced 1939. Rebuilt with shortened O2-type boiler, retaining G.C. smokebox.

O4/8[6] Introduced 1944. Rebuilt with 100A (B1) boiler, retaining original cylinders.

(O4/4 were rebuilds with O2 boilers, since rebuilt again; O5 was a G.C. development of O4 with larger boiler and Belpaire firebox.)

Weight: Loco. { 73 tons 4 cwt.[1]
73 tons 4 cwt.[2]
73 tons 4 cwt.[3]
74 tons 13 cwt.[4]
73 tons 4 cwt.[5]
73 tons 17 cwt.[6]
72 tons 10 cwt.[7] }

Tender { 48 tons 6 cwt. (with scoop)
47 tons 6 cwt. (without scoop) }

Pressure: 180 lb. Su.
Cyls.: (O) 21″ × 26″.
Driving Wheels: 4′ 8″.
T.E.: 31,325 lb.
P.V.

O1[7] Introduced 1944. Thompson rebuild with 100A boiler, Walschaerts valve gear and new cylinders.

Weight: Loco. 73 tons 6 cwt.
Tender as O4.
Pressure: 225 lb. Su.
Cyls.: (O) 20″ × 26″.
Driving Wheels: 4′ 8″.
T.E.: 35,520 lb.
Walschaerts valve gear. P.V.

63570[5]	63594[7]	63613[6]	63637[2]
63571[7]	63595[5]	63615[5]	63639[6]
63573[6]	63596[7]	63616[5]	63641[6]
63574[1]	63597[1]	63617[1]	63643[6]
63575[6]	63598[1]	63618[1]	63644[7]
63576[1]	63599[1]	63619[7]	63645[7]
63577[1]	63600[5]	63621[1]	63646[8]
63578[7]	63601[1]	63622[1]	63647[7]
63579[7]	63602[1]	63623[1]	63648[3]
63584[1]	63603[5]	63624[6]	63649[6]
63585[1]	63604[6]	63626[1]	63650[7]
63586[1]	63605[1]	63628[6]	63651[6]
63587[1]	63606[6]	63630[7]	63652[7]
63588[5]	63607[6]	63631[6]	63653[6]
63589[7]	63608[1]	63632[1]	63655[6]
63590[7]	63609[1]	63633[6]	63656[2]
63591[7]	63610[7]	63634[5]	63657[2]
63592[7]	63611[1]	63635[1]	63658[1]
63593[1]	63612[6]	63636[6]	63659[2]

63661[5]	63718[6]	63775[5]	63840[6]
63662[5]	63719[1]	63776[6]	63841[6]
63663[7]	63720[6]	63777[7]	63842[2]
63664[1]	63721[6]	63779[2]	63843[5]
63665[2]	63722[1]	63780[7]	63845[2]
63666[2]	63724[2]	63781[6]	63846[2]
63669[5]	63725[7]	63782[2]	63848[5]
63670[7]	63726[6]	63783[2]	63850[6]
63671[1]	63727[1]	63784[7]	63852[6]
63672[6]	63728[6]	63785[6]	63853[6]
63674[6]	63730[6]	63786[7]	63854[7]
63675[6]	63731[6]	63787[2]	63856[7]
63676[7]	63732[6]	63788[6]	63857[6]
63677[1]	63734[6]	63789[7]	63858[6]
63678[7]	63735[2]	63791[6]	63859[2]
63679[6]	63736[1]	63792[7]	63860[5]
63681[2]	63737[2]	63793[6]	63861[6]
63683[6]	63738[6]	63794[6]	63862[6]
63684[1]	63739[6]	63795[7]	63863[7]
63685[2]	63740[7]	63796[7]	63864[6]
63686[2]	63741[6]	63798[2]	63865[7]
63687[7]	63742[6]	63799[1]	63867[7]
63688[6]	63743[1]	63800[6]	63868[7]
63689[7]	63744[2]	63801[6]	63869[7]
63690[3]	63746[7]	63802[6]	63870[2]
63691[6]	63747[5]	63803[7]	63872[7]
63692[1]	63748[5]	63805[6]	63873[6]
63693[1]	63750[6]	63806[7]	63874[7]
63695[2]	63752[7]	63807[6]	63877[6]
63697[6]	63754[6]	63808[7]	63878[6]
63698[1]	63755[7]	63813[2]	63879[7]
63700[1]	63757[1]	63816[6]	63880[5]
63701[2]	63758[5]	63817[7]	63881[6]
63702[2]	63759[2]	63818[6]	63882[6]
63703[6]	63760[7]	63819[6]	63883[2]
63704[6]	63762[1]	63821[2]	63884[6]
63705[6]	63763[6]	63822[6]	63885[6]
63706[6]	63764[2]	63823[6]	63886[7]
63707[1]	63765[6]	63824[5]	63887[7]
63708[5]	63766[2]	63827[6]	63888[2]
63709[6]	63767[2]	63828[6]	63890[7]
63711[7]	63768[7]	63829[6]	63891[5]
63712[7]	63770[5]	63832[6]	63893[6]
63713[2]	63771[2]	63833[2]	63894[5]
63715[6]	63772[5]	63836[6]	63895[6]
63716[2]	63773[7]	63837[6]	63897[6]
63717[6]	63774[2]	63838[7]	63898[6]

63899^{6}	63904^{4}	63911^{4}	63915^{6}
63900^{2}	63906^{4}	63912^{4}	63917^{4}
63901^{7}	63907^{4}	63913^{4}	63920^{4}
63902^{4}	63908^{4}	63914^{6}	

Total

Class O1	**58**	**Class O4/6**	**10**
Class O4/1	**40**	**Class O4/7**	**26**
Class O4/2	**2**	**Class O4/8**	**100**
Class O4/3	**43**		

2-8-0 8F Class O2

O2/1* Introduced 1921. Development of experimental Gresley G.N. 3-cyl. loco. (L.N.E.R. 3921). Subsequently rebuilt with side-window cab, and reduced boiler mountings.

O2/2† Introduced 1924. Development of O2/1 with detail differences.

O2/3 Introduced 1932. Development of O2/2 with side-window cab and reduced boiler mountings.

O2/4‡ Introduced 1943. Rebuilt with 100A (B1 type) boiler and smokebox extended backwards (63924 retaining G.N. tender).

Weight: Loco. { 75 tons 16 cwt.*† / 78 tons 13 cwt. / 74 tons 2 cwt.‡

Tender { 43 tons 2 cwt. (63922–46) / 52 tons (63947–87).

Pressure: 180 lb. Su.

Cyls.: (3) $18\frac{1}{2}'' \times 26''$.

Driving Wheels: 4′ 8″.

T.E.: 36,740 lb.

Walschaerts valve gear and derived motion. P.V.

63922*	63925‡	63928*	63931*
63923*	63926*	63929*	63932‡
63924‡	63927*	63930‡	63933‡

63934†	63948‡	63962‡	63976
63935‡	63949‡	63963	63977
63936†	63950‡	63964	63978
63937†	63951	63965‡	63979
63938‡	63952	63966‡	63980
63939†	63953	63967	63981
63940†	63954	63968	63982‡
63941†	63955‡	63969	63983‡
63942†	63956	63970	63984
63943†	63957	63971	63985
63944†	63958	63972	63986
63945‡	63959	63973	63987
63946†	63960	63974	
63947	63961‡	63975	

Total

Class O2/1	**7**	**Class O2/3**	**31**
Class O2/2	**10**	**Class O2/4**	**18**

0-6-0 2P3F Class J6

Introduced 1911. Gresley G.N. design.
Weight: Loco. 50 tons 10 cwt.
Tender 43 tons 2 cwt.
Pressure: 170 lb. Su.
Cyls.: $19'' \times 26''$.
Driving Wheels: 5′ 2″.
T.E.: 21,875 lb.
P.V.

64170	64191	64223	64253
64171	64192	64226	64256
64173	64196	64231	64257
64174	64203	64232	64260
64175	64206	64233	64265
64177	64208	64236	64268
64178	64209	64240	64270
64179	64219	64245	64277
64182	64222	64251	64278
64185			

Total 37

HISTORIC LOCOMOTIVES PRESERVED IN STORE

Type	Originating Company	Pre-Grouping No.	L.N.E.R. No.	Name	Place of Preservation
4-2-2	G.N.R.	1	—	—	York Museum
4-4-2	G.N.R.	990	(3990)	Henry Oakley	York Museum
4-4-2	G.N.R.	251	(3251)	—	York Museum
2-2-4T	N.E.R.	66	66	Aerolite	York Museum
2-4-0	N.E.R.	910	910	—	York Museum
2-4-0	N.E.R.	1463	1463	—	York Museum
4-4-0	N.E.R.	1621	1621	—	York Museum

The unbracketed numbers are the ones at present carried by the locos.

0-6-0 2P3F Class J11

Introduced 1901. Robinson G.C. design. Parts 1 and 4 have 3,250-gallon tenders; Parts 2 and 5, 4,000-gallon. Parts 1 and 2 have high boiler mountings; Parts 4 and 5 low. All of Parts 4 and 5 are superheated, and some of Parts 1 and 2. There are frequent changes between parts.

J11/3* Introduced 1942. Rebuilt with long-travel piston valves and boiler higher pitched.

Weight: Loco. { 51 tons 19 cwt. (Sat.) / 52 tons 2 cwt. (Su.) / 53 tons 6 cwt.* }

Tender { 44 tons 3 cwt. (3,250 gall.) / 48 tons 6 cwt. (4,000 gall.) }

Pressure: 180 lb. SS.

Cyls.: $18\frac{1}{2}'' \times 26''$.

Driving Wheels: 5′ 2″.

T.E.: 21,960 lb.

64284*	64313	64325	64352*
64288	64314*	64329	64354*
64292	64315	64332*	64355
64305	64316*	64333*	64357
64308	64317*	64337	64359*
64310	64318*	64341	64362*
64311	64324*	64346*	64363

64364*	64387	64417*	64440
64368	64393*	64418*	64441*
64371	64394*	64419	64442*
64373*	64395*	64420*	64443
64375*	64396	64423	64444
64377	64397	64425	64445
64379*	64402*	64427*	64446
64383	64403	64434	64447
64384	64404	64435	64450*
64385	64405	64437	64452
64386*	64406*	64439*	

Total

Class J11/3 31

Class J11 (other parts) **40**

0-6-0 3F Class J35

J35/5* Introduced 1906. Reid N.B. design with piston valves.

J35/4 Introduced 1908. Slide valves. (Parts 1, 2 and 3 were variations of Parts 4 and 5 before superheating.)

64461-64674

Weight: Loco. {51 tons.* / 50 tons 15 cwt.}
Tender {38 tons 1 cwt.* / 37 tons 15 cwt.}
Pressure: 180 lb. Su.
Cyls.: 18¼" × 26".
Driving Wheels: 5' 0".
T.E.: 22,080 lb.

64461*	64479	64499	64519
64462*	64480	64500	64523
64463*	64482	64502	64524
64468*	64483	64504	64525
64470*	64487	64505	64527
64471*	64488	64507	64529
64472*	64489	64510	64531
64474*	64491	64512	64532
64476*	64493	64514	64533
64477*	64494	64515	64534
64478	64497	64518	64535

Total
Class J35/4 34 Class J35/5 10

0-6-0 5F Class J37

Introduced 1914. Reid N.B. design. Superheated development of J35.
Weight: Loco. 54 tons 14 cwt.
Tender 40 tons 19 cwt.
Pressure: 180 lb. Su.
Cyls.: 19½" × 26".
Driving Wheels: 5' 0".
T.E.: 25,210 lb.
P.V.

64537	64549	64560	64571
64539	64550	64561	64572
64540	64551	64562	64573
64541	64552	64563	64574
64542	64553	64564	64575
64543	64554	64565	64576
64544	64555	64566	64577
64545	64556	64567	64578
64546	64557	64568	64579
64547	64558	64569	64580
64548	64559	64570	64581

64582	64598	64613	64628
64583	64599	64614	64629
64585	64600	64615	64630
64586	64601	64616	64631
64587	64602	64617	64632
64588	64603	64618	64633
64589	64604	64619	64634
64590	64605	64620	64635
64591	64606	64621	64636
64592	64607	64622	64637
64593	64608	64623	64638
64594	64609	64624	64639
64595	64610	64625	
64596	64611	64626	
64597	64612	64627	

Total 101

0-6-0 3P5F Class J19

Introduced 1916. Hill G.E. design rebuilt with round-topped firebox from 1934.
*Rebuilt with 19" cyls. and 180 lb. pressure.
Weight: Loco. 50 tons 7 cwt.
Tender 38 tons 5 cwt.
Pressure: {170 lb. Su. / 180 lb. Su.*}
Cyls.: {20" × 26". / 19" × 26".*}
Driving Wheels: 4' 11".
T.E.: {27,430 lb. / 26,215 lb.*}

64642	64652	64659	64667
64643	64653	64660	64669
64646	64655	64663	64671*
64647	64656	64664*	64673
64650	64657	64666	64674

Total 20

0-6-0 5F Class J20

J20/1 Introduced 1943. Hill G.E. design with Belpaire firebox (introduced 1920) rebuilt with B12/1-type boiler with round-topped firebox.

Weight: Loco. 54 tons 15 cwt.
Tender 38 tons 5 cwt.
Pressure: 180 lb. Su.
Cyls.: 20″ × 28″.
Driving Wheels: 4′ 11″.
T.E.: 29,045 lb.
P.V.

64676	64681	64687	64693
64677	64682	64689	64696
64678	64684	64690	64697
64679	64685	64691	64698
64680	64686	64692	64699

Total 20

0-6-0 4P5F Class J39

Introduced 1926. Gresley design.
J39/1 Standard 3,500-gallon tender.
J39/2* Standard 4,200-gallon tender.
J39/3† Various N.E. tenders (3,940-gallon on 64843–5, 4,125-gallon on 64855–9).
Weight: Loco. 57 tons 17 cwt.
Tender { 44 tons 4 cwt. / 52 tons 13 cwt.* and others.
Pressure: 180 lb. Su.
Cyls.: 20″ × 26″.
Driving Wheels: 5′ 2″.
T.E.: 25,665 lb.
P.V.

64700†	64719	64741	64765
64701	64720	64742	64767
64703	64723	64743	64770
64704	64724	64744	64772
64705	64725	64745	64775
64706	64726	64746	64778
64707	64727	64747	64779
64708	64729	64748	64783
64709	64730	64749	64784*
64710	64732	64754	64786*
64711	64733	64756	64789*
64713	64736	64757	64790*
64716	64738	64758	64791*
64717	64739	64760	64792*
64718	64740	64764	64794*

64795*	64843†	64884*	64929*
64796	64844†	64885*	64930*
64798	64845†	64886*	64931*
64801	64846	64888*	64932*
64802	64847	64889*	64933
64804	64848	64890*	64934
64806	64849	64891*	64935
64807	64850	64892*	64936
64808	64851	64893*	64938
64809	64852	64895*	64939
64810	64853	64896*	64940
64811	64854	64897*	64941
64812	64855†	64899*	64942
64813	64856†	64901*	64943
64814	64857†	64903*	64944
64815	64858†	64904*	64945*
64816	64859†	64906*	64946*
64817	64860	64907*	64947*
64818	64861	64908*	64948*
64819	64862	64909*	64949*
64820*	64863	64910*	64950*
64821*	64864	64911*	64955*
64822*	64865	64914*	64961*
64823	64866	64915*	64963*
64824	64867	64916*	64964*
64825	64868	64917*	64966*
64826	64869	64918*	64969*
64828	64870	64919*	64970*
64830	64871	64920*	64971†
64831	64872*	64921*	64974†
64833	64874*	64922*	64975†
64835	64875*	64923*	64978†
64836	64877*	64924*	64979†
64837	64878*	64925*	64982†
64839*	64879*	64926†	64986†
64840*	64880*	64927*	64987†
64842*	64882*	64928*	

Total

Class J39/1 114 Class J39/3 18
Class J39/2 75

0-6-0 2F Class J21

Introduced 1886. T. W. Worsdell N.E. design. Majority built as 2-cyl. compounds and later rebuilt as simple locos., subsequently rebuilt with superheater and piston valves, superheater later removed.

Weight: Loco. 42 tons 9 cwt.
Tender 36 tons 19 cwt.

Pressure: 160 lb. SS.
Cyls.: 19" × 24".
Driving Wheels: 5' 1¼".
T.E.: 19,240 lb.

65033 65070 65099 65110

Total 4

0-6-0 2F Class J10

J10/4* Introduced 1896. Pollitt development of J10/2 with larger bearings and larger tender.

J10/6 Introduced 1901. Robinson locos. with larger bearings and small tender.

Weight: Loco. 41 tons 6 cwt.
Tender { 37 tons 6 cwt. / 43 tons.*

Pressure: 160 lb.
Cyls.: 18" × 26".
Driving Wheels: 5' 1".
T.E.: 18,780 lb.

65157* 65192 65198

Total

Class J10/4 1 Class J10/6 2

0-6-0 2F Class J36

Introduced 1888. Holmes N.B. design.

Weight: Loco. 41 tons 19 cwt.
Tender 33 tons 9 cwt.

Pressure: 165 lb.
Cyls.: 18¼" × 26".
Driving Wheels: 5' 0".
T.E.: 19,690 lb.

65210
65211
65214
65216 Byng
65217 French
65218
65222 Somme
65224 Mons
65227
65228
65229
65230
65232
65233 Plumer
65234
65235 Gough
65237
65239
65241
65243 Maude
65246
65249
65251
65252
65253 Joffre

65257	65260	65265	65267
65258	65261	65266	

65268 Allenby

65273	65282	65295	65305
65275	65285	65296	65306
65276	65287	65297	65307
65277	65288	65300	65309
65280	65290	65303	65310
65281	65293	65304	

65311 Haig

65312	65319	65329	65339
65313	65320	65330	65341
65315	65321	65331	65343
65316	65323	65334	65344
65317	65325	65335	65345
65318	65327	65338	65346

Total 81

0-6-0 1P2F Class J15

Introduced 1883. Worsdell G.E. design, modified by J. Holden.
Weight: Loco. 37 tons 2 cwt.
Tender 30 tons 13 cwt.
Pressure: 160 lb.
Cyls.: 17½" × 24".
Driving Wheels: 4' 11".
T.E.: 16,940 lb.

65361	65450	65461	65474
65389	65453	65462	65476
65420	65457	65464	65477
65440	65458	65465	65478
65445	65459	65469	65479
65446	65460	65471	

Total 23

0-6-0 2P4F Class J17

Introduced 1901. J. Holden G.E. design. Many rebuilt from round-top firebox J16, introduced 1900.
*Fitted with small tender.
Weight: Loco. 45 tons 8 cwt.
Tender { 38 tons 5 cwt. / 30 tons 12 cwt.*
Pressure: 180 lb. Su.
Cyls.: 19" × 26".
Driving Wheels: 4' 11".
T.E.: 24,340 lb.

65503*	65532	65564	65578
65506*	65539	65565	65581
65507*	65541	65566	65582
65511*	65549	65567	65583
65513*	65551	65570	65586
65520	65554	65576	65588
65521	65556	65577	65589
65528*	65560		

Total 30

0-6-0 3F Class J25

Introduced 1898. W. Worsdell N.E. design.
*Original design, saturated, with slide valves.
†Rebuilt with superheater and piston valves.
Weight: Loco. { 39 tons 11 cwt.* / 41 tons 14 cwt.†
Tender 36 tons 19 cwt.
Pressure: 160 lb. SS.
Cyls.: 18½" × 26".
Driving Wheels: 4' 7¼".
T.E.: 21,905 lb.

65645†	65670*	65712*	65726*
65662†	65691*	65713*	65727*
65663*	65693*	65714*	65728*
65666*	65695*	65720*	

Total 15

0-6-0 5F Class J26

Introduced 1904. W. Worsdell N.E. design.
Weight: Loco. 46 tons 16 cwt.
Tender 36 tons 19 cwt.
Pressure: 180 lb.
Cyls.: 18½" × 26".
Driving Wheels: 4' 7¼".
T.E.: 24,640 lb.

65731	65751	65762	65776
65735	65753	65763	65777
65736	65755	65768	65778
65741	65756	65769	65779
65743	65757	65772	
65745	65760	65773	
65747	65761	65774	

Total 25

0-6-0 5F Class J27

Introduced 1906. W. Worsdell N.E. design developed from J26.
*Introduced 1921. Raven locos. Superheated, with piston valves.
†Introduced 1943. Piston valves, but superheater removed.
Weight: Loco. { 47 tons Sat. / 49 tons 10 cwt. Su.
Tender 36 tons 19 cwt.
Pressure: 180 lb. SS.
Cyls.: 18½" × 26".
Driving Wheels: 4' 7¼".
T.E.: 24,640 lb.

Class 3 (Fowler) 2-6-2T No. 40063 [K. R. Pirt

Class 3 (Stanier) 2-6-2T No. 40154 [K. R. Pirt

Class 2 (Ivatt) 2-6-2T No. 41210 (push-and-pull fitted) [Brian E. Morrison

Class 2P (ex-Midland) 4-4-0 No. 40540 [*P. J. Sharpe*

Class 2P (ex-L.M.S.) 4-4-0 No. 40671 [*P. J. Sharpe*

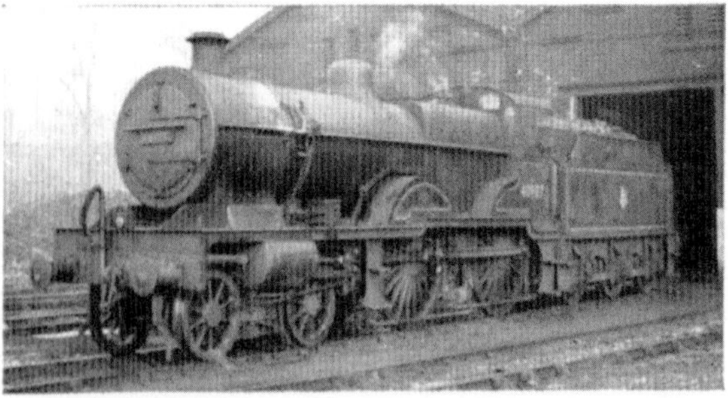

Class 4P 4-4-0 No. 40907 [*K. R. Firt*

Class 4 (Stanier 3-cylinder` 2-6-4T No. 42536 [*J. B. Bucknall*

Class 4 (Stanier 2-cylinder) 2-6-4T No. 42668 [*J. E. Wilkinson*

Class 4 (Fairburn) 2-6-4T No. 42106 [*R. C. Riley*

Class 4 (Ivatt) 2-6-0 No. 43112 [J. E. Wilkinson

Class 2 (Ivatt) 2-6-0 No. 46477 [P. J. Robinson

Class 2 (Riddles) 2-6-0 No. 78023 [Brian E. Morrison

Class 5 4-6-0 No. 45407 [G. Wheeler

Standard Class 5 4-6-0 No. 73140 (with Caprotti valve gear) [F. W. Day

Class 6P5F 4-6-2 No. 72005 *Clan Macgregor* [David A. Anderson

Class 7P 4-6-0 No. 45545 *Planet* [*J. E. Wilkinson*

Class 7P 4-6-0 No. 45736 *Phoenix* [*J. E. Wilkinson*

Class 6P5F 4-6-0 No. 45633 *Aden* [*K. R. Pirt*

Class 6P5F 4-6-0 No. 45517 K. R. Pirt

Class 8P 4-6-2 No. 46253 *City of St. Albans* [G. Wheeler

Class 8P 4-6-2 No. 46203 *Princess Margaret Rose* [David A. Anderson

Standard Class 8P 4-6-2 No. 71000 *Duke of Gloucester* [*A. R. Carpenter*

Class 8F 2-8-0 No. 48634 (the star beneath the number on the cab side indicates that the driving wheels are balanced) [*J. E. Wilkinson*

Class 8F 2-8-0 No. 48752 (with Fowler type tender) [*J. B. Bucknall*

Class 3F 0-6-0 No. 43499 [J. Davenport

Class 4F (ex-Midland) 0-6-0 No. 43914 [P. H. Groom

Class 4F (ex-L.M.S.) 0-6-0 No. 44114 [P. H. Groom

Class 3F 0-6-0T No. 47351 [R. A. Panting

Class 2F 0-6-0T No. 47166 [Brian E. Morrison

Class 0F 0-4-0ST No. 47000 [P. H. Groom

Class 2F 0-6-0ST No. 51412 [*P. J. Robinson*

Class 1F 0-6-0T No. 51537 [*R. C. Riley*

Class 2P 2-4-2T No. 50850 (rebuilt with Belpaire firebox and extended smokebox) [*R. S. Greenwood*

Class 2P 0-4-4T No. 55222 *[D. Penney*

Class 3F 0-6-0T No. 56246 *[David A. Anderson*

Class 2F 0-6-0T No. 56168 *[P. J. Sharpe*

Class 3F 0-6-0 No. 57612 [*K. L. Cook*

Class 3F 0-6-0 No. 57652 [*K. R. Pirt*

Class 2F 0-6-0 No. 57378 [*K. R. Pirt*

Standard Class 9F 2-10-0 No. 92166 (fitted with mechanical stoker and double chimney)
[J. Davenport

Standard Class 9F 2-10-0 No. 92019 alongside Crosti-boilered engine No. 92024
[T. G. Hepburn

Standard Class 4 4-6-0 No. 75042 [P. H. Groom

Class A4 4-6-2 No. 60033 *Seagull* [*J. B. Bucknall*

Class A3 4-6-2 No. 60055 *Woolwinder* (fitted with double chimney and small-type smoke deflectors)

Class B1 4-6-0 No. 61379 *Mayflower* [*K. R. Pirt*

Class A1 4-6-2 No. 60158 *Aberdonian* [G. Wheeler

Class A2/2 4-6-2 No. 60506 *Wolf of Badenoch* [J. P. Wilson

Class A2 4-6-2 No. 60531 *Bahram*

65782	65813	65845	65872†
65786	65814	65846	65873†
65787	65815	65847	65874*
65788	65817	65849	65875†
65789	65818	65850	65876†
65790	65819	65851	65877†
65791	65820	65852	65878*
65792	65821	65853	65879†
65794	65822	65854	65880*
65795	65823	65855	65881*
65796	65825	65857	65882†
65797	65828	65858	65883*
65799	65830	65859	65884†
65800	65831	65860†	65885*
65801	65832	65861†	65887*
65802	65833	65862†	65888†
65804	65834	65863†	65889*
65805	65835	65864†	65890*
65807	65837	65865†	65891†
65808	65838	65867†	65892*
65809	65839	65868†	65893*
65810	65841	65869†	65894*
65811	65842	65870†	
65812	65844	65871*	

Total 94

0-6-0 6F Class J38

Introduced 1926. Gresley design. Predecessor of J39, with 4′ 8″ wheels, boiler 6″ longer than J39 and smokebox 6″ shorter.

*Rebuilt with J39 boiler.

Weight: Loco. 58 tons 19 cwt.
Tender 44 tons 4 cwt.

Pressure: 180 lb. Su.
Cyls.: 20″ × 26″.
Driving Wheels: 4′ 8″.
T.E.: 28,415 lb.
P.V.

65900	65905	65910	65915
65901	65906*	65911	65916
65902	65907	65912	65917*
65903*	65908*	65913	65918*
65904	65909	65914	65919
65920	65924	65928	65932
65921	65925	65929	65933
65922	65926*	65930	65934
65923	65927*	65931	

Total 35

4-4-2T 2P Class C15

Introduced 1911. Reid N.B. design. Push-and-pull fitted.
Weight: 68 tons 15 cwt.
Pressure: 175 lb.
Cyls.: 18″ × 26″.
Driving Wheels: 5′ 9″.
T.E.: 18,160 lb.

67460 67474 **Total 2**

4-4-2T 2P Class C16

Introduced 1915. Reid N.B. design, superheated development of C15.
Weight: 72 tons 10 cwt.
Pressure: 165 lb. Su.
Cyls.: 19″ × 26″.
Driving Wheels: 5′ 9″.
T.E.: 19,080 lb.
P.V.

67484	67489	67492	67501
67485	67490	67494	67502
67486	67491	67496	

Total 11

2-6-2T V1 (3MT) V3 (4MT) Classes V1 & V3

V1 Introduced 1930. Gresley design.
V3* Introduced 1939. Development of V1 with higher pressure (locos. numbered below 67682 rebuilt from V1).

Weight: 84 tons. / 86 tons 16 cwt.*
Pressure: 180 lb. Su. / 200 lb. Su.*

Cyls.: (3) 16″ × 26″.

Driving Wheels: 5′ 8″.

T.E.: { 22,465 lb. / 24,960 lb.*

Walschaerts valve gear and derived motion. P.V.

67600*	67623*	67646*	67669*
67601	67624*	67647*	67670*
67602	67625*	67648*	67671
67603	67626*	67649	67672*
67604*	67627*	67650*	67673
67605*	67628*	67651*	67674*
67606*	67629	67652*	67675*
67607*	67630	67653*	67676
67608	67631	67654*	67677*
67609*	67632*	67655	67678*
67610	67633	67656*	67679*
67611*	67634*	67657*	67680
67612*	67635	67658*	67681*
67613	67636*	67659	67682*
67614*	67637	67660*	67683*
67615*	67638*	67661*	67684*
67616	67639	67662*	67685*
67617*	67640	67663*	67686*
67618*	67641	67664	67687*
67619*	67642	67665	67688*
67620*	67643*	67666	67689*
67621*	67644*	67667*	67690*
67622	67645*	67668*	67691*

Total

Class V1 28 **Class V3 64**

2-6-4T 4MT Class L1

Introduced 1945. Thompson design.

*Introduced 1954. Boiler pressure reduced to 200 lb.

†Introduced 1954. Cylinder diameter reduced.

Weight: 89 tons 9 cwt.

Pressure: { 225 lb. / 200 lb.*

Cyls.: { (O) 20″ × 26″. / (O) 18¾″ × 26″.†

Driving Wheels: 5′ 2″.

T.E.: { 32,080 lb. / 28,515 lb.* / 28,180 lb.†

Walschaerts valve gear. P.V.

67701	67726	67751	67776†
67702	67727	67752	67777
67703	67728	67753	67778
67704	67729	67754	67779†
67705	67730	67755	67780
67706	67731	67756	67781
67707	67732	67757	67782
67708	67733	67758	67783
67709	67734	67759	67784
67710	67735	67760	67785
67711	67736	67761*	67786
67712	67737	67762	67787
67713	67738	67763	67788
67714	67739	67764	67789
67715	67740	67765	67790
67716	67741	67766	67791
67717	67742	67767	67792
67718	67743	67768	67793
67719	67744	67769	67794
67720	67745	67770†	67795
67721	67746	67771†	67796
67722	67747*	67772†	67797
67723	67748	67773	67798*
67724	67749	67774	67799
67725	67750	67775	67800

Total 100

0-6-0ST 4F Class J94

Introduced 1943. Riddles M.o.S. design. (Bought from M.o.S., 1946.)

Weight: 48 tons 5 cwt.

Pressure: 170 lb.

Cyls.: 18″ × 26″.

Driving Wheels: 4′ 3″.

T.E.: 23,870 lb.

68006	68025	68044	68063
68007	68026	68045	68064
68008	68027	68046	68065
68009	68028	68047	68066
68010	68029	68048	68067
68011	68030	68049	68068
68012	68031	68050	68069
68013	68032	68051	68070
68014	68033	68052	68071
68015	68034	68053	68072
68016	68035	68054	68073
68017	68036	68055	68074
68018	68037	68056	68075
68019	68038	68057	68076
68020	68039	68058	68077
68021	68040	68059	68078
68022	68041	68060	68079
68023	68042	68061	68080
68024	68043	68062	

Total 75

0-4-0ST OF Class Y9

Introduced 1882. Holmes N.B. design.
*Locos. running permanently attached to wooden tender.
Weight: Loco. 27 tons 16 cwt.
Tender 6 tons.*
Pressure: 130 lb.
Cyls.: (O) 14" × 20".
Driving Wheels: 3' 8".
T.E.: 9,845 lb.

68095	68104	68114*	68119*
68100*	68110	68117*	68123
68101			

Total 9

0-4-2T OF Class Z4

Introduced 1915. Manning-Wardle design for G.N. of S.
Weight: 25 tons 17 cwt.
Pressure: 160 lb.
Cyls.: (O) 13" × 20".
Driving Wheels: 3' 6".
T.E.: 10,945 lb.

68190 **Total 1**

0-4-2T OF Class Z5

Introduced 1915. Manning-Wardle design for G.N. of S.
Weight: 30 tons 18 cwt.
Pressure: 160 lb.
Cyls.: (O) 14" × 20".
Driving Wheels: 4' 0".
T.E.: 11,105 lb.

68192 **Total 1**

0-6-0T Unclass. Class J71

Introduced 1886. T. W. Worsdell N.E. design.
*Altered cylinder dimensions.
Weight: 37 tons 12 cwt.
Pressure: 140 lb.
Driving Wheels 4' 7¼".
Cyls.: { 16" × 22". / 16¾" × 22".* }
T.E.: { 12,130 lb. / 13,300 lb.* }

68233	68269	68278	68314
68235	68272	68309*	68316*
68254	68275		

Total 10

0-6-0T OF Class J88

Introduced 1904. Reid N.B. design with short wheelbase.
Weight: 38 tons 14 cwt.
Pressure: 130 lb.
Cyls.: (O) 15" × 22".
Driving Wheels: 3' 9".
T.E.: 12,155 lb.

68320	68336	68344	68350
68325	68338	68345	68352
68332	68342	68346	68353
68335	68343	68349	68354

Total 16

DEPARTMENTAL LOCOMOTIVES

(Former running no. in brackets)

0-6-0ST 3F Class J52/2

2 (68816) 9 (68840)

0-4-0T Un-class. Class Y3

Introduced 1927.
Sentinel Wagon Works design. Two-speed Geared Sentinel locos.
Sprocket gear ratio 15: 19.
Weight: 20 tons 16 cwt.
Pressure: 275 lb. Su.
Cyls.: 6¾" × 9".
Driving Wheels: 2' 6".
T.E.: Low Gear: 15,960 lb. High Gear: 5,960 lb.
Poppet valves.

3 (68181)	41 (68177)
7 (68166)	42 (68178)
21 (68162)	57 (68160)
40 (68173)	

Total 7

0-6-0T 2F Class J66

Introduced 1886. J. Holden G.E. design.
Weight: 40 tons 6 cwt.
Pressure: 160 lb.
Cyls.: 16½" × 22".
Driving Wheels: 4' 0".
T.E.: 16,970 lb.

31 (68382) 32 (68370)

Total 2

0-6-0T 2F Class J69

44(68498) 45(68543)

0-4-0T Un-class. Class Y1/1

Sentinel Wagon Works design. Single-speed Geared Sentinel locomotives. The parts of this class differ in details, including size of boiler and fuel capacity.

Y1/1* Introduced 1925.
Y1/2† Introduced 1927.
Sprocket gear ratio 11: 25.
Weight: 20 tons 17 cwt.* 19 tons 16 cwt.†
Pressure: 275 lb. Su.
Cyls.: 6¾" × 9".
Driving Wheels: 2' 6".
T.E.: 7,260 lb.*†
Poppet valves.

39*(68131) 54†(68153)

Total
Class Y1/1 1 Class Y1/2 1

0-4-0 Diesel Mechanical

52 (11104)

0-4-0T Dock Tank Class Y4

Introduced 1913. Hill G.E. design.
Weight: 38 tons 1 cwt.
Pressure: 180 lb.
Cyls.: (O) 17" × 20".
Driving Wheels: 3' 10".
T.E.: 19,225 lb.
Walschaerts valve gear.

33 (68129) Total 1

0-4-0 Diesel Mechanical

56 81

0-6-0 Diesel Mechanical

91 92

Bo-Bo EB1 Electric

100 (26510)

NOTE. (For details of Departmental diesel and electric locomotives, see ABC British Railways Diesels or Electrics and Diesel and Electric Section of combined volume.)

0-6-0T 3F Class J73

Introduced 1891. W. Worsdell N.E. design.

Weight: 46 tons 15 cwt.

Pressure: 160 lb.

Cyls.: 19″ × 24″.

Driving Wheels: 4′ 7¼″.

T.E.: 21,320 lb.

68360 68361 68364

Total 3

0-6-0T 2F Class J77

Introduced 1899. W. Worsdell N.E. rebuild of Fletcher 0-4-4T originally built 1874–84.

Some engines of this class have square-cornered and some round-cornered cab roofs.

Weight: 43 tons.

Pressure: 160 lb.

Cyls.: 17″ × 22″.

Driving Wheels: 4′ 1¼″.

T.E.: 17,560 lb.

68392 68408 68410

Total 3

0-6-0T 2F Class J83

Introduced 1900. Holmes N.B. design.

Weight: 45 tons 5 cwt.

Pressure: 150 lb.

Cyls.: 17″ × 26″.

Driving Wheels: 4′ 6″.

T.E.: 17,745 lb.

68442	68453	68458	68472
68443	68454	68459	68477
68445	68456	68470	68479
68447	68457	68471	68481
68448			

Total 17

0-6-0T 2F Class J69

J69/1† Introduced 1902. Development of Holden J67 with 180 lb. pressure, larger tanks and larger firebox (some rebuilt from J67).

J69/2§ Introduced 1950. J67/1 rebuilt with 180 lb. boiler and larger firebox.

Weight: 40 tons 9 cwt.

Pressure: 180 lb.

Cyls.: 16½″ × 22″.

Driving Wheels: 4′ 0″.

T.E.: 19,090 lb.

(See also E.R. Departmental Locos.)

68497†	68538†	68565†	68612†
68499†	68542†	68566†	68613†
68500†	68545†	68569†	68619†
68501†	68549†	68570†	68621†
68502†	68550†	68571†	68623†
68507†	68552†	68573†	68626†
68508†	68554†	68575†	68633†
68513§	68556†	68577†	68635†
68522§	68558†	68578†	
68526†	68560†	68600†	
68530†	68563†	68609†	

Total

Class J69/2 2 Class J69/1 41

0-6-0T 2F Class J68

Introduced 1912. Hill G.E. development of J69 with side-window cab.

Weight: 42 tons 9 cwt.

Pressure: 180 lb.

Cyls.: 16½″ × 22″.

Driving Wheels: 4′ 0″.

T.E.: 19,090 lb.

68642	68647	68650	68660
68644	68649	68656	68663
68646			

Total 9

0-6-0T 2F Class J72

Introduced 1898. W. Worsdell N.E. design.

*Altered cylinder dimensions.

Weight: 38 tons 12 cwt.

Pressure: 140 lb.

Cyls.: { 17" × 24". / 18" × 24".*

Driving Wheels: 4' 1¼".

T.E.: { 16,760 lb. / 18,790 lb.*

68672	68690	68713	68732
68673	68691	68714	68733
68674	68692	68715	68734
68675	68693	68716	68736
68676	68695	68717	68737
68677	68696	68719	68738
68678	68698	68720	68740
68679	68701	68721	68742
68680	68702	68723	68743
68681	68703	68724	68744
68683	68704	68725	68745
68684	68705	68726	68747
68685*	68706	68728	68749
68686	68707	68729	68750
68687	68708	68730	68753
68688	68709	68731	68754
68689	68711		

(Class continued with No. 69001)

0-6-0ST 3F Class J52

J52/2 Introduced 1897. Ivatt G.N. saddletank with domed boiler.

Weight: 51 tons 14 cwt.

Pressure: 170 lb.

Cyls.: 18" × 26".

Driving Wheels: 4' 8".

T.E.: 21,735 lb.

(See also E.R. Departmental Locos.)

68869 68875

Total 4

0-6-0T 4F Class J50

J50/2* Introduced 1922. Gresley G.N. design (68900–19 rebuilt from smaller J51, built 1915–22).

J50/3† Introduced 1926. Post-grouping development with detail differences.

J50/1‡ Introduced 1929. Rebuilt from smaller J51, built 1913–14.

J50/4§ Introduced 1937. Development of J50/3 with larger bunker.

Weight: { 57 tons.* / 56 tons 6 cwt.‡ / 58 tons 3 cwt.†§

Pressure: 175 lb.

Cyls.: 18½" × 26".

Driving Wheels: 4' 8".

T.E.: 23,635 lb.

68890‡	68915*	68937*	68964†
68891‡	68916*	68939*	68965†
68892‡	68917*	68941†	68966†
68894‡	68918*	68943†	68968†
68895‡	68920*	68944†	68970†
68896‡	68921*	68945†	68971†
68897‡	68922*	68946†	68972†
68899‡	68923*	68947†	68975†
68900‡	68924*	68948†	68976†
68901*	68925*	68950†	68977†
68902*	68926*	68951†	68979§
68903*	68927*	68952†	68981§
68904*	68928*	68954†	68982§
68905*	68929*	68956†	68983§
68907*	68930*	68957†	68984§
68908*	68931*	68958†	68986§
68909*	68932*	68959†	68987§
68910*	68933*	68960†	68988§
68911*	68934*	68961†	68989§
68913*	68935*	68962†	68990§
68914*	68936*	68963†	68991§

Total

Class J50/1 9 Class J50/3 29

Class J50/2 35 Class J50/4 11

0-6-0T 2F Class J72

(*Continued from 68754*)

69001	69008	69015	69022
69002	69009	69016	69023
69003	69010	69017	69024
69004	69011	69018	69025
69005	69012	69019	69026
69006	69013	69020	69027
69007	69014	69021	69028

Total 94

0-6-2T 3F Class N10

Introduced 1902. W. Worsdell N.E. design.

Weight: 57 tons 14 cwt.

Pressure: 160 lb.

Cyls.: 18½" × 26".

Driving Wheels: 4' 7¼".

T.E.: 21,905 lb.

69097	69101	69105	69109

Total 4

0-6-2T 3MT Class N15

N15/2* Introduced 1910. Reid N.B. design developed from N14. Cowlairs Incline banking locos.

N15/1 Introduced 1910. Development of N15/2 with smaller bunker for normal duties.

Weight: {62 tons 1 cwt.* / 60 tons 18 cwt.

Pressure: 175 lb.

Cyls.: 18" × 26".

Driving Wheels: 4' 6".

T.E.: 23,205 lb.

69126*	69132	69135	69138
69128*	69133	69136	69141
69131*	69134	69137	69143
69144	69171	69190	69207
69145	69173	69191	69209
69149	69177	69194	69211
69150	69178	69196	69212
69155	69179	69198	69216
69156	69180	69199	69218
69159	69181	69202	69219
69161	69183	69204	69221
69163	69184	69205	69223
69165	69188	69206	69224

Total

Class N15/1 49 Class N15/2 3

0-6-2T 2MT Class N5

N5/2. Introduced 1891. Parker M.S. & L. design developed from N4.

Weight: 62 tons 7 cwt.

Pressure: 160 lb.

Cyls.: 18" × 26"

Driving Wheels: 5' 1".

T.E.: 18,780 lb.

69258	69274	69296	69354
69263	69286	69307	69360
69266	69293	69309	69370

Total 12

0-6-2T 3P2F Class N2

N2/2* Introduced 1925. Post-grouping development of Gresley G.N. N2/1, introduced 1920, which class is now included in N2/2. Built with condensing apparatus and small chimney.

N2/2† Condensing apparatus removed.

N2/3‡ Introduced 1925. Locos. built non-condensing, originally fitted with large chimney. Some now with small chimney.

N2/4§ Introduced 1928. Development of N2/2, slightly heavier. Built with condensing apparatus and small chimney.

(The small chimneys are to suit the Metropolitan loading gauge, for working to Moorgate. Condensing apparatus has been removed from or added to certain locos. transferred from or to the London area.)

Weight: 70 tons 5 cwt.*†; 70 tons 8 cwt.‡; 71 tons 9 cwt.§

Pressure: 170 lb. Su.
Cyls.: 19" × 26".
Driving Wheels: 5' 8"
T.E.: 19,945 lb.
P.V.

69492*	69521*	69546*	69578§
69498*	69522*	69549*	69579§
69504*	69523*	69552†	69580§
69505†	69528*	69560†	69581§
69506*	69529*	69561†	69582§
69507†	69530*	69563‡	69583§
69509†	69531*	69564‡	69585§
69511†	69533*	69568§	69586§
69512*	69535*	69571§	69587§
69513*	69538*	69572§	69592§
69516†	69540*	69574§	69593§
69518†	69543*	69575§	69596‡
69520*			

Total

Class N2/2 30 Class N2/4 16
Class N2/3 3

0-6-2T 3MT Class N7

N7/3[1] Introduced 1927. Doncaster-built version of N7/2 (see below) but with round-topped firebox.

N7/3[2] Introduced 1943. N7/2 post-grouping development of Hill G.E. design (N7) with long-travel valves, rebuilt with round-topped firebox.

N7/4[3] Introduced 1940. Pre-grouping G.E. design (N7), rebuilt with round-topped firebox, retaining short-travel valves.

N7/5[4] Introduced 1943. Post-grouping development of G.E. design N7/1, rebuilt with round-topped firebox, retaining short-travel valves.

Weight: 64 tons.[1,2,4]; 61 tons 16 cwt.[3]

Pressure: 180 lb. Su.
Cyls.: 18" × 24".
Driving Wheels: 4' 10".
T.E.: 20,515 lb.
Walschaerts valve gear. P.V.

69611[3]	69653[4]	69687[2]	69711[1]
69614[3]	69654[4]	69688[2]	69712[1]
69615[3]	69656[4]	69690[2]	69713[1]
69617[3]	69658[4]	69691[2]	69714[1]
69618[3]	69663[4]	69692[2]	69715[1]
69620[3]	69664[4]	69693[2]	69718[1]
69621[3]	69668[4]	69694[2]	69719[1]
69622[4]	69670[4]	69696[2]	69720[1]
69629[4]	69671[4]	69697[2]	69721[1]
69630[4]	69673[2]	69698[2]	69722[1]
69631[4]	69674[2]	69699[2]	69723[1]
69632[4]	69675[2]	69700[2]	69724[1]
69636[4]	69677[2]	69701[2]	69725[1]
69640[4]	69678[2]	69702[1]	69726[1]
69642[4]	69679[2]	69704[1]	69727[1]
69645[4]	69680[2]	69706[1]	69728[1]
69646[4]	69681[2]	69707[1]	69729[1]
69647[4]	69682[2]	69708[1]	69730[1]
69648[4]	69684[2]	69709[1]	69732[1]
69651[4]	69685[2]	69710[1]	69733[1]
69652[4]	69686[2]		

Total

Class N7/3 52 Class N7/4 7
Class N7/5 23

4-6-2T 3MT Class A5

A5/1 Introduced 1911. Robinson G.C. design.
Weight: 85 tons 18 cwt.
Pressure: 180 lb. Su.
Cyls.: 20" × 26".
Driving Wheels: 5' 7".
T.E.: 23,750 lb.
P.V

69808	69817	69821	69829
69814	69820	69823	

Total 7

4-6-2T 3MT Class A8

Introduced 1931. Gresley rebuild of Raven N.E. Class "D" 4-4-4T (introduced 1913).

Weight: 86 tons 18 cwt.
Pressure: 175 lb. Su.
Cyls.: (3) $16\frac{1}{2}'' \times 26''$.
Driving Wheels: 5′ 9″.
T.E.: 22,940 lb.
P.V.

69850	69861	69875	69885
69854	69869	69878	69886
69858	69870	69880	69889
69859	69873	69883	69894
69860	69874		

Total 18

4-8-0T 5F Class T1

Introduced 1909. W. Worsdell N.E. design.

Weight: 85 tons 8 cwt.
Pressure: 175 lb.
Cyls.: (3) 18″ × 26″.
Driving Wheels: $4' 7\frac{1}{4}''$.
T.E.: 34,080 lb.
P.V.

69921

Total 1

PRESERVED LOCOS IN WORKING ORDER

4-4-0

Introduced 1920. Heywood G. N. of S. superheated, development of Pickersgill 1899 design. Withdrawn 1958 as B.R. No 62277 and restored to original condition, being returned to service for special use in 1959. (L.N.E.R. Class D140)

Weight: Loco. 48 tons 13 cwt.
Tender 37 tons 8 cwt.
Pressure: 165 lb. Su.
Cyls.: 18″ × 26″.
Driving Wheels: 6′ 1″.
T.E.: 16,185 lb.

49 Gordon Highlander

4-4-0

Introduced 1913. Reid N.B. "Glen" class. Withdrawn 1959 as B.R. No. 62469 and restored to original livery. Returned to service for special use 1959. (L.N.E.R. Class D34)

Weight: Loco. 57 tons 4 cwt.
Tender 46 tons 13 cwt.
Pressure: 165 lb. Su.
Cyls.: 20″ × 26″.
Driving Wheels: 6′ 0″.
T.E.: 20,260 lb.
P.V.

256 Glen Douglas

EASTERN REGION DIESEL LOCOMOTIVE CLASSIFICATION

Horse-power	Description	Loco. Nos.	Code
153	Hunslet/Gardner	D2950–2	D1/1
153	Barclay/Gardner	D2953–6	D1/2
165	Ruston & Hornsby	D2957–8	D1/3
200	N.B. Loco. Co./Paxman	D2700–7	D2/1
204	B.R./Gardner	D2000–2142 ...	D2/2
204	Drewry/Gardner (3′ 3″ wheel) ...	D2200–14/42–86 ...	D2/3
204	Drewry/Gardner (3′ 6″ wheel) ...	D2215–41	D2/4
204	Barclay/Gardner (4-speed) ...	D2400–9	D2/5

EASTERN REGION DIESEL LOCOMOTIVE CLASSIFICATION—*(continued)*

Horse-power	Description	Loco. Nos.	Code
204	Barclay/Gardner (5-speed) ...	D2410–44	D2/6
204	Hudswell-Clarke/Gardner	D2500–9	D2/7
204	Hunslet/Gardner	D2550–D2618 ...	D2/3
225	N.B. Loco. Co./M.A.N.	D2708–79	D2/9
330	N.B. Loco. Co./M.A.N.	D2900–10	D3/1
350	B.R./English Electric	D3000–16/27–36/67 –3438/54–72, 3503–3611/52–3899	D3/2
350	B.R./Crossley	D3117–26	D3/3
350	B.R./Blackstone/G.E.C.	D3137–51, 3439–53 /73–3502, 3612–51	D3/4
350	B.R./Blackstone/B.T.H.	D3152–66	D3/5
350	L.M.S./English Electric (4′ 0½″ wheel)	12000–1	D3/6
350	L.M.S./English Electric (4′ 3″ wheel)	12003–32	D3/7
350	B.R./English Electric	12033–12138 ...	D3/8
350	L.N.E./English Electric	15000–3	D3/9
350	G.W./English Electric (4′ 1″ wheel)	15100	D3/10
350	G.W./English Electric (4′ 0½″ wheel)	15101–6	D3/11
350	S.R./English Electric	15201–3	D3/12
350	S.R./English Electric	15211–36	D3/13
360	L.N.E./Petter	15004	D3/14
800	B.T.H./Paxman	D8200–36	D8/1
800	N.B. Loco. Co./Paxman	D8400–9	D8/2
1,000	N.B. Loco. Co./M.A.N./G.E.C. ...	D6101–6/8/9 ...	D10/1
1,000	N.B. Loco. Co./M.A.N./Voith ...	D6300–57	D10/2
1,000	English Electric	D8000–49	D10/3
1,100	English Electric/Napier	D5900–9	D11/1
1,100	N.B. Loco. Co./M.A.N./G.E.C. ...	D6100/7/10–57 ...	D11/2
1,160	B.R./Sulzer	D5000–D5150 ...	D11/3
1,160	Birmingham/Sulzer	D5300–46	D11/4
1,200	Metro. Vickers/Crossley	D5700–19	D12/1
1,250	Brush/Mirlees	D5500–19	D12/2
1,365	Brush/Mirlees	D5520–5679 ...	D13/1
1,550	Birmingham/Sulzer	D6500–76	D15/1
1,600	L.M.S./English Electric	10000–1	D16/1
1,600	S.R./English Electric	10201–2	D16/2
1,750	English Electric	D6700–41	D17/1
2,000	English Electric	D200–324	D20/1
2,000	N.B. Loco. Co./M.A.N./Voith ...	D600–4	D20/2
2,000	S.R./English Electric	10203	D20/3
2,200	Maybach/Mekydro	D800–32	D22/1
2,200	N.B. Loco. Co./	D833–65	D22/2
2,200	B.R./	D866–70	D22/3
2,300	B.R./Sulzer	D1–D124	D23/1
2,500	B.R./Sulzer	D125–47	D25/1
3,300	English Electric/Napier Deltic ...	D1500–21	D33/1

BRITISH RAILWAYS
EASTERN & NORTH EASTERN REGIONS

CHIEF MECHANICAL ENGINEER

A. H. Peppercorn ... 1948–1949
(post abolished)

LOCOMOTIVE SUPERINTENDENTS AND CHIEF MECHANICAL ENGINEERS OF THE L.N.E.R.

Sir Nigel Gresley ... ... 1923–1941 | E. Thompson 1941–1946
A. H. Peppercorn 1946–1947

GREAT NORTHERN RAILWAY

A. Sturrock 1850–1866
P. Stirling 1866–1895
H. A. Ivatt 1896–1911
H. N. Gresley 1911–1922

NORTH EASTERN RAILWAY

E. Fletcher 1854–1883
A. McDonnell* 1883–1884
T. W. Worsdell 1885–1890
W. Worsdell 1890–1910
Sir Vincent Raven ... 1910–1922

GREAT EASTERN RAILWAY

R. Sinclair 1862–1866
S. W. Johnson 1866–1873
W. Adams 1873–1878
M. Bromley 1878–1881
T. W. Worsdell 1881–1885
J. Holden 1885–1907
S. D. Holden 1908–1912
A. J. Hill 1912–1922

LANCASHIRE, DERBYSHIRE AND EAST COAST RAILWAY

R. A. Thom 1902–1907

MANCHESTER, SHEFFIELD AND LINCOLNSHIRE RAILWAY

Richard Peacock ... ... –1854
W. G. Craig 1854–1859
Charles Sacré 1859–1886
T. Parker 1886–1893
H. Pollitt 1893–1897

GREAT CENTRAL RAILWAY

H. Pollitt 1897–1900
J. G. Robinson 1900–1922

HULL AND BARNSLEY RAILWAY

M. Stirling 1885–1922

MIDLAND AND GREAT NORTHERN JOINT RAILWAY

W. Marriott 1884–1924

NORTH BRITISH RAILWAY

T. Wheatley† 1867–1874
D. Drummond 1875–1882
M. Holmes 1882–1903
W. P. Reid 1903–1919
W. Chalmers 1919–1922

GREAT NORTH OF SCOTLAND RAILWAY

D. K. Clark 1853–1855
J. F. Ruthven 1855–1857
W. Cowan 1857–1883
J. Manson 1883–1890
J. Johnson 1890–1894
W. Pickersgill 1894–1914
T. E. Heywood 1914–1922

* Between McDonnell and T. W. Worsdell there was an interval during which the office was covered by a Locomotive Committee.

† Previous to whom the records are indeterminate.

Chief Mechanical Engineer
J. F. HARRISON

4-6-2 7P6F

Introduced 1951. Designed at Derby.
Weight: Loco. 94 tons 0 cwt.
Pressure: 250 lb. Su.
Cyls.: (O) 20″ × 28″.
Driving Wheels: 6′ 2″. T.E.: 32,150 lb.
Walschaerts valve gear. P.V.

70000 Britannia
70001 Lord Hurcomb
70002 Geoffrey Chaucer
70003 John Bunyan
70004 William Shakespeare
70005 John Milton
70006 Robert Burns
70007 Coeur-de-Lion
70008 Black Prince
70009 Alfred the Great
70010 Owen Glendower
70011 Hotspur
70012 John of Gaunt
70013 Oliver Cromwell
70014 Iron Duke
70015 Apollo
70016 Ariel
70017 Arrow
70018 Flying Dutchman
70019 Lightning
70020 Mercury
70021 Morning Star
70022 Tornado
70023 Venus
70024 Vulcan
70025 Western Star
70026 Polar Star
70027 Rising Star
70028 Royal Star
70029 Shooting Star
70030 William Wordsworth
70031 Byron
70032 Tennyson
70033 Charles Dickens
70034 Thomas Hardy
70035 Rudyard Kipling
70036 Boadicea
70037 Hereward the Wake
70038 Robin Hood
70039 Sir Christopher Wren
70040 Clive of India
70041 Sir John Moore
70042 Lord Roberts
70043 Lord Kitchener
70044 Earl Haig
70045 Lord Rowallan
70046 Anzac
70047
70048 The Territorial Army 1908-1958
70049
70050 Firth of Clyde
70051 Firth of Forth
70052 Firth of Tay
70053 Moray Firth
70054 Dornoch Firth

Total 55

4-6-2 8P

Introduced 1954. Designed at Derby.
Weight: Loco. 101 tons 5 cwt.
Pressure: 250 lb. Su.
Cyls: (3) 18″ × 28″.
Driving Wheels: 6′ 2″. T.E.: 39,080 lb.
Caprotti valve gear.

71000 Duke of Gloucester

Total 1

4-6-2 6P5F

Introduced 1952. Designed at Derby.
Weight: Loco. 86 tons 19 cwt.
Pressure: 225 lb. Su.
Cyls.: (O) 19½″ × 28″.
Driving Wheels: 6′ 2″. T.E.: 27,520 lb.
Walschaerts valve gear. P.V.

72000 Clan Buchanan
72001 Clan Cameron
72002 Clan Campbell

72003 Clan Fraser
72004 Clan Macdonald
72005 Clan Macgregor
72006 Clan Mackenzie
72007 Clan Mackintosh
72008 Clan Macleod
72009 Clan Stewart **Total 10**

4-6-0 5

Introduced 1951. Designed at Doncaster.
*Introduced 1956. Fitted with Caprotti valve gear.
Weight: Loco. 76 tons 4 cwt.
Pressure: 225 lb. Su.
Cyls.: (O) 19″ × 28″.
Driving Wheels: 6′ 2″. T.E.: 26,120 lb.
Walschaerts valve gear. P.V.

73000	73020	73040	73060
73001	73021	73041	73061
73002	73022	73042	73062
73003	73023	73043	73063
73004	73024	73044	73064
73005	73025	73045	73065
73006	73026	73046	73066
73007	73027	73047	73067
73008	73028	73048	73068
73009	73029	73049	73069
73010	73030	73050	73070
73011	73031	73051	73071
73012	73032	73052	73072
73013	73033	73053	73073
73014	73034	73054	73074
73015	73035	73055	73075
73016	73036	73056	73076
73017	73037	73057	73077
73018	73038	73058	73078
73019	73039	73059	73079

73080 Merlin
73081 Excalibur
73082 Camelot
73083 Pendragon
73084 Tintagel
73085 Melisande
73086 The Green Knight
73087 Linette
73088 Joyous Gard
73089 Maid of Astolat

73090	73095	73100	73105
73091	73096	73101	73106
73092	73097	73102	73107
73093	73098	73103	73108
73094	73099	73104	73109

73110 The Red Knight
73111 King Uther
73112 Morgan le Fay
73113 Lyonnesse
73114 Etarre
73115 King Pellinore
73116 Iseult
73117 Vivien
73118 King Leodegrance
73119 Elaine

73120	73133*	73146*	73159
73121	73134*	73147*	73160
73122	73135*	73148*	73161
73123	73136*	73149*	73162
73124	73137*	73150*	73163
73125*	73138*	73151*	73164
73126*	73139*	73152*	73165
73127*	73140*	73153*	73166
73128*	73141*	73154*	73167
73129*	73142*	73155	73168
73130*	73143*	73156	73169
73131*	73144*	73157	73170
73132*	73145*	73158	73171

Total 172

4-6-0 4

Introduced 1951. Designed at Brighton.
*Introduced 1957. Fitted with double chimney.
Weight: Loco. 69 tons 0 cwt.
Pressure: 225 lb. Su.
Cyls.: (O) 18″ × 28″.
Driving Wheels: 5′ 8″. T.E.: 25,100 lb.
Walschaerts valve gear. P.V.

75000	75008	75016	75024
75001	75009	75017	75025
75002	75010	75018	75026
75003	75011	75019	75027
75004	75012	75020	75028
75005	75013	75021	75029*
75006	75014	75022	75030
75007	75015	75023	75031

75032	75044	75056	75068
75033	75045	75057	75069
75034	75046	75058	75070
75035	75047	75059	75071
75036	75048	75060	75072
75037	75049	75061	75073
75038	75050	75062	75074
75039	75051	75063	75075
75040	75052	75064	75076
75041	75053	75065	75077
75042	75054	75066	75078
75043	75055	75067	75079

Total 80

2-6-0 4

Introduced 1953. Designed at Doncaster.
Weight: Loco. 59 tons 2 cwt.
Pressure: 225 lb. Su.
Cyls.: (O) 17½" × 26".
Driving Wheels: 5' 3". T.E.: 24,170 lb.
Walschaerts valve gear. P.V.

76000	76026	76052	76078
76001	76027	76053	76079
76002	76028	76054	76080
76003	76029	76055	76081
76004	76030	76056	76082
76005	76031	76057	76083
76006	76032	76058	76084
76007	76033	76059	76085
76008	76034	76060	76086
76009	76035	76061	76087
76010	76036	76062	76088
76011	76037	76063	76089
76012	76038	76064	76090
76013	76039	76065	76091
76014	76040	76066	76092
76015	76041	76067	76093
76016	76042	76068	76094
76017	76043	76069	76095
76018	76044	76070	76096
76019	76045	76071	76097
76020	76046	76072	76098
76021	76047	76073	76099
76022	76048	76074	76100
76023	76049	76075	76101
76024	76050	76076	76102
76025	76051	76077	76103

76104	76107	76110	76113
76105	76108	76111	76114
76106	76109	76112	

Total 115

2-6-0 3

Introduced 1954. Designed at Swindon.
Weight: Loco. 57 tons 9 cwt.
Pressure: 200 lb. Su.
Cyls.: (O) 17½" × 26".
Driving Wheels: 5' 3". T.E.: 21,490 lb.
Walschaerts valve gear. P.V.

77000	77005	77010	77015
77001	77006	77011	77016
77002	77007	77012	77017
77003	77008	77013	77018
77004	77009	77014	77019

Total 20

2-6-0 2

Introduced 1953. Designed at Derby.
Weight: Loco. 49 tons 5 cwt.
Pressure: 200 lb. Su.
Cyls.: (O) 16½" × 24".
Driving Wheels: 5' 0". T.E.: 18,515 lb.
Walschaerts valve gear. P.V.

78000	78017	78033	78049
78001	78018	78034	78050
78002	78019	78035	78051
78003	78020	78036	78052
78004	78021	78037	78053
78005	78022	78038	78054
78006	78023	78039	78055
78007	78024	78040	78056
78008	78025	78041	78057
78009	78026	78042	78058
78010	78027	78043	78059
78011	78028	78044	78060
78012	78029	78045	78061
78013	78030	78046	78062
78014	78031	78047	78063
78015	78032	78048	78064
78016			

Total 65

2-6-4T 4

Introduced 1951. Designed at Brighton.
Weight: 88 tons 10 cwt.
Pressure: 225 lb. Su.
Cyls.: (O) 18" × 28".
Driving Wheels: 5' 8". T.E.: 25,100 lb.
Walschaerts valve gear. P.V.

80000	80039	80078	80117
80001	80040	80079	80118
80002	80041	80080	80119
80003	80042	80081	80120
80004	80043	80082	80121
80005	80044	80083	80122
80006	80045	80084	80123
80007	80046	80085	80124
80008	80047	80086	80125
80009	80048	80087	80126
80010	80049	80088	80127
80011	80050	80089	80128
80012	80051	80090	80129
80013	80052	80091	80130
80014	80053	80092	80131
80015	80054	80093	80132
80016	80055	80094	80133
80017	80056	80095	80134
80018	80057	80096	80135
80019	80058	80097	80136
80020	80059	80098	80137
80021	80060	80099	80138
80022	80061	80100	80139
80023	80062	80101	80140
80024	80063	80102	80141
80025	80064	80103	80142
80026	80065	80104	80143
80027	80066	80105	80144
80028	80067	80106	80145
80029	80068	80107	80146
80030	80069	80108	80147
80031	80070	80109	80148
80032	80071	80110	80149
80033	80072	80111	80150
80034	80073	80112	80151
80035	80074	80113	80152
80036	80075	80114	80153
80037	80076	80115	80154
80038	80077	80116	

Total 155

2-6-2T 3

Introduced 1952. Designed at Swindon.
Weight: 73 tons 10 cwt.
Pressure: 200 lb. Su.
Cyls.: (O) $17\frac{1}{2}$" × 26".
Driving Wheels: 5' 3". T.E.: 21,490 lb.
Walschaerts valve gear. P.V.

82000	82012	82024	82036
82001	82013	82025	82037
82002	82014	82026	82038
82003	82015	82027	82039
82004	82016	82028	82040
82005	82017	82029	82041
82006	82018	82030	82042
82007	82019	82031	82043
82008	82020	82032	82044
82009	82021	82033	
82010	82022	82034	
82011	82023	82035	

Total 45

2-6-2T 2

Introduced 1953. Designed at Derby.
Weight: 63 tons 5 cwt.
Pressure: 200 lb. Su.
Cyls.: (O) $16\frac{1}{2}$" × 24".
Driving Wheels: 5' 0". T.E.: 18,515 lb.
Walschaerts valve gear. P.V.

84000	84008	84016	84023
84001	84009	84017	84024
84002	84010	84018	84025
84003	84011	84019	84026
84004	84012	84020	84027
84005	84013	84021	84028
84006	84014	84022	84029
84007	84015		

Total 30

2-8-0 8F WD

Ministry of Supply "Austerity" 2-8-0 locomotives purchased by British Railways, 1948.
Introduced 1943. Riddles M.o.S. design.
Weight: Loco. 70 tons 5 cwt.
Tender 55 tons 10 cwt.
Pressure: 225 lb. Su.
Cyls.: (O) 19" × 28".
Driving Wheels: 4' $8\frac{1}{2}$". T.E.: 34,215 lb.
Walschaerts valve gear. P.V.

90000	90047	90096	90143	90190	90238	90285	90332
90001	90048	90097	90144	90192	90239	90286	90333
90002	90049	90098	90145	90193	90240	90287	90334
90003	90050	90099	90146	90194	90241	90288	90335
90004	90051	90100	90147	90195	90242	90289	90336
90005	90052	90101	90148	90196	90243	90290	90337
90006	90053	90102	90149	90197	90244	90291	90338
90007	90054	90103	90150	90198	90245	90292	90339
90008	90055	90104	90151	90199	90246	90293	90340
90009	90056	90105	90152	90200	90247	90294	90341
90010	90057	90106	90153	90201	90248	90295	90342
90011	90058	90107	90154	90202	90249	90296	90343
90012	90059	90108	90155	90203	90250	90297	90344
90013	90060	90109	90156	90204	90251	90298	90345
90014	90061	90110	90157	90205	90252	90299	90346
90015	90063	90111	90158	90206	90253	90300	90347
90016	90064	90112	90159	90207	90254	90301	90348
90017	90065	90113	90160	90208	90255	90302	90349
90018	90066	90114	90161	90209	90256	90303	90350
90019	90067	90115	90162	90210	90257	90304	90351
90020	90068	90116	90163	90211	90258	90305	90352
90021	90069	90117	90164	90212	90259	90306	90353
90022	90070	90118	90165	90213	90260	90307	90354
90023	90071	90119	90166	90214	90261	90308	90355
90024	90072	90120	90167	90215	90262	90309	90356
90025	90073	90121	90168	90216	90263	90310	90357
90026	90074	90122	90169	90217	90264	90311	90358
90027	90075	90123	90170	90218	90265	90312	90359
90028	90076	90124	90171	90219	90266	90313	90360
90029	90077	90125	90172	90220	90267	90314	90361
90030	90078	90126	90173	90221	90268	90315	90362
90031	90079	90127	90174	90222	90269	90316	90363
90032	90080	90128	90175	90223	90270	90317	90364
90033	90081	90129	90176	90224	90271	90318	90365
90034	90082	90130	90177	90225	90272	90319	90366
90035	90084	90131	90178	90226	90273	90320	90367
90036	90085	90132	90179	90227	90274	90321	90368
90037	90086	90133	90180	90228	90275	90322	90369
90038	90087	90134	90181	90229	90276	90323	90370
90039	90088	90135	90182	90230	90277	90324	90371
90040	90089	90136	90183	90231	90278	90325	90372
90041	90090	90137	90184	90232	90279	90326	90373
90042	90091	90138	90185	90233	90280	90327	90374
90043	90092	90139	90186	90234	90281	90328	90375
90044	90093	90140	90187	90235	90282	90329	90376
90045	90094	90141	90188	90236	90283	90330	90377
90046	90095	90142	90189	90237	90284	90331	90378

90379
90380
90381
90382
90383
90384
90385
90386
90387
90388
90389
90390
90391
90392
90393
90394
90395
90396
90397
90398
90399
90400
90401
90402
90403
90404
90405
90406
90407
90408
90409
90410
90411
90412
90413
90414
90415
90416
90417
90418
90419
90420
90421
90422
90423
90424
90425
90426
90427
90428
90429
90430
90431
90432
90433
90434
90435
90436
90437
90438
90439
90440
90441
90442
90443
90444
90445
90446
90447
90448
90449
90450
90451
90452
90453
90454
90455
90456
90457
90458
90459
90460
90461
90462
90463
90464
90465
90466
90467
90468
90469
90470
90471
90472
90473
90474
90475
90476
90477
90478
90479
90480
90481
90482
90483
90484
90485
90486
90487
90488
90489
90490
90491
90492
90493
90494
90495
90496
90497
90498
90499
90500
90501
90502
90503
90504
90505
90506
90507
90508
90509
90510
90511
90512
90513
90514
90515
90516
90517
90518
90519
90520
90521
90522
90523
90524
90525
90526
90527
90528
90529
90530
90531
90532
90533
90534
90535
90536
90537
90538
90539
90540
90541
90542
90543
90544
90545
90546
90547
90548
90549
90550
90551
90552
90553
90554
90555
90556
90557
90558
90559
90560
90561
90562
90563
90564
90565
90566
90567
90568
90569
90570
90571
90572
90573
90574
90575
90576
90577
90578
90579
90580
90581
90582
90583
90584
90585
90586
90587
90588
90589
90590
90591
90592
90593
90594
90595
90596
90597
90598
90599
90600
90601
90602
90603
90604
90605
90606
90607
90608
90609
90610
90611
90612
90613
90614
90615
90616
90617
90618
90619
90620
90621
90622
90623
90624
90625
90626
90627
90628
90629
90630
90631
90632
90633
90634
90635
90636
90637
90638
90639
90640
90641
90642
90643
90644
90645
90646
90647
90648
90649
90650
90651
90652
90653
90654
90655
90656
90657
90658
90659
90660
90661
90662
90663
90664
90665
90666
90667
90668
90669
90670
90671
90672
90673
90674
90675
90676
90677
90678
90679
90680
90681
90682
90683
90684
90685
90686
90687
90688
90689
90690
90691
90692
90693
90694
90695
90696
90697
90698
90699
90700
90701
90702
90703
90704
90705
90706
90707
90708
90709
90710
90711
90712
90713
90714
90715
90716
90717
90718
90719
90720
90721
90722
90723
90724
90725
90726
90727
90728
90729
90730
90731
90732
Vulcan

Total 730

2-10-0 WD

Ministry of Supply "Austerity" 2-10-0 locomotives purchased by British Railways, 1948.
Introduced 1943. Riddles M.o.S. design.
Weight: Loco. 78 tons 6 cwt.
Tender 55 tons 10 cwt.
Pressure: 225 lb. Su.
Cyls.: (O) 19″ × 28″.
Driving Wheels: 4′ 8½″. T.E.: 34,215 lb.
Walschaerts valve gear. P.V.

90750	90757	90763	90769
90751	90758	90764	90770
90752	90759	90765	90771
90753	90760	90766	90772
90754	90761	90767	90773
90755	90762	90768	90774
90756			

Total 25

2-10-0 9F

Introduced 1954. Designed at Brighton.
*Introduced 1955. Fitted with Crosti boiler, some engines later having Crosti pre-heater sealed off for orthodox working.
†Introduced 1957. Fitted with double chimney.
‡Introduced 1958. Fitted with Mechanical Stoker and double chimney.
Weight: Loco. { 86 tons 14 cwt. / 90 tons 4 cwt.*
Pressure: 250 lb. Su.
Cyls.: (O) 20″ × 28″.
Driving Wheels: 5′ 0″. T.E.: 39,670 lb.
Walschaerts valve gear. P.V.

92000†	92018	92036	92054
92001	92019	92037	92055
92002	92020*	92038	92056
92003	92021*	92039	92057
92004	92022*	92040	92058
92005	92023*	92041	92059
92006	92024*	92042	92060
92007	92025*	92043	92061
92008	92026*	92044	92062
92009	92027*	92045	92063
92010	92028*	92046	92064
92011	92029*	92047	92065
92012	92030	92048	92066
92013	92031	92049	92067
92014	92032	92050	92068
92015	92033	92051	92069
92016	92034	92052	92070
92017	92035	92053	92071

92072	92117	92162	92207†
92073	92118	92163	92208†
92074	92119	92164	92209†
92075	92120	92165‡	92210†
92076	92121	92166‡	92211†
92077	92122	92167‡	92212†
92078	92123	92168	92213†
92079†	92124	92169	92214†
92080	92125	92170	92215†
92081	92126	92171	92216†
92082	92127	92172	92217†
92083	92128	92173	92218†
92084	92129	92174	92219†
92085	92130	92175	92220†§
92086	92131	92176	92221†
92087	92132	92177	92222†
92088	92133	92178†	92223†
92089	92134	92179	92224†
92090	92135	92180	92225†
92091	92136	92181	92226†
92092	92137	92182	92227†
92093	92138	92183†	92228†
92094	92139	92184†	92229†
92095	92140	92185†	92230†
92096	92141	92186†	92231†
92097	92142	92187†	92232†
92098	92143	92188†	92233†
92099	92144	92189†	92234†
92100	92145	92190†	92235†
92101	92146	92191†	92236†
92102	92147	92192†	92237†
92103	92148	92193†	92238†
92104	92149	92194†	92239†
92105	92150	92195†	92240†
92106	92151	92196†	92241†
92107	92152	92197†	92242†
92108	92153	92198†	92243†
92109	92154	92199†	92244†
92110	92155	92200†	92245†
92111	92156	92201†	92246†
92112	92157	92202†	92247†
92113	92158	92203†	92248†
92114	92159	92204†	92249†
92115	92160	92205†	92250†
92116	92161	92206†	

Total 251

§ 92220 named *Evening Star*.

BRITISH RAILWAYS DIESEL LOCOMOTIVE CLASSES

The lists of numbers include all locomotives on order at the time of going to press. For details of delivery, see the Locomotive Stock change list each month in Trains Illustrated.

1Co-Co1 "4"

"PEAK" CLASS

Introduced: 1959.

Locomotive manufacturer: B.R.

Total b.h.p.: 2,300. / 2,500*

Engine: Sulzer 12LDA28 twin bank pressure charged, 12-cyl. type of 2,300 b.h.p. (2,500 b.h.p.*) at 750 r.p.m.

Transmission: **Electric.** Six Crompton Parkinson 305 h.p. axle-hung nose-suspended traction motors.

Weight: 138 tons 2 cwt.

Driving Wheels: 3′ 9″.

Maximum tractive effort: 70,000 lb.

D1 Scafell Pike
D2* Helvellyn
D3 Skiddaw
D4 Great Gable
D5 Cross Fell
D6 Whernside
D7 Ingleborough
D8 Penyghent
D9 Snowdon
D10 Tryfan

D11	D15	D19	D23
D12	D16	D20	D24
D13	D17	D21	D25
D14	D18	D22	D26

D27	D58	D89	D120
D28	D59	D90	D121
D29	D60	D91	D122
D30	D61	D92	D123
D31	D62	D93	D124
D32	D63	D94	D125
D33	D64	D95	D126
D34	D65	D96	D127
D35	D66	D97	D128
D36	D67	D98	D129
D37	D68	D99	D130
D38	D69	D100	D131
D39	D70	D101	D132
D40	D71	D102	D133
D41	D72	D103	D134
D42	D73	D104	D135
D43	D74	D105	D136
D44	D75	D106	D137
D45	D76	D107	D138
D46	D77	D108	D139
D47	D78	D109	D140
D48	D79	D110	D141
D49	D80	D111	D142
D50	D81	D112	D143
D51	D82	D113	D144
D52	D83	D114	D145
D53	D84	D115	D146
D54	D85	D116	D147
D55	D86	D117	
D56	D87	D118	
D57	D88	D119	

1Co-Co1 "4"

Introduced: 1958.
Locomotive manufacturer: English Electric.
Total b.h.p.: 2,000.
Engine: English Electric 16SVT. Mk. II of 2,000 b.h.p. at 850 r.p.m.
Transmission: **Electric.** Six English Electric nose-suspended traction motors.
Weight: 133 tons.
Driving Wheels: 3′ 9″
Maximum tractive effort: 52,000 lb.
Classified **D20/1** by the E. & N.E.R.

D200	D227	D254	D281
D201	D228	D255	D282
D202	D229	D256	D283
D203	D230	D257	D284
D204	D231	D258	D285
D205	D232	D259	D286
D206	D233	D260	D287
D207	D234	D261	D288
D208	D235	D262	D289
D209	D236	D263	D290
D210	D237	D264	D291
D211	D238	D265	D292
D212	D239	D266	D293
D213	D240	D267	D294
D214	D241	D268	D295
D215	D242	D269	D296
D216	D243	D270	D297
D217	D244	D271	D298
D218	D245	D272	D299
D219	D246	D273	D300
D220	D247	D274	D301
D221	D248	D275	D302
D222	D249	D276	D303
D223	D250	D277	D304
D224	D251	D278	
D225	D252	D279	
D226	D253	D280	

A1A-A1A "4"

"WARSHIP" CLASS

Introduced: 1958.
Locomotive manufacturer: North British Locomotive Co.
Total b.h.p.: 2,000.
Engines: Two N.B.L./M.A.N. type L12V 18/21S 12-cyl. of 1,000 b.h.p.
Transmission: **Hydraulic.** Two Hardy Spicer cardan shafts to Voith-North British type L306r hydraulic transmissions each containing three torque converters.
Weight: 117 tons 8 cwt.
Driving Wheels: 3′ 7″.
Maximum tractive effort: 50,000 lb.

D600 Active
D601 Ark Royal
D602 Bulldog
D603 Conquest
D604 Cossack

B-B "4"

"WARSHIP" CLASS

Introduced: 1958.
Locomotive manufacturer: Swindon Works, B.R.
Total b.h.p.: 2,000*
2,200.
2,400†
Engines: Two-Bristol-Siddeley-Maybach MD 650 V-type of 1,152 b.h.p. at 1,530 r.p.m. (*1,056 b.h.p. at 1.400 r.p.m.)
†Two Paxman 12-cyl. high-speed 12YJXL of 1,200 b.h.p. at 1,500 r.p.m.
Transmission: **Hydraulic.** Two Mekydro type K104 hydraulic transmissions containing permanently filled single torque converter and four-speed automatic gearbox.
Weight: 78 tons.
Driving Wheels: 3′ 3½″.
Maximum tractive effort: 52,400 lb.

D800* Sir Brian Robertson
D801* Vanguard
D802* Formidable
D803 Albion
D804 Avenger
D805 Benbow
D806 Cambrian
D807 Caradoc
D808 Centaur
D809 Champion
D810 Cockade
D811 Daring
D812 Royal Naval Reserve 1859-1959
D813 Diadem
D814 Dragon

D815 Druid
D816 Eclipse
D817 Foxhound
D818 Glory
D819 Goliath
D820 Grenville
D821 Greyhound
D822 Hercules
D823 Hermes
D824 Highflyer
D825 Intrepid
D826 Jupiter
D827 Kelly
D828 Magnificent
D829 Magpie
D830 Majestic
D831 Monarch
D832† Onslaught

B-B "4"

"WARSHIP" CLASS

To be introduced.
Locomotive manufacturer: North British Locomotive Co.
Total b.h.p.: 2,200.
Engines:
Transmission: **Hydraulic.**
Weight:
Driving Wheels:
Maximum tractive effort:

D833 Panther
D834 Pathfinder
D835 Pegasus
D836 Powerful
D837 Ramillies
D838 Rapid
D839 Relentless
D840 Resistance
D841 Roebuck
D842 Royal Oak
D843 Sharpshooter
D844 Spartan
D845 Sprightly
D846 Steadfast
D847 Strongbow
D848 Sultan
D849 Superb
D850 Swift
D851 Temeraire
D852 Tenacious
D853 Thruster
D854 Tiger
D855 Triumph
D856 Trojan
D857 Undaunted
D858 Valorous
D859 Vanquisher
D860 Victorious
D861 Vigilant
D862 Viking
D863 Warrior
D864 Zealous
D865 Zenith
D866
D867
D868
D869
D870

Co-Co Deltic "5"

To be introduced.
Locomotive manufacturer: English Electric.
Total b.h.p.: 3,300.
Engines:
Transmission: **Electric.**
Weight:
Driving Wheels.
Maximum tractive effort.

D1500	D1506	D1512	D1518
D1501	D1507	D1513	D1519
D1502	D1508	D1514	D1520
D1503	D1509	D1515	D1521
D1504	D1510	D1516	
D1505	D1511	D1517	

Co-Co "Deltic"

NOTE: British Railways are providing facilities for road tests of this locomotive, which remains the property of the manufacturer, and is not included in B.R. stock. An order has been placed for 22 of these locomotives to work on the E., N.E. & Scottish Regions, (D1500-21).

Introduced: 1955.
Locomotive manufacturer: English Electric.
Total b.h.p.: 3,300.
Engines: Two Napier "Deltic" 18-cyl. engines of 1,650 b.h.p.
Transmission: **Electric.** Six axle-hung nose-suspended traction motors.
Weight: 106 tons.
Driving Wheels: 3′ 7″.
Maximum tractive effort: 60,000 lb.

0-6-0 Shunter

Introduced: 1957.
Locomotive manufacturer: B.R.
Total b.h.p.: 204
Engine: Gardner type 8L3 of 204 b.h.p. at 1,200 r.p.m.
Transmission: **Mechanical.** Vulcan-Sinclair type 23 fluid coupling. Wilson-Drewry C.A.5 type five-speed epicyclic gearbox. Type RF 11 spiral bevel reverse and final drive unit.
Weight: 30 tons 16 cwt.
Driving Wheels: 3′ 7″.
Maximum tractive effort: 15,650 lb.
Classified **D2/2** by the E. & N.E.R.

(**Original numbers in brackets**)

D2000 (11187)	D2012 (11199)
D2001 (11188)	D2013 (11200)
D2002 (11189)	D2014 (11201)
D2003 (11190)	D2015 (11202)
D2004 (11191)	D2016 (11203)
D2005 (11192)	D2017 (11204)
D2006 (11193)	D2018 (11205)
D2007 (11194)	D2019 (11206)
D2008 (11195)	D2020 (11207)
D2009 (11196)	D2021 (11208)
D2010 (11197)	D2022 (11209)
D2011 (11198)	

D2023	D2032	D2041	D2050
D2024	D2033	D2042	D2051
D2025	D2034	D2043	D2052
D2026	D2035	D2044	D2053
D2027	D2036	D2045	D2054
D2028	D2037	D2046	D2055
D2029	D2038	D2047	D2056
D2030	D2039	D2048	D2057
D2031	D2040	D2049	D2058

D2059	D2088	D2117	D2146
D2060	D2089	D2118	D2147
D2061	D2090	D2119	D2148
D2062	D2091	D2120	D2149
D2063	D2092	D2121	D2150
D2064	D2093	D2122	D2151
D2065	D2094	D2123	D2152
D2066	D2095	D2124	D2153
D2067	D2096	D2125	D2154
D2068	D2097	D2126	D2155
D2069	D2098	D2127	D2156
D2070	D2099	D2128	D2157
D2071	D2100	D2129	D2158
D2072	D2101	D2130	D2159
D2073	D2102	D2131	D2160
D2074	D2103	D2132	D2161
D2075	D2104	D2133	D2162
D2076	D2105	D2134	D2163
D2077	D2106	D2135	D2164
D2078	D2107	D2136	D2165
D2079	D2108	D2137	D2166
D2080	D2109	D2138	D2167
D2081	D2110	D2139	D2168
D2082	D2111	D2140	D2169
D2083	D2112	D2141	D2170
D2084	D2113	D2142	D2171
D2085	D2114	D2143	D2172
D2086	D2115	D2144	D2173
D2087	D2116	D2145	D2174

0-6-0 Shunter

Introduced: 1952.
Locomotive manufacturer: Drewry.
Total b.h.p.: 204.
Engine: Gardner type 8L3 of 204 b.h.p. at 1,200 r.p.m.
Transmission: **Mechanical.** Vulcan-Sinclair type 23 fluid coupling. Wilson-Drewry C.A.5 type five-speed epicyclic gearbox. Type RF 11 spiral bevel reverse and final drive unit.
Weight: 29 tons 15 cwt.
Driving Wheels: 3′ 3″.
Maximum tractive effort: 16,850 lb.
Classified **D2/3** by the E. & N.E.R.

(**Original numbers in brackets**)

D2200 (11100)	D2202 (11102)
D2201 (11101)	D2203 (11103)

D2204 (11105)	D2210 (11111)
D2205 (11106)	D2211 (11112)
D2206 (11107)	D2212 (11113)
D2207 (11108)	D2213 (11114)
D2208 (11109)	D2214 (11115)
D2209 (11110)	

0-6-0 Shunter

Introduced: 1955.
Locomotive manufacturer: Drewry.
Total b.h.p.: 204.
Engine: Gardner type 8L3 of 204 b.h.p. at 1,200 r.p.m.
Transmission: **Mechanical.** Vulcan-Sinclair type 23 fluid coupling. Wilson-Drewry C.A.5 type five-speed epicyclic gearbox. Type RF 11 spiral bevel reverse and final drive unit.
Weight: 29 tons 15 cwt.
Driving Wheels: 3′ 6″.
Maximum tractive effort: 15,650 lb.
Classified **D2/4** by the E. & N.E.R.

(**Original numbers in brackets**)

D2215 (11121)	D2229 (11135)
D2216 (11122)	D2230 (11149)
D2217 (11123)	D2231 (11150)
D2218 (11124)	D2232 (11151)
D2219 (11125)	D2233 (11152)
D2220 (11126)	D2234 (11153)
D2221 (11127)	D2235 (11154)
D2222 (11128)	D2236 (11155)
D2223 (11129)	D2237 (11156)
D2224 (11130)	D2238 (11157)
D2225 (11131)	D2239 (11158)
D2226 (11132)	D2240 (11159)
D2227 (11133)	D2241 (11160)
D2228 (11134)	

0-6-0 Shunter

D2242-D2295, FOR PARTICULARS SEE D2200-D2214.

(**Original numbers in brackets**)

D2242 (11212)	D2248 (11218)
D2243 (11213)	D2249 (11219)
D2244 (11214)	D2250 (11220)
D2245 (11215)	D2251 (11221)
D2246 (11216)	D2252 (11222)
D2247 (11217)	D2253 (11223)
D2254 (11224)	D2257 (11227)
D2255 (11225)	D2258 (11228)
D2256 (11226)	D2259 (11229)

D2260	D2269	D2278	D2287
D2261	D2270	D2279	D2288
D2262	D2271	D2280	D2289
D2263	D2272	D2281	D2290
D2264	D2273	D2282	D2291
D2265	D2274	D2283	D2292
D2266	D2275	D2284	D2293
D2267	D2276	D2285	D2294
D2268	D2277	D2286	D2295

0-6-0 Shunter

Introduced: 1956.
Locomotive manufacturer: Barclay.
Total b.h.p.: 204.
Engine: Gardner type 8L3 or 204 b.h.p. at 1,200 r.p.m.
Transmission: **Mechanical.** Vulcan-Sinclair type 23 fluid coupling. Wilson C.A.4 type four-speed epicyclic gearbox. Wiseman type 15 RLGB reverse and final drive unit.
Weight: 32 tons 0 cwt.
Driving Wheels: 3′ 6″.
Maximum tractive effort: 15,340 lb.
Classified **D2/5** by the E. & N.E.R.
(**Original numbers in brackets**)

D2400 (11177)	D2405 (11182)
D2401 (11178)	D2406 (11183)
D2402 (11179)	D2407 (11184)
D2403 (11180)	D2408 (11185)
D2404 (11181)	D2409 (11186)

0-4-0 Shunter

Introduced: 1958.
Locomotive manufacturer: Barclay.
Total b.h.p.: 204.
Engine: Gardner type 8L3 of 204 b.h.p. at 1,200 r.p.m.
Transmission: **Mechanical.** Vulcan-Sinclair type 23 fluid coupling. Wilson-Drewry C.A.5 type five-speed epicyclic gearbox. Wiseman type 15. R.L.G.B. reverse and final drive unit.
Weight: 35 tons.
Driving Wheels: 3′ 7″.
Maximum tractive effort: 20,000 lb.
Classified **D2/6** by the E. & N.E.R.

D2410	D2413	D2416	D2419
D2411	D2414	D2417	D2420
D2412	D2415	D2418	D2421

D2422	D2428	D2434	D2440
D2423	D2429	D2435	D2441
D2424	D2430	D2436	D2442
D2425	D2431	D2437	D2443
D2426	D2432	D2438	D2444
D2427	D2433	D2439	

0-6-0 Shunter

Introduced: 1956.
Locomotive manufacturer. Hudswell-Clarke.
Total b.h.p.: 204
Engine: Gardner type 8L3 of 204 b.h.p. at 1,200 r.p.m.
Transmission: **Mechanical.** S.C.R.5 type, size 23 scoop control fluid coupling. Three-speed "SSS Powerflow" double synchro-type gearbox and final drive.
Weight: 36 tons 7 cwt.
Driving Wheels: 3′ 6″.
Maximum tractive effort: 16,100 lb.
Classified **D2/7** by the E. & N.E.R.

(Original numbers in brackets)

D2500 (11116)	D2505 (11144)
D2501 (11117)	D2506 (11145)
D2502 (11118)	D2507 (11146)
D2503 (11119)	D2508 (11147)
D2504 (11120)	D2509 (11148)

0-6-0 Shunter

Introduced: 1955.
Locomotive manufacturer: Hunslet.
Total b.h.p.: 204.
Engine: Gardner type 8L3 of 204 b.h.p. at 1,200 r.p.m.
Transmission: **Mechanical.** Hunslet patent friction clutch. Hunslet four-speed gearbox incorporating reverse and final drive gears.
Weight: 30 tons 0 cwt.
Driving Wheels: 3′ 4″.
Maximum tractive effort: 14,500 lb.
Classified **D2/8** by E. & N.E.R.

(Original numbers in brackets)

D2550 (11136)	D2556 (11142)
D2551 (11137)	D2557 (11143)
D2552 (11138)	D2558 (11161)
D2553 (11139)	D2559 (11162)
D2554 (11140)	D2560 (11163)
D2555 (11141)	D2561 (11164)

D2562 (11165)	D2568 (11171)
D2563 (11166)	D2569 (11172)
D2564 (11167)	D2570 (11173)
D2565 (11168)	D2571 (11174)
D2566 (11169)	D2572 (11175)
D2567 (11170)	D2573 (11176)

D2574	D2586	D2598	D2610
D2575	D2587	D2599	D2611
D2576	D2588	D2600	D2612
D2577	D2589	D2601	D2613
D2578	D2590	D2602	D2614
D2579	D2591	D2603	D2615
D2580	D2592	D2604	D2616
D2581	D2593	D2605	D2617
D2582	D2594	D2606	D2618
D2583	D2595	D2607	
D2584	D2596	D2608	
D2585	D2597	D2609	

0-4-0 Shunter

Introduced: 1953.
Locomotive manufacturer: North British Locomotive Co.
Total b.h.p.: 200.
Engine: Paxman type **6RPH** of 200 b.h.p. at 1,000 r.p.m.
Transmission: **Hydraulic.** Voith-North British hydraulic torque converter type L33YU. North British bevel gears and reversing dog clutch coupled through reduction gearing to jackshaft.
Weight: 32 tons.
Driving Wheels: 3′ 6″.
Maximum tractive effort: 21,500 lb.
Classified **D2/1** by the E. & N.E.R.

(Original numbers in brackets)

D2700 (11700)	D2704 (11704)
D2701 (11701)	D2705 (11705)
D2702 (11702)	D2706 (11706)
D2703 (11703)	D2707 (11707)

0-4-0 Shunter

Introduced: 1957.
Locomotive manufacturer: North British Locomotive Co.
Total b.h.p.: 225.
Engine: North British type M.A.N. W6V 17.5/22A of 225 b.h.p. at 1,100 r.p.m. (12 hr. rating).

Transmission: **Hydraulic.** Voith-North British hydraulic torque converter type LCCYU. North British bevel gears and reversing dog clutch coupled through reduction gearing to jackshaft.
Weight: 30 tons.
Driving Wheels: 3′ 6″.
Maximum tractive effort: 20,080 lb.
Classified **D2/9** by the E. & N.E.R.

(Original numbers in brackets)

D2708 (11708)	D2714 (11714)
D2709 (11709)	D2715 (11715)
D2710 (11710)	D2716 (11716)
D2711 (11711)	D2717 (11717)
D2712 (11712)	D2718 (11718)
D2713 (11713)	D2719 (11719)

D2720	D2735	D2750	D2765
D2721	D2736	D2751	D2766
D2722	D2737	D2752	D2767
D2723	D2738	D2753	D2768
D2724	D2739	D2754	D2769
D2725	D2740	D2755	D2770
D2726	D2741	D2756	D2771
D2727	D2742	D2757	D2772
D2728	D2743	D2758	D2773
D2729	D2744	D2759	D2774
D2730	D2745	D2760	D2775
D2731	D2746	D2761	D2776
D2732	D2747	D2762	D2777
D2733	D2748	D2763	D2778
D2734	D2749	D2764	D2779

0-4-0 Shunter

Introduced: 1958.
Locomotive manufacturer: North British Locomotive Co.
Total b.h.p.: 330.
Engine: North British/M.A.N. type W6V 17.5/22 AS, super-charged.
Transmission: **Hydraulic.** Voith-North British hydraulic torque converter type L24V. North British spiral bevel gears, reversing and reduction gears to jackshaft.
Weight: 36 tons.
Driving Wheels: 3′ 9″.
Maximum tractive effort: 24,100 lb.
Classified **D3/1** by the E. & N.E.R.

D2900	D2906	D2912	D2918
D2901	D2907	D2913	D2919
D2902	D2908	D2914	D2920
D2903	D2909	D2915	
D2904	D2910	D2916	
D2905	D2911	D2917	

0-4-0 Shunter

Introduced: 1955.
Locomotive manufacturer: Hunslet.
Total b.h.p.: 153.
Engine: Gardner type 6L3 of 153 b.h.p. at 1,200 r.p.m.
Transmission.: **Mechanical.** Hunslet patent friction clutch and four-speed gearbox incorporating reverse and final drive gears.
Weight: 22 tons 9 cwt.
Driving Wheels: 3′ 4″.
Maximum tractive effort: 10,800 lb.
Classified **D1/1** by E. & N.E.R.

(Original numbers in brackets)

D2950 (11500)	D2952 (11502)
D2951 (11501)	

0-4-0 Shunter

Introduced: 1956.
Locomotive manufacturer: Barclay.
Total b.h.p.: 153.
Engine: Gardner type 6L3 of 153 b.h.p. at 1,200 r.p.m.
Transmission: **Mechanical.** Vulcan-Sinclair rigid type hydraulic coupling. Wilson S.E. 4 type four-speed epicyclic gearbox. Wiseman type 15 RLGB reverse and final drive unit.
Weight: 25 tons.
Driving Wheels: 3′ 2″.
Maximum tractive effort: 12,750 lb.
Classified **D1/2** by E. & N.E.R.

(Original numbers in brackets)

D2953 (11503)	D2955 (11505)
D2954 (11504)	D2956 (11506)

0-4-0 Shunter

Introduced: 1956.
Locomotive manufacturer: Ruston & Hornsby.
Total b.h.p.: 165.
Engine: Ruston type 6VPHL of 165 b.h.p. at 1,250 r.p.m. (1 hr. rating).
Transmission: **Mechanical.** Oil pressure-operated S.L.M. type friction

clutches incorporated in Ruston constant mesh type gearbox. Reverse gear and final drive unit incorporating bevel gears and dog clutches and reduction gear to final drive.
Weight: 28 tons.
Driving Wheels: 3′ 4″.
Maximum tractive effort: 14,350 lb.
Classified **D1/3** by the E. & N.E.R.

(Original numbers in brackets)

D2957 (11507) D2958 (11508)

0-6-0 Shunter

Engines D3000-D3336 were originally numbered 13000-13336 and are being renumbered as they are overhauled.

Introduced: 1953.
Locomotive manufacturer: British Railways.
Total b.h.p.: 400.
Engine: English Electric 6-cyl. type 6KT of 400 b.h.p. at 630 r.p.m.
Transmission: **Electric.** Two English Electric nose-suspended traction motors. Double reduction gear drive.
Weight: 49 tons 0 cwt.
Driving Wheels: 4′ 6″.
Maximum tractive effort: 35,000 lb.
Classified **D3/2** by the E. & N.E.R.
Note: Nos. D3000-91 and 3102-3116 fitted for vacuum brake operation.

D3000	D3019	D3038	D3057
D3001	D3020	D3039	D3058
D3002	D3021	D3040	D3059
D3003	D3022	D3041	D3060
D3004	D3023	D3042	D3061
D3005	D3024	D3043	D3062
D3006	D3025	D3044	D3063
D3007	D3026	D3045	D3064
D3008	D3027	D3046	D3065
D3009	D3028	D3047	D3066
D3010	D3029	D3048	D3067
D3011	D3030	D3049	D3068
D3012	D3031	D3050	D3069
D3013	D3032	D3051	D3070
D3014	D3033	D3052	D3071
D3015	D3034	D3053	D3072
D3016	D3035	D3054	D3073
D3017	D3036	D3055	D3074
D3018	D3037	D3056	D3075

D3076	D3087	D3098	D3109
D3077	D3088	D3099	D3110
D3078	D3089	D3100	D3111
D3079	D3090	D3101	D3112
D3080	D3091	D3102	D3113
D3081	D3092	D3103	D3114
D3082	D3093	D3104	D3115
D3083	D3094	D3105	D3116
D3084	D3095	D3106	
D3085	D3096	D3107	
D3086	D3097	D3108	

0-6-0 Shunter

Introduced: 1955.
Locomotive manufacturer: British Railways.
Total b.h.p.: 350.
Engine: Crossley 6-cyl. type ESNT 6 of 350 b.h.p. at 825 r.p.m. (continuous rating).
Transmission: **Electric.** Two Crompton Parkinson nose-suspended traction motors. Double reduction gear drive.
Weight: 47 tons 10 cwt.
Driving Wheels: 4′ 6″
Maximum tractive effort: 35,000 lb.
Classified **D3/3** by the E. & N.E.R.

D3117	D3120	D3123	D3126
D3118	D3121	D3124	
D3119	D3122	D3125	

0-6-0 Shunter

Introduced: 1953.
Locomotive manufacturer: British Railways.
Total b.h.p.: 400.
Engine: English Electric 6-cyl. type 6KT of 400 b.h.p. at 680 r.p.m.
Transmission: **Electric.** Two English Electric nose-suspended traction motors. Double reduction gear drive.
Weight: 48 tons 0 cwt.
Driving Wheels: 4′ 6″.
Maximum tractive effort: 35,000 lb.
Fitted for vacuum brake operation
Classified **D3/2** by the E. & N.E.R.

D3127	D3130	D3133	D3136
D3128	D3131	D3134	
D3129	D3132	D3135	

0-6-0 Shunter

Introduced: 1955.
Locomotive manufacturer: British Railways.
Total b.h.p.: 370.
Engine: Blackstone 6-cyl. type ER6T of 370 b.h.p. at 750 r.p.m.
Transmission: **Electric.** Two G.E.C. nose-suspended traction motors, Double reduction gear drive.
Weight: 47 tons 10 cwts.
Driving Wheels: 4′ 6″.
Maximum tractive effort: 35,000 lb.
Fitted for vacuum brake operation.
Classified **D3/4** by the E. & N.E.R.

D3137	D3141	D3145	D3149
D3138	D3142	D3146	D3150
D3139	D3143	D3147	D3151
D3140	D3144	D3148	

0-6-0 Shunter

Introduced: 1955.
Locomotive manufacturer: British Railways.
Total b.h.p.: 370.
Engine: Blackstone 6-cyl. type ER6T of 370 b.h.p. at 750 r.p.m.
Transmission: **Electric.** Two B.T.H. nose-suspended traction motors. Double reduction gear drive.
Weight: 47 tons 0 cwt.
Driving Wheels: 4′ 6″.
Maximum tractive effort: 35,000 lb.
Classified **D3/5** by the E. & N.E.R.

D3152	D3156	D3160	D3164
D3153	D3157	D3161	D3165
D3154	D3158	D3162	D3166
D3155	D3159	D3163	

D3167 D3438. FOR PARTICULARS SEE Nos. D3127-D3136.

D3167	D3178	D3189	D3200
D3168	D3179	D3190	D3201
D3169	D3180	D3191	D3202
D3170	D3181	D3192	D3203
D3171	D3182	D3193	D3204
D3172	D3183	D3194	D3205
D3173	D3184	D3195	D3206
D3174	D3185	D3196	D3207
D3175	D3186	D3197	D3208
D3176	D3187	D3198	D3209
D3177	D3188	D3199	D3210

D3211	D3256	D3301	D3346
D3212	D3257	D3302	D3347
D3213	D3258	D3303	D3348
D3214	D3259	D3304	D3349
D3215	D3260	D3305	D3350
D3216	D3261	D3306	D3351
D3217	D3262	D3307	D3352
D3218	D3263	D3308	D3353
D3219	D3264	D3309	D3354
D3220	D3265	D3310	D3355
D3221	D3266	D3311	D3356
D3222	D3267	D3312	D3357
D3223	D3268	D3313	D3358
D3224	D3269	D3314	D3359
D3225	D3270	D3315	D3360
D3226	D3271	D3316	D3361
D3227	D3272	D3117	D3362
D3228	D3273	D3318	D3363
D3229	D3274	D3319	D3364
D3230	D3275	D3320	D3365
D3231	D3276	D3321	D3366
D3232	D3277	D3322	D3367
D3233	D3278	D3323	D3368
D3234	D3279	D3324	D3369
D3235	D3280	D3325	D3370
D3236	D3281	D3326	D3371
D3237	D3282	D3327	D3372
D3238	D3283	D3328	D3373
D3239	D3284	D3329	D3374
D3240	D3285	D3330	D3375
D3241	D3286	D3331	D3376
D3242	D3287	D3332	D3377
D3243	D3288	D3333	D3378
D3244	D3289	D3334	D3379
D2345	D3290	D3335	D3380
D3246	D3291	D3336	D3381
D3247	D3292	D3337	D3382
D3248	D3293	D3338	D3383
D3249	D3294	D3339	D3384
D3250	D3295	D3340	D3385
D3251	D3296	D3341	D3386
D3252	D3297	D3342	D3387
D3253	D3298	D3343	D3388
D3254	D3299	D3344	D3389
D3255	D3300	D3345	D3390

D3391	D3403	D3415	D3427
D3392	D3404	D3416	D3428
D3393	D3405	D3417	D3429
D3394	D3406	D3418	D3430
D3395	D3407	D3419	D3431
D3396	D3408	D3420	D3432
D3397	D3409	D3421	D3433
D3398	D3410	D3422	D3434
D3399	D3411	D3423	D3435
D3400	D3412	D3424	D3436
D3401	D3413	D3425	D3437
D3402	D3414	D3426	D3438

D3439 D3453. FOR PARTICULARS SEE D3137-D3151.

D3439	D3443	D3447	D3451
D3440	D3444	D3448	D3452
D3441	D3445	D3449	D3453
D3442	D3446	D3450	

D3454 D3472. FOR PARTICULARS SEE D3127-D3136.

D3454	D3459	D3464	D3469
D3455	D3460	D3465	D3470
D3456	D3461	D3466	D3471
D3457	D3462	D3467	D3472
D3458	D3463	D3468	

D3473 D3502. FOR PARTICULARS SEE D3137-D3151.

D3473	D3481	D3489	D3497
D3474	D3482	D3490	D3498
D3475	D3483	D3491	D3499
D3476	D3484	D3492	D3500
D3477	D3485	D3493	D3501
D3478	D3486	D3494	D3502
D3479	D3487	D3495	
D3480	D3488	D3496	

D3503-D3611. FOR PARTICULARS SEE D3127-D3136.

D3503	D3506	D3509	D3512
D3504	D3507	D3510	D3513
D3505	D3508	D3511	D3514

D3515	D3540	D3565	D3590
D3516	D3541	D3566	D3591
D3517	D3542	D3567	D3592
D3518	D3543	D3568	D3593
D3519	D3544	D3569	D3594
D3520	D3545	D3570	D3595
D3521	D3546	D3571	D3596
D3522	D3547	D3572	D3597
D3523	D3548	D3573	D3598
D3524	D3549	D3574	D3599
D3525	D3550	D3575	D3600
D3526	D3551	D3576	D3601
D3527	D3552	D3577	D3602
D3528	D3553	D3578	D3603
D3529	D3554	D3579	D3604
D3530	D3555	D3580	D3605
D3531	D3556	D3581	D3606
D3532	D3557	D3582	D3607
D3533	D3558	D3583	D3608
D3534	D3559	D3584	D3609
D3535	D3560	D3585	D3610
D3536	D3561	D3586	D3611
D3537	D3562	D3587	
D3538	D3563	D3588	
D3539	D3564	D3589	

D3612-D3651. FOR PARTICULARS SEE D3137-D3151.

D3612	D3622	D3632	D3642
D3613	D3623	D3633	D3643
D3614	D3624	D3634	D3644
D3615	D3625	D3635	D3645
D3616	D3626	D3636	D3646
D3617	D3627	D3637	D3647
D3618	D3628	D3638	D3648
D3619	D3629	D3639	D3649
D3620	D3630	D3640	D3650
D3621	D3631	D3641	D3651

D3652-D4094. FOR PARTICULARS SEE D3127-D3136.

D3652	D3655	D3658	D3661
D3653	D3656	D3659	D3662
D3654	D3657	D3660	D3663

D3664	D3709	D3754	D3799	D3844	D3889	D3934	D3979
D3665	D3710	D3755	D3800	D3845	D3890	D3935	D3980
D3666	D3711	D3756	D3801	D3846	D3891	D3936	D3981
D3667	D3712	D3757	D3802	D3847	D3892	D3937	D3982
D3668	D3713	D3758	D3803	D3848	D3893	D3938	D3983
D3669	D3714	D3759	D3804	D3849	D3894	D3939	D3984
D3670	D3715	D3760	D3805	D3850	D3895	D3940	D3985
D3671	D3716	D3761	D3806	D3851	D3896	D3941	D3986
D3672	D3717	D3762	D3807	D3852	D3897	D3942	D3987
D3673	D3718	D3763	D3808	D3853	D3898	D3943	D3988
D3674	D3719	D3764	D3809	D3854	D3899	D3944	D3989
D3675	D3720	D3765	D3810	D3855	D3900	D3945	D3990
D3676	D3721	D3766	D3811	D3856	D3901	D3946	D3991
D3677	D3722	D3767	D3812	D3857	D3902	D3947	D3992
D3678	D3723	D3768	D3813	D3858	D3903	D3948	D3993
D3679	D3724	D3769	D3814	D3859	D3904	D3949	D3994
D3680	D3725	D3770	D3815	D3860	D3905	D3950	D3995
D3681	D3726	D3771	D3816	D3861	D3906	D3951	D3996
D3682	D3727	D3772	D3817	D3862	D3907	D9352	D3997
D3683	D3728	D3773	D3818	D3863	D3908	D3953	D3998
D3684	D3729	D3774	D3819	D3864	D3909	D3954	D3999
D3685	D3730	D3775	D3820	D3865	D3910	D3955	D4000
D3686	D3731	D3776	D3821	D3866	D3911	D3956	D4001
D3687	D3732	D3777	D3822	D3867	D3912	D3957	D4002
D3688	D3733	D3778	D3823	D3868	D3913	D3958	D4003
D3689	D3734	D3779	D3824	D3869	D3914	D3959	D4004
D3690	D3735	D3780	D3825	D3870	D3915	D3960	D4005
D3691	D3736	D3781	D3826	D3871	D3916	D3961	D4006
D3692	D3737	D3782	D3827	D3872	D3917	D3962	D4007
D3693	D3738	D3783	D3828	D3873	D3918	D3963	D4008
D3694	D3739	D3784	D3829	D3874	D3919	D3964	D4009
D3695	D3740	D3785	D3830	D3875	D3920	D3965	D4010
D3696	D3741	D3786	D3831	D3876	D3921	D3966	D4011
D3697	D3742	D3787	D3832	D3877	D3922	D3967	D4012
D3698	D3743	D3788	D3833	D3878	D3923	D3968	D4013
D3699	D3744	D3789	D3834	D3879	D3924	D3969	D4014
D3700	D3745	D3790	D3835	D3880	D3925	D3970	D4015
D3701	D3746	D3791	D3836	D3881	D3926	D3971	D4016
D3702	D3747	D3792	D3837	D3882	D3927	D3972	D4017
D3703	D3748	D3793	D3838	D3883	D3928	D3973	D4018
D3704	D3749	D3794	D3839	D3884	D3929	D3974	D4019
D3705	D3750	D3795	D3840	D3885	D3930	D3975	D4020
D3706	D3751	D3796	D3841	D3886	D3931	D3976	D4021
D3707	D3752	D3797	D3842	D3887	D3932	D3977	D4022
D3708	D3753	D3798	D3843	D3888	D3933	D3978	D4023

D4024	D4042	D4060	D4078
D4025	D4043	D4061	D4079
D4026	D4044	D4062	D4080
D4027	D4045	D4063	D4081
D4028	D4046	D4064	D4082
D4029	D4047	D4065	D4083
D4030	D4048	D4066	D4084
D4031	D4049	D4067	D4085
D4032	D4050	D4068	D4086
D4033	D4051	D4069	D4087
D4034	D4052	D4070	D4088
D4035	D4053	D4071	D4089
D4036	D4054	D4072	D4090
D4037	D4055	D4073	D4091
D4038	D4056	D4074	D4092
D4039	D4057	D4075	D4093
D4040	D4058	D4076	D4094
D4041	D4059	D4077	

Bo-Bo "2"

Introduced: 1958.
Locomotive manufacturer: B.R.
Total b.h.p.: 1,160.
Engine: Sulzer 6-cyl. type 6LDA28 of 1,160 b.h.p. at 750 r.p.m.
Transmission: **Electric.** Four B.T.H. axle-hung, nose-suspended traction motors of 213 h.p. (continuous rating).
Weight: { 75 tons. / 72 tons 17 cwt.*
Driving Wheels: 3′ 9″.
Maximum tractive effort: 40,000 lb.
Classified **D11/3** by the E. & N.E.R.

D5000	D5015	D5030	D5045
D5001	D5016	D5031	D5046
D5002	D5017	D5032	D5047
D5003	D5018	D5033	D5048
D5004	D5019	D5034	D5049
D5005	D5020	D5035	D5050
D5006	D5021	D5036	D5051
D5007	D5022	D5037	D5052
D5008	D5023	D5038	D5053
D5009	D5024	D5039	D5054
D5010	D5025	D5040	D5055
D5011	D5026	D5041	D5056
D5012	D5027	D5042	D5057
D5013	D5028	D5043	D5058
D5014	D5029	D5044	D5059

D5060	D5084	D5108	D5132
D5061	D5085	D5109	D5133
D5062	D5086	D5110	D5134
D5063	D5087	D5111	D5135
D5064	D5088	D5112	D5136
D5065	D5089	D5113	D5137
D5066	D5090	D5114	D5138
D5067	D5091	D5115	D5139
D5068	D5092	D5116	D5140
D5069	D5093	D5117	D5141
D5070	D5094*	D5118	D5142
D5071	D5095	D5119	D5143
D5072	D5096	D5120	D5144
D5073	D5097	D5121	D5145
D5074	D5098	D5122	D5146
D5075	D5099	D5123	D5147
D5076	D5100	D5124	D5148
D5077	D5101	D5125	D5149
D5078	D5102	D5126	D5150
D5079	D5103	D5127	
D5080	D5104	D5128	
D5081	D5105	D5129	
D5082	D5106	D5130	
D5083	D5107	D5131	

Bo-Bo "2"

Introduced: 1958.
Locomotive manufacturer: Birmingham R.C. & W. Co.
Total b.h.p.: 1,160.
Engine: Sulzer 6-cyl. type 6LDA28 of 1,160 b.h.p. at 750 r.p.m.
Transmission: **Electric.** Four Crompton Parkinson axle-hung, nose-suspended traction motors.
Weight: { 77 tons 10 cwt.*. / 74 tons.
Driving Wheels: 3′ 7″.
Maximum tractive effort: 42,000 lb.
Classified **D11/4** by the E. & N.E.R.

D5300*	D5309*	D5318*	D5327
D5301*	D5310*	D5319*	D5328
D5302*	D5311*	D5320	D5329
D5303*	D5312*	D5321	D5330
D5304*	D5313*	D5322	D5331
D5305*	D5314*	D5323	D5332
D5306*	D5315*	D5324	D5333
D5307*	D5316*	D5325	D5334
D5308*	D5317*	D5326	D5335

D5336	D5339	D5342	D5345
D5337	D5340	D5343	D5346
D5338	D5341	D5344	

A1A-A1A "2"

Introduced: 1957.
Locomotive manufacturer: Brush Traction Ltd.
Total b.h.p.: 1,250*; 1,365; 1,600†
Engine: Mirrlees, Bickerton & Day 12-cyl. JVS12T of 1,250*, 1,365 or 1,600† b.h.p. at 850 r.p.m.
Transmission: **Electric.** Four Brush 250 h.p. traction motors, single reduction gear drive.
Weight: 104 tons.
Driving Wheels: 3' 7".
Maximum tractive effort: 42,000 lb.
Classified (**D12/2***) **D13/1** by the E. & N.E.R.

D5500*	D5527	D5554	D5581
D5501*	D5528	D5555	D5582
D5502*	D5529	D5556	D5583
D5503*	D5530	D5557	D5584
D5504*	D5531	D5558	D5585
D5505*	D5532	D5559	D5586
D5506*	D5533	D5560	D5587
D5507*	D5534	D5561	D5588
D5508*	D5535	D5562	D5589
D5509*	D5536	D5563	D5590
D5510*	D5537	D5564	D5591
D5511*	D5538	D5565	D5592
D5512*	D5539	D5566	D5593
D5513*	D5540	D5567	D5594
D5514*	D5541	D5568	D5595
D5515*	D5542	D5569	D5596
D5516*	D5543	D5570	D5597
D5517*	D5544	D5571	D5598
D5518*	D5545†	D5572	D5599
D5519*	D5546	D5573	D5600
D5520	D5547	D5574	D5601
D5521	D5548	D5575	D5602
D5522	D5549	D5576	D5603
D5523	D5550	D5577	D5604
D5524	D5551	D5578	D5605
D5525	D5552	D5579	D5606
D5526	D5553	D5580	D5607

D5608	D5626	D5644	D5662
D5609	D5627	D5645	D5663
D5610	D5628	D5646	D5664
D5611	D5629	D5647	D5665
D5612	D5630	D5648	D5666
D5613	D5631	D5649	D5667
D5614	D5632	D5650	D5668
D5615	D5633	D5651	D5669
D5616	D5634	D5652	D5670
D5617	D5635	D5653	D5671
D5618	D5636	D5654	D5672
D5619	D5637	D5655	D5673
D5620	D5638	D5656	D5674
D5621	D5639	D5657	D5675
D5622	D5640	D5658	D5676
D5623	D5641	D5659	D5677
D5624	D5642	D5660	D5678
D5625	D5643	D5661	D5679

Co-Bo "2"

Introduced: 1958.
Lcoomotive manufacturer: Metropolitan Vickers.
Total b.h.p.: 1,200.
Engine: Crossley 8-cyl. HST Vee 8 of 1,200 b.h.p. at 625 r.p.m. (continuous).
Transmission: **Electric.** Five Metropolitan-Vickers 180 h.p. axle-hung nose-suspended traction motors.
Weight: 97 tons.
Driving Wheels: 3' 3½".
Maximum tractive effort: 50,000 lb.

D5700	D5705	D5710	D5715
D5701	D5706	D5711	D5716
D5702	D5707	D5712	D5717
D5703	D5708	D5713	D5718
D5704	D5709	D5714	D5719

Bo-Bo "2"

Introduced: 1959.
Locomotive manufacturer: English Electric.
Total b.h.p.: 1,100.
Engine: Napier "Deltic" T9-29 9 cyl., two-stroke pressure charged type of 1,100 b.h.p. at 1,600 r.p.m.

Transmission: **Electric.** Four English Electric axle-hung nose-suspended traction motors.
Weight: 73 tons 17 cwt.
Driving Wheels: 3′ 7″.
Maximum tractive effort.: 47,000 lb.
Classified **D11/1** by the E. & N.E.R.

D5900	D5903	D5906	D5909
D5901	D5904	D5907	
D5902	D5905	D5908	

Bo-Bo "2"

Introduced: 1959.
Locomotive manufacturer: North British Locomotive Co.
Total b.h.p.: 1,000* / 1,100.
Engine: N.B.L./M.A.N. 12-cyl. pressure charged L12V/18/21S of (1,000*) 1,100 b.h.p.
Transmission: **Electric.** Four G.E.C. nose-suspended traction motors.
Weight: 72 tons 10 cwt.
Driving Wheels: 3′ 7″.
Maximum tractive effort: 45,000 lb.
Classified (**D10/1***) **D11/2** by the E .& N.E.R.

D6100	D6115	D6130	D6145
D6101*	D6116	D6131	D6146
D6102*	D6117	D6132	D6147
D6103*	D6118	D6133	D6148
D6104*	D6119	D6134	D6149
D6105*	D6120	D6135	D6150
D6106*	D6121	D6136	D6151
D6107	D6122	D6137	D6152
D6108*	D6123	D6138	D6153
D6109*	D6124	D6139	D6154
D6110	D6125	D6140	D6155
D6111	D6126	D6141	D6156
D6112	D6127	D6142	D6157
D6113	D6128	D6143	
D6114	D6129	D6144	

B-B "2"

Introduced: 1959.
Locomotive manufacturer: North British Locomotive Co.
Total b.h.p.: 1,000.* / 1,100.
Engine: N. B. L. / M. A. N. 12-cyl. L12V18/21M of 1,000 b.h.p.* or 1,100 b.h.p.
Transmission: **Hydraulic.** Voith—N.B.L. L.T.306r hydraulic transmission and cardan shafts to primary gear-boxes on the inner axles and secondary gear-boxes on the outer axles.
Weight: 68 tons.* / 65 tons.
Driving Wheels: 3′ 7″.
Maximum tractive effort: 40,000 lbs.

D6300*	D6315	D6330	D6345
D6301*	D6316	D6331	D6346
D6302*	D6317	D6332	D6347
D6303*	D6318	D6333	D6348
D6304*	D6319	D6334	D6349
D6305*	D6320	D6335	D6350
D6306	D6321	D6336	D6351
D6307	D6322	D6337	D6352
D6308	D6323	D6338	D6353
D6309	D6324	D6339	D6354
D6310	D6325	D6340	D6355
D6311	D6326	D6341	D6356
D6312	D3627	D6342	D6357
D6313	D6328	D6343	
D6314	D6329	D6344	

Bo-Bo "3"

Introduced: 1960.
Locomotive manufacturer: Birmingham R.C. & W. Co.
Total b.h.p.: 1,550.
Engines: Sulzer 8LDA28 pressure-charged 8-cyl of 1,550 b.h.p. at 750 r.p.m. (continuous).
Transmission: **Electric.** Four Crompton Parkinson 305 h.p. axle-hung nose-suspended traction motors.
Weight: 73 tons 8 cwt.
Driving Wheels: 3′ 7″.
Maximum tractive effort: 45,000 lb.

D6500	D6512	D6524	D6536
D6501	D6513	D6525	D6537
D6502	D6514	D6526	D6538
D6503	D6515	D6527	D6539
D6504	D6516	D6528	D6540
D6505	D6517	D6529	D6541
D6506	D6518	D6530	D6542
D6507	D6519	D6531	D6543
D6508	D6520	D6532	D6544
D6509	D6521	D6533	D6545
D6510	D6522	D6534	D6546
D6511	D6523	D6535	D6547

Class B16/1 4-6-0 No. 61414 [*David A. Anderson*

Class B16/2 4-6-0 No. 61475 [*P. Ransome-Wallis*

Class B17/6 4-6-0 No. 61657 *Doncaster Rovers* [*K. R. Pirt*

Class K4 2-6-0 No. 61998 *MacLeod of MacLeod* [W. S. Sellar

Class K1 2-6-0 No. 62055 [R. E. Vincent

Class K2/2 2-6-0 (with side-window cab) No. 61794 *Loch Oich* [K. R. Pirt

Class D16/3 4-4-0 No. 62618 (since withdrawn) [D. Penney

Class D49/2 4-4-0 No. 62759 *The Craven* [P. J. Lynch

Class D49/1 4-4-0 No. 62709 *Berwickshire* [David A. Anderson

Class O4/8 2-8-0 No. 63837 [J. B. Bucknall

Class O4/7 2-8-0 No. 63775 [K. R. Pirt

Class O4/3 2-8-0 No. 63782 [K. R. Pirt

Class O2/2 2-8-0 No. 63940 [P. H. Groom

Class O2/4 2-8-0 No. 63925 [P. H. Groom

Class WD 2-10-0 No. 90761 [R. K. Evans

Class J6 0-6-0 No. 64178 [K. R. Pirt

Class J38 0-6-0 No. 65916 [David A. Anderson

Class J39 0-6-0 No. 64930 [K. R. Pirt

Class J15 0-6-0 No. 65389 [R. C. Riley

Class J11/3 0-6-0 No. 64439 [R. A. Panting

Class J11 0-6-0 No. 64348 [P. H. Wells

Top: Class A8 4-6-2T No. 69853 [*R. K. Evans*

Centre: Class C16 4-4-2T No. 67484 [*Brian E. Morrison*

Left: Class C15 4-4-2T No. 67460 [*A. W. Martin*

Class A5 4-6-2T No. 69820 [*J. B. Bucknall*

Class L1 2-6-4T No. 67764 [*N. Fields*

Class V3 2-6-2T No. 67632 [*K. R. Pirt*

Class N7/5 0-6-2T No. 69632 [*A. R. Carpenter*

Class N7/3 0-6-2T No. 69715 [*K. L. Cook*

Class N2/2 0-6-2T No. 69505 [*P. H. Groom*

Class N2/2 0-6-2T No. 69492 (with condensing apparatus) [*A. R. Carpenter*

Class J50 0-6-0T No. 68936 [*R. C. Riley*

Class J52 0-6-0ST No. 68869 [*R. C. Riley*

Class Y9 0-4-0ST No. 68123 — [*T. Booth*

Class Y4 0-4-0T Departmental No. 33 — [*R. C. Riley*

Class Y3 0-4-0T Departmental No. 38 — [*R. E. Vincent*

204 b.h.p. 0-6-0 diesel-mechanical shunter No. D2028 *[P. H. Groom*

Drewry 204 b.h.p. 0-6-0 diesel-mechanical shunter No. D2272 *[J. B. Bucknall*

Barclay 153 b.h.p. 0-4-0 diesel-mechanical shunter No. 11506 *[P. J. Sharpe*

Birmingham/Sulzer Type 2 1,160 b.h.p. diesel-electric Bo-Bo No. D5329

Metropolitan-Vickers Type 2 1,200 b.h.p. diesel-electric Co-Bo No. D5708

[P. J. Sharpe

Derby/Sulzer Type 2 1,160 b.h.p. diesel-electric Bo-Bo No. D5006 *[P. H. Groom*

English Electric Type 1 1,000 b.h.p. diesel-electric Bo-Bo No. D8015 [*J. B. Bucknall*

B.T.H. Type 1 800 b.h.p. diesel-electric Bo-Bo No. D8208 [*J. B. Bucknall*

North British Type 1 800 b.h.p. diesel-electric Bo-Bo No. D8400 [*J. B. Bucknall*

Two Park Royal two-car sets at Birmingham (New Street) [*M. Mensing*

Wickham two-car unit leaving Ely [*M. Mensing*

Cravens motor brake second No. M50773 and motor composite No. M50806 forming a two-car unit [*J. E. Wilkinson*

D6548	D6556	D6564	D6572
D6549	D6557	D6565	D6573
D6550	D6558	D6566	D6574
D6551	D6559	D6567	D6575
D6552	D6560	D6568	D6576
D6553	D6561	D6569	
D6554	D6562	D6570	
D6555	D6563	D6571	

Bo-Bo "3"

To be introduced:
Locomotive manufacturer: English Electric.
Total b.h.p.: 1,750.
Engine:
Transmission: **Electric.**
Weight:
Driving Wheels:
Maximum tractive effort:

D6700	D6711	D6722	D6733
D6701	D6712	D6723	D6734
D6702	D6713	D6724	D6735
D6703	D6714	D6725	D6736
D6704	D6715	D6726	D6737
D6705	D6716	D6727	D6738
D6706	D6717	D6728	D6739
D6707	D6718	D6729	D6740
D6708	D6719	D6730	D6741
D6709	D6720	D6731	
D6710	D6721	D6732	

Bo-Bo "1"

Introduced: 1957.
Locomotive manufacturer: English Electric Co./Vulcan Foundry Ltd.
Total b.h.p.: 1,000.
Engine: English Electric 8 SVT Mk. II of 1,000 b.h.p. at 850 r.p.m. (continuous).
Transmission: **Electric.** Four axle-hung, nose-suspended d.c. traction motors.
Weight: 72 tons.
Driving Wheels: 3′ 7″.
Maximum tractive effort: 42,000 lb.
Classified **D10/3** by the E. & N.E.R.

D8000	D8013	D8026	D8039
D8001	D8014	D8027	D8040
D8002	D8015	D8028	D8041
D8003	D8016	D8029	D8042
D8004	D8017	D8030	D8043
D8005	D8018	D8031	D8044
D8006	D8019	D8032	D8045
D8007	D8020	D8033	D8046
D8008	D8021	D8034	D8047
D8009	D8022	D8035	D8048
D8010	D8023	D8036	D8049
D8011	D8024	D8037	
D8012	D8025	D8038	

Bo-Bo "1"

Introduced: 1957.
Locomotive manufacturer: British Thomson-Houston Co.
Total b.h.p.: 800.
Engine: Paxman 16-cyl. YHXL "V"-type pressure charged by two Napier exhaust gas-driven turbo chargers. 800 b.h.p. at 1,250 r.p.m.
Transmission: **Electric.** Four B.T.H. nose-suspended traction motors with single reduction gear drive.
Weight: 68 tons.
Driving Wheels: 3′ 3½″.
Maximum tractive effort: 37,500 lb.
Classified **D8/1** by the E. & N.E.R.

D8200	D8210	D8220	D8230
D8201	D8211	D8221	D8231
D8202	D8212	D8222	D8232
D8203	D8213	D8223	D8233
D8204	D8214	D8224	D8234
D8205	D8215	D8225	D8235
D8206	D8216	D8226	D8236
D8207	D8217	D8227	
D8208	D8218	D8228	
D8209	D8219	D8229	

Bo-Bo "1"

Introduced: 1958.
Locomotive manufacturer: North British Locomotive Co.
Total b.h.p.: 800.
Engine: Paxman 16-cyl. type 16YHXL of 800 b.h.p. at 1,250 r.p.m.
Transmission: **Electric.** Four G.E.C. axle-hung nose-suspended traction motors.

Weight: 68 tons.
Driving Wheels: 3′ 7″.
Maximum tractive effort: 42,000 lb.
Classified **D8/2** by the E. & N.E.R.

D8400	D8403	D8406	D8408
D8401	D8404	D8407	D8409
D8402	D8405		

Co-Co 5P/5F

Introduced: 1947.
Locomotive manufacturer: Derby Works, B.R.
Total b.h.p.: 1,600.
Engine : English Electric 16-cyl. of 1,600 b.h.p. at 750 r.p.m. (continuous rating).
Transmission: **Electric.** Six nose-suspended motors, single reduction gear drive.
Weight: 127 tons 13 cwt.
Driving Wheels: 3′ 6″.
Maximum tractive effort: 41,400 lb.

10000 10001 **Total 2**

1Co-Co1 {10201/2 5P/5F; 10203 6P/6F}

Introduced: {1951; 1954*}
Locomotive manufacturer: Ashford Works, B.R.
Total b.h.p.: {1,750; 2,000*}
Engine: English Electric Co. 16-cyl 1,750 b.h.p. (2,000 b.h.p.*)
Transmission: **Electric.** six nose-suspended, axle-hung motors of 260 h.p. (1-hour rating).
Weight: {135 tons.; 132 tons*}
Driving Wheels: 3′ 7″.
Maximum tractive effort: {48,000 lb.; 50,000 lb.*}

10201 10202 *10203
Total 3

NOTE

Also on order are 45 Type "3" B-B diesel-hydraulic locomotives of 1,700 b.h.p. with Maybach engines and Mekydro transmission to be built by Beyer Peacock (Hymek) Ltd., the numbers of which are not known at the time of going to press.

0-6-0 Shunter

Introduced: 1936.
Locomotive manufacturer: English Electric for L.M.S.
Total b.h.p.: 350.
Engine: English Electric 6-cyl. 350 b.h.p.
Transmission: **Electric.** Two nose-suspended motors, single reduction gear drive.
Weight. 51 tons.
Driving Wheels: 4′ 0½″.
Maximum tractive effort: 30,000 lb.

12000 12001 **Total 2**

0-6-0 Shunter

Introduced: 1939.
Locomotive manufacturer: Derby Works, B.R.
Total b.h.p.: 350.
Engine: English Electric, 6-cyl. 350 b.h.p.
Transmission: **Electric.** Single motor; jackshaft drive.
Weight: 54 tons 16 cwt.
Driving Wheels: 4′ 3″.
Maximum tractive effort: 33,000 lb.
Classified **D3/7** by the E. & N.E.R.

12003	12011	12019	12027
12004	12012	12020	12028
12005	12013	12021	12029
12006	12014	12022	12030
12007	12015	12023	12031
12008	12016	12024	12032
12009	12017	12025	
12010	12018	12026	

Total 30

0-6-0 Shunter

Introduced: 1945.
Locomotive manufacturer: Derby Works, B.R.
Total b.h.p.: 350.
Engine: English Electric, 6-cyl. 350 b.h.p.
Transmission: **Electric.** Two 135 h.p., nose-suspended motors, double reduction gear drive.
Weight: 47 tons 5 cwt.
Driving Wheels: 4′ 0½″.
Maximum tractive effort: 35,000 lb.
Classified **D3/8** by the E. & N.E.R.

12033	12060	12087	12114
12034	12061	12088	12115
12035	12062	12089	12116
12036	12063	12090	12117
12037	12064	12091	12118
12038	12065	12092	12119
12039	12066	12093	12120
12040	12067	12094	12121
12041	12068	12095	12122
12042	12069	12096	12123
12043	12070	12097	12124
12044	12071	12098	12125
12045	12072	12099	12126
12046	12073	12100	12127
12047	12074	12101	12128
12048	12075	12102	12129
12049	12076	12103	12130
12050	12077	12104	12131
12051	12078	12105	12132
12052	12079	12106	12133
12053	12080	12107	12134
12054	12081	12108	12135
12055	12082	12109	12136
12056	12083	12110	12137
12057	12084	12111	12138
12058	12085	12112	
12059	12086	12113	

Total 106

0-6-0 Shunter

Introduced: 1944.
Locomotive manufacturer: Doncaster Works, B.R.
Total b.h.p.: 350.
Engine: English Electric, 6-cyl. 350 b.h.p.
Transmission: **Electric.** Two 135 h.p. nose-suspended motors, double reduction gear drive.
Weight: 50 tons.
Driving Wheels: 4′ 0″.
Maximum tractive effort: 32,000 lb.
Classified **D3/9** by the E. & N.E.R.

15000 15001 15002 15003

Total 4

0-6-0 Shunter

Introduced: 1949.
Locomotive manufacturer: Doncaster Works, B.R.
Total b.h.p.: 360.
Engine: Petter SS4 4-cyl. 360 b.h.p.
Transmission: **Electric.** Two 135 h.p. nose-suspended traction motors double reduction gear drive.
Weight: 51 tons.
Driving Wheels: 4′ 0″.
Maximum tractive effort: 32,000 lb.
Classified **D3/14** by the E. & N.E.R.

15004 **Total 1**

0-6-0 Shunter

Introduced: 1936.
Locomotive manufacturer: English Electric for G.W.R.
Total b.h.p.: 350.
Engine: English Electric 6-cyl. 350 b.h.p.
Transmission: **Electric.** Two nose-suspended motors, single reduction gear drive.
Weight: 51 tons 10 cwt.
Driving Wheels: 4′ 1″.
Maximum tractive effort: 30,000 lb.

15100 **Total 1**

0-6-0 Shunter

Introduced: 1948.
Locomotive manufacturer: Swindon Works, B.R.
Total b.h.p.: 350.
Engine: English Electric, 6-cyl. 350 b.h.p.
Transmission: **Electric.** Two 135 h.p. nose-suspended motors, double reduction gear drive.
Weight: 50 tons.
Driving Wheels: 4′ 0½″.
Maximum tractive effort: 33,500 lb.

15101	15103	15105
15102	15104	15106

Total 6

0-6-0 Shunter

Introduced: 1937.
Locomotive manufacturer: Ashford Works, B.R.
Total b.h.p. 350.
Engine: English Electric, 6-cyl. 350 b.h.p.
Transmission: **Electric.** Two nose-suspended motors, single reduction gear drive.
Weight: 55 tons 5 cwt.
Driving Wheels: 4′ 6″.
Maximum tractive effort: 30,000 lb.

15201 15202 15203 **Total 3**

0-6-0 Shunter

Introduced: 1949.
Locomotive manufacturer: Ashford Works, B.R.
Total b.h.p.: 350.
Engine: English Electric, 6-cyl. 350 b.h.p.
Transmission: **Electric.** Two 135 h.p. nose-suspended motors, double reduction gear drive.
Weight: 45 tons.
Driving Wheels: 4′ 6″.
Maximum tractive effort: 24,000 lb.

15211	15218	15225	15232
15212	15219	15226	15233
15213	15220	15227	15234
15214	15221	15228	15235
15215	15222	15229	15236
15216	15223	15230	
15217	15224	15231	

Total 26

NOTE: British Railways are providing facilities for road tests of the following two locomotives, which remain the property of the manufacturer and are not included in B.R. stock.

0-6-0 Shunter

Introduced: 1957.
Locomotive manufacturer: English Electric.
Total b.h.p.: 500.
Engine: English Electric 6RKT of 500 b.h.p. at 750 r.p.m.
Transmission: **Electric.** One English Electric traction motor coupled to double-reduction gear box final drive.
Weight: 48 tons.
Driving Wheels: 4′ 0″.
Maximum tractive effort: 33,000 lb.

D0226

0-6-0 Shunter

Introduced: 1957.
Locomotive manufacturer: English Electric.
Total b.h.p.: 500.
Engine: English Electric, 6RKT of 500 b.h.p. at 750 r.p.m.
Transmission: **Hydraulic.** Lysholm-Smith torque-converter and three-speed reduction gear to final drive.
Weight: 48 tons.
Driving Wheels: 4′ 0″.
Maximum tractive effort: 33,000 lb.

D022

A1A-A1A Gas Turbine

Introduced: 1949.
Locomotive manufacturer: Swiss Locomotive & Machine Works, Winterthur.
Total b.h.p.: 2,500.
Engine: Brown-Boveri 2,500 b.h.p. Gas Turbine.
Transmission: **Electric.** Four frame-mounted traction motors driving through spring drive.
Weight: 115 tons.
Driving Wheels: 4′ 0½″.
Maximum tractive effort: 60,000 lb.

18000

SERVICE LOCOMOTIVES

Western Region

0-4-0

Introduced: 1957.
Locomotive manufacturer: Ruston & Hornsby.
Total b.h.p.: 88.
Engine: Ruston & Hornsby 4-cyl. type of 88 b.h.p.
Transmission: **Mechanical.** Chain driven from gearbox.
Weight: 17 tons.
Wheel Diameter: 3′ 0″.
Maximum tractive effort: 9,500 lb.

20

0-6-0

Introduced: 1953.
Locomotive manufacturer: Ruston & Hornsby.
Total b.h.p.: 165.
Engine: Ruston & Hornsby 6-cyl. type of 165 b.h.p.
Transmission: **Electric.** One B.T.H. nose-suspended traction motor.
Weight: 30 tons.
Driving Wheels: 3′ 2½″.
Maximum tractive effort: 17,000 lb.

PWM650	PWM652	PWM654
PWM651	PWM653	

Also Petrol Locomotives 24 and 27.

Southern Region

0-4-0

Introduced: 1947.
Locomotive manufacturer: John Fowler & Co.
Total b.h.p.: 150.
Engine: Fowler.
Transmission: **Mechanical.** Four-speed gearbox.
Weight: 29 tons.
Driving Wheels: 3′ 3″.
Maximum tractive effort: 15,000 lb.

DS600

0-4-0

Introduced:
Locomotive manufacturer: Ruston & Hornsby.
Total b.h.p.:
Engine:
Transmission:
Weight:
Driving Wheels:
Maximum tractive effort:

DS1169

0-6-0

Introduced: 1947.
Locomotive manufacturer: Drewry.
Total b.h.p.: 204.
Engine: Gardner 8L3 or 204 b.h.p.
Transmission: **Mechanical.** Five-speed gearbox.
Weight: 24 tons 15 cwt.
Driving Wheels: 3′ 3″.
Maximum tractive effort: 16,850 lb.

DS1173

London Midland Region

0-4-0

Introduced: 1936.
Locomotive manufacturer: John Fowler & Co.
Total b.h.p.: 88.
Engine: Ruston & Hornsby 6-cyl. type VQ of 88 b.h.p.
Transmission: **Mechanical.** Four-speed constant-mesh gearbox with multiple-disc dry clutch manually operated.
Weight: 25 tons.
Driving Wheels: 3′ 0″.
Maximum tractive effort: 8,940 lb.

ED1

0-4-0

Introduced: 1936.
Locomotive manufacturer: John Fowler & Co.
Total b.h.p.: 150.
Engine: Fowler type 4C vertical or 150 b.h.p. at 1,000 r.p.m. (1 hr. rating).
Transmission: **Mechanical.** Four speed gearbox.
Weight: 29 tons.
Driving Wheels: 3′ 3″.
Maximum tractive effort: 15,000 lb.

ED2	ED4	ED5
ED3		ED6

0-4-0

Introduced: 1955.
Locomotive manufacturer: John Fowler & Co.
Total b.h.p.: 150.
Engine: Fowler 4-cyl. type C of 150 b.h.p.
Transmission: **Mechanical.** Three-lobe synchromesh gearbox with multiple disc dry clutch manually operated.
Weight: 29 tons.
Driving Wheels: 3′ 3″.
Maximum tractive effort: 15,000 lb.

ED7

0-4-0

Introduced: 1958.
Locomotive manufacturer: Ruston & Hornsby.
Total b.h.p.:
Engine: Ruston type 4YCL.
Transmission: **Mechanical.** Chain drive.
Weight: 8 tons 4 cwt.
Driving Wheel: 2′ 6″.
Maximum tractive effort: 4,200 lb
Gauge: 3′ 0″.

ED10

0-4-0

Introduced: 1958.
Locomotive manufacturer: Ruston & Hornsby.
Total b.h.p.: 20.
Engine:
Transmission:
Weight: 3 tons 10 cwt.
Driving Wheels:
Maximum tractive effort: 1 890 lb.
Gauge: 1′ 6″.

ZM32

Eastern Region

0-4-0

Introduced: 1950.
Locomotive manufactuer: Hibberd & Co.
Total b.h.p.: 52.
Engine: English National 4-cyl. Gas type. DA4 of 52 b.h.p. at 1,250 r.p.m.
Transmission: **Mechanical.** Spur-type three-speed gearbox with roller chains.
Weight: 11 tons.
Driving Wheels:
Maximum tractive effort:

52 (11104)

0-4-0

Introduced: 1955.
Locomotive manufacturer: Ruston & Hornsby.
Total b.h.p.: 88.
Engine: Ruston & Hornsby Mark 4V vertical 4-cyl. of 88 b.h.p.
Transmission: **Mechanical.**
Weight: 17 tons.
Driving Wheels: 3′ 0″.
Maximum tractive effort: 9,500 lb.

56

0-4-0

Introduced: 1958.
Locomotive manufacturer: Andrew Barclay.
Total b.h.p.: 150.
Engine:
Transmission: **Mechanical.**
Weight:
Driving Wheels:
Maximum tractive effort:

81

0-4-0

Introduced: 1959.
Locomotive manufacturer: Ruston & Hornsby.
Total b.h.p.:
Engine:
Transmission:
Weight:
Driving Wheels:
Maximum tractive effort:

85

0-6-0

Introduced: 1958.
Locomotive manufacturer: Swindon Works, B.R.
Total b.h.p.: 200.
Engine: Gardner type 8L3 of 204 b.h.p at 1,200 r.p.m.
Transmission. **Mechanical.** Wilson-Drewry Director air-operated epicyclic gearbox. R.F.11 Spiral Bevel reverse/final drive unit.
Weight: 30 tons 4 cwt.
Driving Wheels: 3′ 7″.
Maximum tractive effort: 15,300 lb.

91 92

DIESEL MULTIPLE UNITS

Motor Brake Second ■
(TWIN UNITS)

Built by: **Derby Works, B.R.**
Engines: Two B.U.T. (Leyland) 6-cyl. horizontal type of 230 b.h.p.
*Two Rolls Royce 8-cyl. horizontal type of 238 b.h.p.
†Two B.U.T. (Leyland) 6-cyl. horizontal type of 230 b.h.p.
Transmission: **Mechanical.** Cardan shaft and freewheel to four-speed epicyclic gearbox and further cardan shaft to final drive.
***Hydraulic.** Twin Disc Torque converter
†**Mechanical.** Cardan shaft and free wheel to Self Changing Gears Ltd. automatic four-speed gearbox and further cardan shaft to final drive.
Body: 64′ 6″ × 9′ 3″.
Weight: 35 tons 10 cwt. / 37 tons 10 cwt.†
Seats 2nd: 62

E50000*	E50017	E50034
E50001	E50018	E50035
E50002	E50019	E50036
E50003	E50020	E50037
E50004	E50021	E50038
E50005	E50022	E50039
E50006	E50023	E50040
E50007	E50024	E50041
E50008	E50025	E50042
E50009	E50026	E50043
E50010	E50027	E50044
E50011	E50028	E50045
E50012	E50029	E50046
E50013	E50030	E50047
E50014	E50031	E50048
E50015	E50032	E50049†
E50016	E50033	

Motor Brake Second ■
(THREE-CAR SUBURBAN)

Built by: **Derby Works, B.R.**
Engines: Two B.U.T. (Leyland) 6-cyl. horizontal type of 150 b.h.p.
Transmission: **Mechanical.** Cardan shaft and freewheel to four-speed epicyclic gearbox and further cardan shaft to final drive.
Body: 64′ 0″ × 9′ 3″. Non-gangwayed, side doors to each seating bay.
Weight: 35 tons 10 cwt.
Seats 2nd: 65.

W50050	W50064	W50078
W50051	W50065	W50079
W50052	W50066	W50080
W50053	W50067	W50081
W50054	W50068	W50082
W50055	W50069	W50083
W50056	W50070	W50084
W50057	W50071	W50085
W50058	W50072	W50086
W50059	W50073	W50087
W50060	W50074	W50088
W50061	W50075	W50089
W50062	W50076	W50090
W50063	W50077	W50091

Motor Second ■
(THREE-CAR SUBURBAN)

Built by: **Derby Works, B.R.**
Engines: Two B.U.T. (Leyland) 6-cyl. horizontal type of 150 b.h.p.
Transmission: **Mechanical.** Cardan shaft and freewheel to four-speed epicyclic gearbox and further cardan shaft to final drive.
Body: 64′ 0″ × 9′ 3″. Non-gangwayed, side doors to each seating bay.
Weight: 35 tons 10 cwt.
Seats 2nd: 95.

W50092	W50106	W50120
W50093	W50107	W50121
W50094	W50108	W50122
W50095	W50109	W50123
W50096	W50110	W50124
W50097	W50111	W50125
W50098	W50112	W50126
W50099	W50113	W50127
W50100	W50114	W50128
W50101	W50115	W50129
W50102	W50116	W50130
W50103	W50117	W50131
W50104	W50118	W50132
W50105	W50119	W50133

Motor Brake Second ■

(TWIN UNITS)

Built by: **Metropolitan Cammell.**
Engines: Two Rolls Royce 6-cyl. horizontal type of 180 b.h.p.
*Two Rolls Royce 6-cyl. type supercharged to 230 b.h.p.
Transmission: **Mechanical.** Cardan shaft and freewheel to four-speed epicyclic gearbox and further cardan shaft to final drive.
Body: 57′ 0″ × 9′ 3″
Weight: 33 tons.
Seats 2nd: 52.

M50134	M50136*	M50137
M50135		

Motor Composite (L) ■

(FOUR-CAR UNITS)

Built by: **Metropolitan Cammell.**
Engines: Two B.U.T. (A.E.C.) 6-cyl. horizontal type of 150 b.h.p.
Transmission: **Mechanical.** Cardan shaft and freewheel to four-speed epicyclic gearbox and further cardan shaft to final drive.
Body: 57′ 0″ × 9′ 3″
Weight: 32 tons.
Seats 1st: 12.
2nd: 45

E50138	E50143	E50148
E50139	E50144	E50149
E50140	E50145	E50150
E50141	E50146	E50151
E50142	E50147	

Motor Brake Second ■

(TWIN UNITS)

Built by: **Metropolitan Cammell.**
Engines: Two B.U.T. (A.E.C.) 6 cyl. horizontal type of 150 b h.p.
Transmission: **Mechanical.** Cardan shaft and freewheel to four-speed epicyclic gearbox and further cardan shaft to final drive.
Body: 57′ 0″ × 9′ 3″.
Weight: 31 tons 10 cwt
Seats: 2nd: 52.

E50152	E50154	E50156
E50153	E50155	E50157

Motor Composite (L) ■

(TWIN UNITS)

Built by: **Metropolitan Cammell.**
Engines: Two B.U.T. (A.E.C.) 6-cyl. horizontal type of 150 b.h.p.
Transmission: **Mechanical.** Cardan shaft and freewheel to four-speed epicyclic gearbox and further cardan shaft to final drive.
Body: 57′ 0″ × 9′ 3″.
Weight: 32 tons.
Seats: 1st: 12.
2nd: 53

E50158	E50160	E50162
E50159	E50161	E50163

Motor Brake Second ■

(TWIN UNITS)

For Details see E50152-7

E50164	E50166	E50167
E50165		

Motor Composite (L) ■

(TWIN UNITS)

For Details see E50158-63

E50168	E50170	E50171
E50169		

Motor Composite (L) ■

(FOUR-CAR UNITS)

Built by: **Metropolitan Cammell.**
Engines: B.U.T. (A.E.C.), 6-cyl. horizontal type of 150 b.h.p.
Transmission: **Mechanical.** Cardan shaft and freewheel to four-speed epicyclic gearbox and further cardan shaft to final drive.
Body: 57′ 0″ × 9′ 3″.
Weight: 32 tons.
Seats 1st: 12.
2nd: 53.

E50172	E50182	E50191
E50174	E50183	E50192
E50175	E50184	E50193
E50176	E50185	E50194
E50177	E50186	E50195
E50178	E50187	E50196
E50179	E50188	E50197
E50180	E50189	
E50181	E50190	

Motor Brake Second ■

(TWIN UNITS)

Built by: **Metropolitan Cammell.**
Engines: Two B.U.T. (A.E.C.) 6-cyl. horizontal type of 150 b.h.p
Transmission: **Mechanical.** Cardan shaft and freewheel to four-speed epicyclic gearbox and further cardan shaft to final drive.
Body: 57′ 0″ × 9′ 3″.
Weight: 32 tons.
Seats 2nd: 52.

E50198	E50210	E50222
E50199	E50211	E50223
E50200	E50212	E50224
E50201	E50213	E50225
E50202	E50214	E50226
E50203	E50215	E50227
E50204	E50216	E50228
E50205	E50217	E50229
E50206	E50218	E50230
E50207	E50219	E50231
E50208	E50220	E50232
E50209	E50221	E50233

Motor Composite (L) ■

(FOUR-CAR UNITS)

For Details see E50138-45

E50234	E50238	E50242
E50235	E50239	E50243
E50236	E50240	E50244
E50237	E50241	E50245

Motor Brake Second ■

(TWIN UNITS)

Built by: **Metropolitan Cammell.**
Engines: Two B.U.T. (A.E.C.) 6-cyl. horizontal type of 150 b.h.p.
Transmission: **Mechanical.** Cardan shaft and freewheel to four-speed epicyclic gearbox and further cardan shaft to final drive.
Body: 57′ 0″ × 9′ 3″.
Weight: 31 tons 10 cwt.
Seats 2nd: 44.

E50246 E50247 E50248

Motor Brake Second ■

Built by: **Cravens.**
Engines: Two B.U.T. (A.E.C.) 6-cyl. horizontal type of 150 b.h.p.
Transmission: **Mechanical.** Cardan shaft and freewheel to four-speed epicyclic gearbox and further cardan shaft to final drive.
Body: 57′ 6″ × 9′ 3″.
Weight: 30 tons.
Seats 2nd: 52.

E50249

Motor Brake Second ■

(TWIN UNITS)

Built by: **Metropolitan Cammell.**
Engines: Two B.U.T. (A.E.C.) 6-cyl. horizontal type of 150 b.h.p.
Transmission: **Mechanical.** Cardan shaft and freewheel to four-speed epicyclic gearbox and further cardan shaft to final drive.
Body: 57′ 0″ × 9′ 3″.
Weight: 31 tons 10 cwt.
Seats 2nd: 52.

E50250	E50254	E50258
E50251	E50255	E50259
E50252	E50256	
E50253	E50257	

Motor Composite (L) ■

(TWIN UNITS)

Built by: **Metropolitan Cammell.**
Engines: Two B.U.T. (A.E.C.) 6 cyl. horizontal type of 150 b.h.p.
Transmission: **Mechanical.** Cardan shaft and freewheel to four-speed epicyclic gearbox and further cardan shaft to final drive.
Body: 57′ 0″ × 9′ 3″.
Weight: 31 tons 10 cwt.
Seats 1st: 12.
2nd: 53

E50260	E50264	E50268
E50261	E50265	E50269
E50262	E50266	
E50263	E50267	

Motor Composite (L) ■

(THREE-CAR UNITS)

Built by: **Metropolitan Cammell.**
Engines: Two Rolls Royce 6-cyl. horizontal type of 180 b.h.p.
Transmission: **Mechanical.** Cardan shaft and freewheel to four-speed epicyclic gearbox and further cardan shaft to final drive.
Body: 57′ 0″ × 9′ 3″
Weight: 32 tons
Seats 1st: 12.
2nd: 53.

E50270	E50274	E50278
E50271	E50275	E50279
E50272	E50276	
E50273	E50277	

Motor Brake Second ■

(THREE-CAR UNITS)

Built by: **Metropolitan Cammell.**
Engine: Two Rolls Royce 6-cyl. horizontal type of 180 b.h.p.
Transmission: **Mechanical.** Cardan shaft and freewheel to four-speed epicyclic gearbox and further cardan shaft to final drive.
Body: 57′ 0″ × 9′ 3″.
Weight: 33 tons.
Seats 2nd: 52.

E50280	E50285	E50290
E50281	E50286	E50291
E50282	E50287	E50292
E50283	E50288	
E50284	E50289	

Motor Brake Second ■

(TWIN UNITS)

Built by: **Metropolitan Cammell.**
Engines: Two B.U.T. (A.E.C.) 6-cyl. horizontal type of 150 b.h.p.
Transmission: **Mechanical.** Cardan. shaft and freewheel to four-speed epicyclic gearbox and further cardan shaft to final drive.
Body: 57′ 0″ × 9′ 3″.
Weight: 31 tons 10 cwt.
Seats 2nd: 52.

E50293	E50295	E50296
E50294		

Motor Brake Second ■

(THREE-CAR UNITS)

Built by: **Metropolitan Cammell.**
Engines: Two B.U.T. 6-cyl. horizontal type of 150 b.h.p.
Transmission: **Mechanical.** Cardan shaft and freewheel to four-speed epicyclic gearbox and further cardan shaft to final drive.
Body: 57′ 0″ × 9′ 3″.
Weight: 31 tons 10 cwt.
Seats 2nd: 52.

M50303	M50309	M50315
M50304	M50310	M50316
M50305	M50311	M50317
M50306	M50312	M50318
M50307	M50313	M50319
M50308	M50314	M50320

Motor Composite (L) ■

(THREE-CAR UNITS)

Built by: **Metropolitan Cammell.**
Engines: Two B.U.T. 6-cyl. horizontal type of 150 b.h.p.
Transmission: **Mechanical.** Cardan shaft and freewheel to four-speed epicyclic gearbox and further cardan shaft to final drive.
Body: 57′ 0″ × 9′ 3″.
Weight: 31 tons 10 cwt.
Seats 1st: 12.
2nd: 53.

M50321	M50327	M50333
M50322	M50328	M50334
M50323	M50329	M50335
M50324	M50330	M50336
M50325	M50331	M50337
M50326	M50332	M50338

Motor Brake Second ■

(TWIN UNITS)

Built by: **Gloucester R.C. & W. Co.**
Engines: Two B.U.T. (A.E.C.) 6-cyl. horizontal type of 150 b.h.p.
Transmission: **Mechanical.** Cardan shaft and freewheel to four-speed epicyclic gearbox and further cardan shaft to final drive.
Body: 57′ 6″ × 9′ 3″.
Weight: 30 tons 5 cwt.
Seats. 2nd: 52.

SC50339	SC50346	M50353
SC50340	SC50347	M50354
SC50341	SC50348	M50355
SC50342	SC50349	M50356
SC50343	M50350	M50357
SC50344	M50351	M50358*
SC50345	M50352	

*Fitted with C.A.V. Ltd. automatic gear change equipment.

Motor Brake Second ■
(TWIN UNITS)

Built by: **Cravens.**
Engines: Two B.U.T. (Leyland) (A.E.C.*) 6-cyl. horizontal type of 150 b.h.p.
Transmission: **Mechanical.** Cardan shaft and freewheel to four-speed epicyclic gearbox and further cardan shaft to final drive.
Body: 57′ 6″ × 9′ 3″.
Weight: 29 tons.
Seats 2nd: 52.

E50359	E50371*	E50383*
E50360	E50372*	E50384*
E50361	E50373*	E50385*
E50362	E50374*	E50386*
E50363	E50375*	E50387*
E50364	E50376*	E50388*
E50365	E50377*	E50389*
E50366	E50378*	M50390*
E50367	E50379*	M50391*
E50368	E50380*	M50392*
E50369	E50381*	M50393*
E50370	E50382*	M50394*

Motor Brake Second ■
(TWIN UNITS)

Built by: **Park Royal Vehicles.**
Engines: Two B.U.T. (A.E.C.) 6-cyl. horizontal type of 150 b.h.p.
Transmission: **Mechanical.** Cardan shaft and freewheel to four-speed epicyclic gearbox and further cardan shaft to final drive.
Body: 57′ 6″ × 9′ 3′.
Weight: 33 tons 8 cwt.
Seats 2nd: 52.

M50395	M50402	M50409
M50396	M50403	M50410
M50397	M50404	M50411
M50398	M50405	M50412
M50399	M50406	M50413
M50400	M50407	M50414
M50401	M50408	

Motor Brake Second ■
(TWIN UNITS)

Built by: **D. Wickham & Co. Ltd.**
Engines: Two B.U.T. (Leyland) 6-cyl. horizontal type of 150 b.h.p.
Transmission: **Mechanical.** Cardan shaft and freewheel to four-speed epicyclic gearbox and further cardan shaft to final drive.
Body: 57′ 0″ × 9′ 3″.
Weight: 27 tons 10 cwt.
Seats 2nd: 59.

E50415	E50417	E50419
E50416	E50418	

Motor Brake Second ■
(L.M. THREE-CAR UNITS)

Built by: **Birmingham R.C. & W. Co.**
Engines: Two B.U.T. (Leyland) 6-cyl. horizontal type of 150 b.h.p.
Transmission: **Mechanical.** Cardan shaft and freewheel to four-speed epicyclic gearbox and further cardan shaft to final drive.
Body: 57′ 6″ × 9′ 3″.
Weight: 31 tons.
Seats 2nd: 52.

M50420	M50422	M50423
M50421		

Motor Composite (L) ■
(THREE-CAR UNITS)

Built by: **Birmingham R. C. & W. Co.**
Engines: Two B.U.T. (Leyland) 6-cyl. horizontal type of 150 b.h.p.
Transmission: **Mechanical.** Cardan shaft and freewheel to four-speed epicyclic gearbox and further cardan shaft to final drive.
Body: 57′ 6″ × 9′ 3″.
Weight: 31 tons.
Seats 1st: 12.
2nd 54.

M50424	M50426	M50427
M50425		

Motor Brake Second ■

(THREE-CAR UNITS)

For Details see M50420-3

M50428	M50446	M50464
M50429	M50447	M50465
M50430	M50448	M50466
M50431	M50449	M50467
M50432	M50450	M50468
M50433	M50451	M50469
M50434	M50452	M50470
M50435	M50453	M50471
M50436	M50454	M50472
M50437	M50455	M50473
M50438	M50456	M50474
M50439	M50457	M50475
M50440	M50458	M50476
M50441	M50459	M50477
M50442	M50460	M50478
M50443	M50461	M50479
M50444	M50462	
M50445	M50463	

Motor Composite (L) ■

(THREE-CAR UNITS)

For Details see M50424-7.

M50480	M50498	M50516
M50481	M50499	M50517
M50482	M50500	M50518
M50483	M50501	M50419
M50484	M50502	M50520
M50485	M50503	M50521
M50486	M50504	M50522
M50487	M50505	M50523
M50488	M50506	M50524
M50489	M50507	M50525
M50490	M50508	M50526
M50491	M50509	M50527
M50492	M50510	M50528
M50493	M50511	M50529
M50494	M50512	M50530
M50495	M50513	M50531
M50496	M50514	
M50497	M50515	

Motor Brake Second ■

(TWIN UNITS)

Built by: **Birmingham R. C. & W. Co.**
Engines: Two B.U.T. (Leyland) 6-cyl. horizontal type of 150 b.h.p .
Transmission: **Mechanical.** Cardan shaft and freewheel to four-speed epicyclic gearbox and further cardan shaft to final drive.
Body: 57′ 6″ × 9′ 3″
Weight: 31 tons.
Seats 2nd: 52.

M50532	M50536	M50540
M50533	M50537	M50541
M50534	M50538	
M50535	M50539	

Motor Composite (L) ■

(FOUR-CAR UNITS)

Built by: **Birmingham R. C. & W. Co.**
Engines: Two B.U.T. (Leyland) 6-cyl. horizontal type of 150 b.h.p.
Transmission: **Mechanical.** Cardan shaft and freewheel to four-speed epicyclic gearbox and further cardan shaft to final drive.
Body: 57′ 6″ × 9′ 3″.
Weight: 31 tons.
Seats 1st: 12.
2nd 41.

E50542	E50560	E50578
E50543	E50561	E50579
E50544	E50562	E50580
E50545	E50563	E50581
E50546	E50564	E50582
E50547	E50565	E50583
E50548	E50566	E50584
E50549	E50567	E50585
E50550	E50568	E50586
E50551	E50569	E50587
E50552	E50570	E50588
E50553	E50571	E50589
E50554	E50572	E50590
E50555	E50573	E50591
E50556	E50574	E50592
E50557	E50575	E50593
E50558	E50576	
E50559	E50577	

Motor Brake Second ■
(TWIN UNITS)

Built by: **Birmingham R. C. & W. Co.**
Engines: Two B.U.T. (Leyland) 6-cyl. horizontal type of 150 b.h.p.
Transmission: **Mechanical.** Cardan shaft and freewheel to four-speed epicyclic gearbox and further cardan shaft to final drive.
Body: 57′ 6″ × 9′ 3″
Weight: 31 tons.
Seats 2nd: 52.

E50594	E50596	E50598
E50595	E50597	

Motor Brake Second ■
(TWIN OR THREE*-CAR UNITS)

Built by: **Derby Works, B.R.**
Engines: Two B.U.T. (A.E.C.) 6-cyl. horizontal type of 150 b.h.p.
Transmission: **Mechanical.** Cardan shaft and freewheel to four-speed epicyclic gearbox and further cardan shaft to final drive.
Body: 57′ 6″ × 9′ 2″.
Weight: 28 tons 10 cwt.
Seats 2nd: 52.

E50599	E50610	E50621*
E50600	E50611	E50622*
E50601	E50612	E50623*
E50602	E50613	E50624*
E50603	E50614	M50625
E50604	E50615	M50626
E50605	E50616	M50627
E50606	E50617	M50628
E50607	E50618	M50629
E50608	E50619	
E50609	E50620*	

Motor Composite (L) ■
(THREE* AND FOUR-CAR UNITS

Built by: **Derby Works, B R.**
Engines: Two B.U.T. (A.E.C.) 6-cyl. horizontal type of 150 b.h.p.
Transmission: **Mechanical.** Cardan shaft and freewheel to four-speed epicyclic gearbox and further cardan shaft to final drive.
Body: 57′ 6″ × 9′ 2″.
Weight: 28 tons
Seats 2nd: 12.
2nd: 50

E50630	E50636	E50642*
E50631	E50637	E50643*
E50632	E50638	E50644*
E50633	E50639	E50645*
E50634	E50640	E50646*
E50635	E50641	

Motor Second (L) ■
(THREE-CAR CROSS-COUNTRY)

Built by: **Swindon Works B.R.**
Engines: Two B.U.T. 6-cyl horizontal type of 150 b.h.p.
Transmission: **Mechanical.** Cardan shaft and freewheel to four-speed epicyclic gearbox and further cardan shaft to final drive.
Body: 64′ 6″ × 9′ 3″.
Weight: 36 tons 10 cwt
Seats 2nd: 63.

W50647	W50664	W50681
W50648	W50665	W50682
W50649	W50666	W50683
W50650	W50667	W50684
W50651	W50668	W50685
W50652	W50669	W50686
W50653	W50670	W50687
W50654	W50671	W50688
W50655	W50672	W50689
W50656	W50673	W50690
W50657	W50674	W50691
W50658	W50675	W50692
W50659	W50676	W50693
W50660	W50677	W50694
W50661	W50678	W50695
W50662	W50679	
W50663	W50680	

Motor Brake Composite ■
(THREE-CAR CROSS-COUNTRY)

Built by: **Swindon Works B.R.**
Engines: Two B.U.T. 6-cyl. horizontal type of 150 b.h.p.
Transmission: **Mechanical.** Cardan shaft and freewheel to four-speed epicyclic gearbox and further cardan shaft to final drive.
Body: 64′ 6″ × 9′ 3″.
Weight: 36 tons 7 cwt.
Seats 1st: 18.
2nd: 16

W50696	W50713	W50730
W50697	W50714	W50731
W50698	W50715	W50732
W50699	W50716	W50733
W50700	W50717	W50734
W50701	W50718	W50735
W50702	W50719	W50736
W50703	W50720	W50737
W50704	W50721	W50738
W50705	W50722	W50739
W50706	W50723	W50740
W50707	W50724	W50741
W50708	W50725	W50742
W50709	W50726	W50743
W50710	W50727	W50744
W50711	W50728	
W50712	W50729	

Motor Composite (L) ■

(THREE-CAR UNITS)

Built by: **Metropolitan Cammell.**
Engines: Two Rolls Royce 6-cyl. horizontal type of 180 b.h.p.
Transmission: **Mechanical:** Cardan shaft and freewheel to four-speed epicyclic gearbox and further cardan shaft to final drive.
Body: 57′ 0″ × 9′ 3″.
Weight: 31 tons 10 cwt.
Seats 1st: 12.
2nd: 53.

E50745 E50746 E50747

Motor Composite (L) ■

(N.E. FOUR-CAR UNITS)

Built by: **Metropolitan Cammell.**
Engines: Two B.U.T. (A.E.C.) 6-cyl. horizontal type of 150 b.h p.
Transmission: **Mechanical.** Cardan shaft and freewheel to four-speed epicyclic gearbox and further cardan shaft to final drive.
Body: 57′ 0″ × 9′ 3″.
Weight: 31 tons 10 cwt.
Seats 1st: 12.
2nd: 53.

E50748	E50750	E50751
E50749		

Motor Brake Second ■

(THREE-CAR UNITS)

Built by: **Cravens.**
Engines: Two B.U.T. (Leyland) 6-cyl. horizontal type of 150 b.h.p.
Transmission: **Mechanical.** Cardan shaft and freewheel to four-speed epicyclic gearbox and further cardan shaft to final drive.
Body: 57′ 6″ × 9′ 3″
Weight: 30 tons.
Seats 2nd: 52.

M50752	M50759	M50766
M50753	M50760	M50767
M50754	M50761	M50768
M50755	M50762	M50769
M50756	M50763	M50770
M50757	M50764	
M50758	M50765	

Motor Brake Second ■

(TWIN UNITS)

Built by: **Cravens.**
Engines: Two B.U.T. (A.E.C.) 6-cyl. horizontal type of 150 b.h.p.
Transmission: **Mechanical.** Cardan shaft and freewheel to four-speed epicyclic gearbox and further cardan shaft to final drive.
Body: 57′ 6″ × 9′ 3″.
Weight: 30 tons.
Seats 2nd: 52.

M50771	M50776	M50781
M50772	M50777	M50782
M50773	M50778	M50783
M50774	M50779	M50784
M50775	M50780	

Motor Composite (L) ■

(L.M. THREE-CAR UNITS)

Built by: **Cravens.**
Engines: Two B.U.T. (Leyland) 6-cyl. horizontal type of 150 b.h.p.
Transmission: **Mechanical.** Cardan shaft and freewheel to four-speed epicyclic gearbox and further cardan shaft to final drive.
Body: 57′ 6″ × 9′ 3″.
Weight: 30 tons.
Seats 1st: 12.
2nd: 51

M50785	M50792	M50799
M50786	M50793	M50800
M50787	M50794	M50801
M50788	M50795	M50802
M50789	M50796	M50803
M50790	M50797	
M50791	M50798	

Motor Composite (L) ■

(TWIN UNITS)

Built by: **Cravens.**
Engines: Two B.U.T. (A.E.C.) 6-cyl. horizontal type of 150 b.h.p.
Transmission: **Mechanical.** Cardan shaft and freewheel to four-speed epicyclic gearbox and further cardan shaft to final drive.
Body: 57′ 6″ × 9′ 3″.
Weight: 30 tons.
Seats *1st:* 12.
2nd: 51.

M50804	M50809	M50814
M50805	M50810	M50815
M50806	M50811	M50816
M50807	M50812	M50817
M50808	M50813	

Motor Brake Second ■

(THREE-CAR SUBURBAN)
For Details see W50050-91

W50818	W50836	W50854
W50819	W50837	W50855
W50820	W50838	W50856
W50821	W50839	W50857
W50822	W50840	W50858
W50823	W50841	W50859
W50824	W50842	W50860
W50825	W50843	W50861
W50826	W50844	W50862
W50827	W50845	W50863
W50828	W50846	W50864
W50829	W50847	W50865
W50830	W50848	W50866
W50831	W50849	W50867
W50832	W50850	W50868
W50833	W50851	W50869
W50834	W50852	W50870
W50835	W50853	

Motor Second ■

(THREE-CAR SUBURBAN)
For Details see W50092-50133

W50871	W50889	W50907
W50872	W50890	W50908
W50873	W50891	W50909
W50874	W50892	W50910
W50875	W50893	W50911
W50876	W50894	W50912
W50877	W50895	W50913
W50878	W50896	W50914
W50879	W50897	W50915
W50880	W50898	W50916
W50881	W50899	W50917
W50882	W50900	W50918
W50883	W50901	W50919
W50884	W50902	W50920
W50885	W50903	W50921
W50886	W50904	W50922
W50887	W50905	W50923
W50888	W50906	

Motor Brake Second ■

(TWIN UNITS)

Built by: **Derby Works, B.R.**
Engines: Two B.U.T. (A.E.C.) 6-cyl. horizontal type of 150 b.h.p.
Transmission: **Mechanical.** Cardan shaft and freewheel to four-speed epicyclic gearbox and further cardan shaft to final drive.
Body: 57′ 6″ × 9′ 2″.
Weight: 28 tons 10 cwt.
Seats 2nd: 52.

M50924	M50928	M50932
M50925	M50929	M50933
M50926	M50930	M50934
M50927	M50931	M50935

Motor Second (L) ●

(INTER CITY UNITS)

Built by: **Swindon Works, B.R.**
Engines: Two B.U.T. 6-cyl. horizontal type of 150 b.h.p.
Transmission: **Mechanical.** Cardan shaft and freewheel to four-speed epicyclic gearbox and further cardan shaft to final drive.
Body: 64′ ″6 × 9′ 3″ Gangwayed both ends, side driving compartment at one end.
Weight:
Seats 2nd: 64.

SC50936

Motor Brake Second ■

(TWIN UNITS)

Built by: **Derby Works, B.R.**
Engines: Two B.U.T. (A.E.C.) 6-cyl. horizontal type of 150 b.h.p.
Transmission: **Mechanical.** Cardan shaft and freewheel to four-speed epicyclic gearbox and further cardan shaft to final drive.
Body: 57′ 6″ × 9′ 2″.
Weight:
Seats 2nd:

M50938	M50955	M50972
M50939	M50956	M50973
M50940	M50957	M50974
M50941	M50958	M50975
M50942	M50959	M50976
M50943	M50960	M50977
M50944	M50961	M50978
M50945	M50962	M50979
M50946	M50963	M50980
M50947	M50964	M50981
M50948	M50965	M50982
M50949	M50966	M50983
M50950	M50967	M50984
M50951	M50968	M50985
M50952	M50969	M50986
M50953	M50970	M50987
M50954	M50971	

Motor Second ★

(THREE-CAR SUBURBAN)

Built by: **Derby Works, B.R.**
Engines: Two Rolls Royce horizontal type of 238 b.h.p.
Transmission: **Hydraulic.** Twin-disc torque converter.
Body: 64′ 0″ × 9′ 3″. Non-gangwayed, side doors to each seating bay.
Weight: 39 tons 10 cwt.
Seats 2nd: 95.

E50988	E50995	E51002
E50989	E50996	E51003
E50990	E50997	E51004
E50991	E50998	E51005
E50992	E50999	E51006
E50993	E51000	E51007
E50994	E51001	

Motor Second (L) ●

(INTER CITY UNITS)

Built by : **Swindon Works, B.R.**
Engines: Two B.U.T. 6-cyl. horizontal type of 150 b.h.p.
Transmission: **Mechanical.** Cardan shaft and freewheel to four-speed epicyclic gearbox and further cardan shaft to final drive.
Body: 64′ 6″ × 9′ 3″. Gangwayed both ends, side driving compartment at one end.
Weight:
Seats 2nd: 64.

SC51008	SC51016	SC51024
SC51009	SC51017	SC51025
SC51010	SC51018	SC51026
SC51011	SC51019	SC51027
SC51012	SC51020	SC51028
SC51013	SC51021	SC51029
SC51014	SC51022	
SC51015	SC51023	

Motor Brake Second (L) ●

(INTER CITY UNITS)

Built by : **Swindon Works, B.R.**
Engines: Two B.U.T. (A.E.C.) 6-cyl. horizontal type of 150 b.h.p.
Transmission: **Mechanical.** Cardan shaft and freewheel to four-speed epicyclic gearbox and further cardan shaft to final drive.
Body: 64′ 6″ × 9′ 3″.
Weight: 38 tons.
Seats 2nd: 52.

SC51030	SC51038	SC51046
SC51031	SC51039	SC51047
SC51032	SC51040	SC51048
SC51033	SC51041	SC51049
SC51034	SC51042	SC51050
SC51035	SC51043	SC51051
SC51036	SC51044	
SC51037	SC51045	

Motor Brake Composite ■
(THREE-CAR CROSS-COUNTRY)

Built by: **Gloucester R.C. & W. Co.**
Engines: Two B.U.T. 6-cyl. horizontal type of 150 b.h.p.
Transmission: **Mechanical.** Cardan shaft and freewheel to four-speed epicyclic gearbox and further cardan shaft to final drive.
Body: 64′ 6″ × 9′ 3″.
Weight: 36 tons 19 cwt.
Seats 1st: 18.
2nd: 16

W51052	W51062	W51072
W51053	W51063	W51073
W51054	W51064	W51074
W51055	W51065	W51075
W51056	W51066	W51076
W51057	W51067	W51077
W51058	W51068	W51078
W51059	W51069	W51079
W51060	W51070	
W51061	W51071	

Motor Second (L) ■
(THREE-CAR CROSS-COUNTRY)

Built by: **Gloucester R.C. & W. Co.**
Engines: Two B.U.T. 6-cyl. horizontal type of 150 b.h.p.
Transmission: **Mechanical.** Cardan shaft and freewheel to four-speed epicyclic gearbox and further cardan shaft to final drive.
Body: 64′ 6″ × 9′ 3″.
Weight: 37 tons 10 cwt.
Seats 2nd: 68.

W51080	W51083	W51086
W51081	W51084	W51087
W51082	W51085	W51088

W51089	W51096	W51103
W51090	W51097	W51104
W51091	W51098	W51105
W51092	W51099	W51106
W51093	W51100	W51107
W51094	W51101	
W51095	W51102	

Motor Brake Second ■
(TWIN UNITS)
For Details see SC50339-M50358

SC51108	SC51115	SC51122
SC51109	SC51116	SC51123
SC51110	SC51117	SC51124
SC51111	SC51118	SC51125
SC51112	SC51119	SC51126
SC51113	SC51120	SC51127
SC51114	SC51121	

Motor Brake Second ■
(THREE-CAR SUBURBAN)
For Details see W50050-91

W51128	W51133	W51138
W51129	W51134	W51139
W51130	W51135	W51140
W51131	W51136	
W51132	W51137	

Motor Second ■
(THREE-CAR SUBURBAN)
For Details see W50092-50133

W51141	W51146	W51151
W51142	W51147	W51152
W51143	W51148	W51153
W51144	W51149	
W51145	W51150	

Motor Brake Second ★
(E.R. THREE-CAR SUBURBAN)

Built by: **Derby Works, B.R.**
Engines: Two Rolls Royce horizontal type of 238 b.h.p.
Transmission: **Hydraulic.** Twin-disc torque converter.
Body: 64′ 0″ × 9′ 3″. Non-gangwayed, side doors to each seating bay.
Weight: 39 tons 10 cwt.
Seats 2nd: 65.

E51154	E51161	E51168
E51155	E51162	E51169
E51156	E51163	E51170
E51157	E51164	E51171
E51158	E51165	E51172
E51159	E51166	E51173
E51160	E51167	

Motor Brake Second ■
(TWIN UNITS)

Built by: **Meteropolitan Cammell.**
Engines: Two B.U.T. (A.E.C.) 6-cyl. horizontal type of 150 b.h.p.
Transmission: **Mechanical.** Cardan shaft and freewheel to four-speed epicyclic gearbox and further cardan shaft to final drive.
Body: 57′ 0″ × 9′ 3″.
Weight: 32 tons.
Seats 2nd: 52.

M51174	M51201	SC51228
M51175	M51202	SC51229
M51176	M51203	SC51230
M51177	E51204	SC51231
M51178	E51205	SC51232
M51179	E51206	SC51233
M51180	E51207	SC51234
M51181	E51208	SC51235
M51182	E51209	SC51236
M51183	E51210	SC51237
M51184	E51211	SC51238
M51185	E51212	SC51239
M51186	E51213	SC51240
M51187	E51214	SC51241
M51188	E51215	SC51242
M51189	E51216	SC51243
M51190	E51217	SC51244
M51191	E51218	SC51245
M51192	E51219	SC51246
M51193	E51220	SC51247
M51194	E51221	SC51248
M51195	E51222	SC51249
M51196	E51223	SC51250
M51197	SC51224	SC51251
M51198	SC51225	SC51252
M51199	SC51226	SC51253
M51200	SC51227	

Motor Brake Second ■
(TWIN UNITS)

Built by: **Cravens.**
Engines: Two B.U.T. (A.E.C.) 6-cyl. horizontal type of 150 b.h.p.
Transmission: **Mechanical.** Cardan shaft and freewheel to four-speed epicyclic gearbox and further cardan shaft to final drive.
Body: 57′ 6″ × 9′ 3″
Weight: 30 tons.
Seats 2nd: 52.

E51254	E51270	E51286
E51255	E51271	E51287
E51256	E51272	E51288
E51257	E51273	E51289
E51258	E51274	E51290
E51259	E51275	E51291
E51260	E51276	E51292
E51261	E51277	E51293
E51262	E51278	E51294
E51263	E51279	E51295
E51264	E51280	E51296
E51265	E51281	E51297
E51266	E51282	E51298
E51267	E51283	E51299
E51268	E51284	E51300
E51269	E51285	E51301

Motor Brake Second ■
(THREE-CAR SUBURBAN)

Built by: **Pressed Steel Co.**
Engines: Two B.U.T. 6-cyl. horizontal type of 150 b.h.p.
Transmission: **Mechanical.** Cardan shaft and freewheel to four-speed epicyclic gearbox and further cardan shaft to final drive.
Body: 64′ 0″ × 9′ 3″. Non-gangwayed, side doors to each seating bay.
Weight:
Seats 2nd:

W51332	W51335	W51338
W51333	W51336	W51339
W51334	W51337	W51340

Motor Brake Second ■
(THREE-CAR SUBURBAN)

Built by: **Pressed Steel Co.**
Engines: Two B.U.T. 6-cyl. horizontal type of 150 b.h.p.

Transmission: **Mechanical.** Cardan shaft and freewheel to four-speed epicyclic gearbox and further cardan shaft to final drive.
Body: 64′ 0″ × 9′ 3″. Non-gangwayed, side doors to each seating bay.
Weight:
Seats 2nd:

W51374	W51377	W51380
W51375	W51378	W51381
W51376	W51379	W51382

Motor Brake Second ■
(TWIN UNITS)

Built by: **Derby Works, B.R.**
Engines: Two B.U.T. (A.E.C.) 6-cyl. horizontal type of 150 b.h.p.
Transmission: **Mechanical.** Cardan shaft and freewheel to four-speed epicyclic gearbox and further cardan shaft to final drive.
Body: 57′ 6″ × 9′ 2″.
Weight:
Seats 2nd:

M51416	M51419	M51422
M51417	M51420	M51423
M51418	M51421	M51424

Motor Brake Second ■
(TWIN UNITS)

Built by: **Metropolitan Cammell.**
Engines: Two B.U.T. (A.E.C.) 6-cyl. horizontal type of 150 b.h.p.
Transmission: **Mechanical.** Cardan shaft and freewheel to four-speed epicyclic gearbox and further cardan shaft to final drive.
Body: 57′ 0″ × 9′ 3″.
Weight: 31 tons 10 cwt.
Seats 2nd: 52.

E51425	E51429	E51433
E51426	E51430	E51434
E51427	E51431	
E51428	E51432	

Motor Brake Second ■
THREE OR *FOUR-CAR UNITS)

Built by: **Metropolitan Cammell.**
Engines: Two B.U.T. (A.E.C.) 6-cyl. horizontal type of 150 b.h.p.
Transmission: **Mechanical** Cardan shaft and freewheel to four-speed epicyclic gearbox and further cardan shaft to final drive.
Body: 57′ 0″ × 9′ 3″.
Weight: 32 tons.
Seats 2nd: 52.

E51435*	SC51447	SC51459
E51436*	SC51448	SC51460
E51437*	SC51449	SC51461
E51438*	SC51450	SC51462
E51439*	SC51451	SC51463
E51440*	SC51452	SC51464
E51441*	SC51453	SC51465
E51442*	SC51454	SC51466
E51443*	SC51455	SC51467
E51444*	SC51456	SC51468
SC51445	SC51457	SC51469
SC51446	SC51458	SC51470

Motor Brake Second ■
(TWIN UNITS)

Built by: **Cravens.**
Engines: Two B.U.T. (A.E.C.) 6-cyl. horizontal type of 150 b.h.p.
Transmission: **Mechanical.** Cardan shaft and freewheel to four-speed epicyclic gearbox and further cardan shaft to final drive.
Body: 57′ 6″ × 9′ 3″.
Weight:
Seats 2nd:

E51471	SC51479	SC51487
E51472	SC51480	SC51488
SC51473	SC51481	SC51489
SC51474	SC51482	SC51490
SC51475	SC51483	SC51491
SC51476	SC51484	SC51492
SC51477	SC51485	SC51493
SC51478	SC51486	SC51494

Motor Composite (L) ■
(TWIN UNITS)

Built by: **Metropolitan Cammell.**
Engines: Two B.U.T. (A.E.C.) 6-cyl. horizontal type of 150 b.h.p.
Transmission: **Mechanical.** Cardan shaft and freewheel to four-speed epicyclic gearbox and further cardan shaft to final drive.
Body: 57′ 0″ × 9′ 3″.
Weight: 31 tons 10 cwt.
Seats 1st: 12.
2nd: 53.

E51495	E51499	E51503
E51496	E51500	E51504
E51497	E51501	
E51498	E51502	

Motor Composite (L) ■
(THREE OR *FOUR-CAR UNITS)

Built by: **Metropolitan Cammell.**
Engines: Two B.U.T. (A.E.C.) 6-cyl. horizontal type of 150 b.h.p.
Transmission: **Mechanical.** Cardan shaft and freewheel to four-speed epicyclic gearbox and further cardan shaft to final drive.
Body: 57′ 0″ × 9′ 3″.
Weight: 31 tons 10 cwt.
Seats 1st: 12.
2nd: 53.

E51505*	SC51517	SC51529
E51506*	SC51518	SC51530
E51507*	SC51519	SC51531
E51508*	SC51520	SC51532
E51509*	SC51521	SC51533
E51510*	SC51522	SC51534
E51511*	SC51523	SC51535
E51512*	SC51524	SC51536
E51513*	SC51525	SC51537
E51514*	SC51526	SC51538
SC51515	SC51527	SC51539
SC51516	SC51528	SC51540

Motor Brake Second ■
(THREE-CAR UNITS)

For Details see E51435-SC51470

E51541	E51544	E51547
E51542	E51545	
E51543	E51546	

Motor Brake Second ■
(TWIN UNITS)

Built by: **Metropolitan Cammell.**
Engines: Two B.U.T. (A.E.C.) 6-cyl. horizontal type of 150 b.h.p.
Transmission: **Mechanical.** Cardan shaft and freewheel to four-speed epicyclic gearbox and further cardan shaft to final drive.
Body: 57′ 0″ × 9′ 3″.
Weight: 31 tons 10 cwt.
Seats 2nd: 52.

M51548 M51549 M51550

Motor Composite (L) ■
(THREE-CAR UNITS)

For Details see E51505-SC51540

E51551	E51554	E51557
E51552	E51555	
E51553	E51556	

Motor Composite (L) ■
(TWIN UNITS)

Built by: **Metropolitan Cammell.**
Engines: Two B.U.T. (A.E.C.) 6-cyl. horizontal type of 150 b.h.p.
Transmission: **Mechanical.** Cardan shaft and freewheel to four-speed epicyclic gearbox and further cardan shaft to final drive.
Body: 57′ 0″ × 9′ 3″.
Weight: 31 tons 10 cwt.
Seats 1st: 12
2nd: 53

M51558 M51559 M51560

Motor Composite (L) ■
(TWIN UNITS)

Built by: **Derby Works, B.R.**
Engines: Two B.U.T. (A.E.C.) 6-cyl. horizontal type of 150 b.h.p.
Transmission: **Mechanical.** Cardan shaft and freewheel to four-speed epicyclic gearbox and further cardan shaft to final drive.
Body: 57′ 6″ × 9′ 2″.
Weight: 27 tons.
Seats 1st: 12.
2nd: 53.

E51561	E51565	E51569
E51562	E51566	E51570
E51563	E51567	E51571
E51564	E51568	E51572

Motor Brake Second ■
(FOUR-CAR SUBURBAN)

Built by: **Derby Works, B.R.**
Engines: Two Rolls Royce 8-cyl. horizontal type of 238 b.h.p.
Transmission: **Hydraulic.** Torque converter.
Body: 64′ 0″ × 9′ 3″.
Non-gangwayed, side doors to each seating bay.
Weight:
Seats 2nd: 76.

M51591	M51594	M51597
M51592	M51595	M51598
M51593	M51596	M51599

M51600	M51617	M51634
M51601	M51618	M51635
M51602	M51619	M51636
M51603	M51620	M51637
M51604	M51621	M51638
M51605	M51622	M51639
M51606	M51623	M51640
M51607	M51624	M51641
M51608	M51625	M51642
M51609	M51626	M51643
M51610	M51627	M51644
M51611	M51628	M51645
M51612	M51629	M51646
M51613	M51630	M51647
M51614	M51631	M51648
M51615	M51632	M51649
M51616	M51633	M51650

Motor Brake Second ■
(FOUR-CAR SUBURBAN)

Built by: **Derby Works, B.R.**
Engines: Two B.U.T. 6-cyl. horizontal type of 230 b.h.p.
Transmission: **Mechanical.** Cardan shaft and freewheel to four-speed epicyclic gearbox and further cardan shaft to final drive.
Body: 64′ 0″ × 9′ 3″. Non-gangwayed, side doors to each seating bay.
Weight:
Seats 2nd:

M51651	M51661	M51671
M51652	M51662	M51672
M51653	M51663	M51673
M51654	M51664	M51674
M51655	M51665	M51675
M51656	M51666	M51676
M51657	M51667	M51677
M51658	M51668	M51678
M51659	M51669	M51679
M51660	M51670	M51680

Motor Brake Second
(TWIN UNITS)

Built by: **Cravens.**
Engine: One Rolls Royce 8-cyl. horizontal type of 238 b.h.p.
Transmission:
Body: 57′ 6″ × 9′ 3″.
Weight:
Seats 2nd: 52.

M51681	M51690	M51699
M51682	M51691	M51700
M51683	M51692	M51701
M51684	M51693	M51702
M51685	M51694	M51703
M51686	M51695	M51704
M51687	M51696	M51705
M51688	M51697	
M51689	M51698	

Motor Composite (L)
(TWIN UNITS)

Built by : **Cravens.**
Engine: One Rolls Royce 8-cyl. horizontal type of 238 b.h.p.
Transmission:
Body: 57′ 6″ × 9′ 3″.
Weight:
Seats 1st: 12.
2nd: 51.

M51706	M51715	M51724
M51707	M51716	M51725
M51708	M51717	M51726
M51709	M51718	M51727
M51710	M51719	M51728
M51711	M51720	M51729
M51712	M51721	M51730
M51713	M51722	
M51714	M51723	

Motor Brake Second
(TWIN UNITS)

Built by: **Cravens.**
Engines: One Rolls Royce 8-cyl. horizontal type of 238 b.h p.
Transmission: **Hydraulic.** Torque converter.
Body: 57′ 6″ × 9′ 3″
Weight:
Seats 2nd: 52.

M51731	M51740	M51749
M51732	M51741	M51750
M51733	M51742	M51751
M51734	M51743	M51752
M51735	M51744	M51753
M51736	M51745	M51754
M51737	M51746	M51755
M51738	M51747	
M51739	M51748	

Motor Composite (L)
(TWIN UNITS)

Built by: **Cravens.**
Engine: One Rolls Royce 8-cyl. horizontal type of 238 b.h.p.
Transmission: **Hydraulic.** Torque converter.
Body: 57′ 6″ × 9′ 3″.
Weight:
Seats 1st: 12.
2nd: 51.

M51756	M51765	M51774
M51757	M51766	M51775
M51758	M51767	M51776
M51759	M51768	M51777
M51760	M51769	M51778
M51761	M51770	M51779
M51762	M51771	M51780
M51763	M51772	
M51764	M51773	

Motor Brake Composite ■
(THREE-CAR CROSS-COUNTRY)

Built by: **Swindon Works, B.R.**
Engines: Two B.U.T. 6-cyl. horizontal type of 150 b.h.p.
Transmission: **Mechanical.** Cardan shaft and freewheel to four-speed epicyclic gearbox and further cardan shaft to final drive.
Body: 64′ 6″ × 9′ 3″.
Weight: 36 tons 7 cwt.
Seats 1st: 18.
2nd: 16.

SC51781	SC51784	SC51787
SC51782	SC51785	
SC51783	SC51786	

Motor Second (L) ■
(THREE-CAR CROSS-COUNTRY)

Built by: **Swindon Works, B.R.**
Engines: Two B.U.T. 6-cyl. horizontal type of 150 b.h.p.
Transmission: **Mechanical.** Cardan shaft and freewheel to four-speed epicyclic gearbox and further cardan shaft to final drive.
Body: 64′ 6″ × 9′ 3″.
Weight: 36 tons 10 cwt.
Seats 2nd: 68.

SC51788	SC51791	SC51794
SC51789	SC51792	
SC51790	SC51793	

Motor Brake Second ■
(THREE-CAR UNITS)

Built by: **Metropolitan Cammell.**
Engines: Two B.U.T. (A.E.C.) 6-cyl. horizontal type of 150 b.h.p.
Transmission: **Mechanical.** Cardan shaft and freewheel to four-speed epicyclic gearbox and further cardan shaft to final drive.
Body: 57′ 0″ × 9′ 3″.
Weight: 32 tons.
Seats 2nd: 52.

SC51795	SC51798	SC51801
SC51796	SC51799	
SC51797	SC51800	

Motor Composite (L) ■
(THREE-CAR UNITS)

Built by: **Metropolitan Cammell.**
Engines: Two B.U.T. (A.E.C.) 6-cyl. horizontal type of 150 b.h.p.
Transmission: **Mechanical.** Cardan shaft and freewheel to four-speed epicyclic gearbox and further cardan shaft to final drive.
Body: 57′ 0″ × 9′ 3″.
Weight: 31 tons 10 cwt.
Seats 1st: 12.
2nd: 53.

SC51802	SC51805	SC51808
SC51803	SC51806	
SC51804	SC51807	

Motor Brake Second ■
(FOUR-CAR SUBURBAN)

Built by: **Derby Works, B.R.**
Engines: Two B.U.T. 6-cyl. horizontal type of 230 b.h.p.
Transmission: **Mechanical.** Cardan shaft and freewheel to four-speed epicyclic gearbox and further cardan shaft to final drive.
Body: 64′ 0″ × 9′ 3″.
Non-gangwayed, side doors to **each** seating bay.
Weight:
Seats 2nd:

M51849	M51857	M51865
M51850	M51858	M51866
M51851	M51859	M51867
M51852	M51860	M51868
M51853	M51861	M51869
M51854	M51862	M51870
M51855	M51863	M51871
M51856	M51864	M51872

M51873	M51883	M51893
M51874	M51884	M51894
M51875	M51885	M51895
M51876	M51886	M51896
M51877	M51887	M51897
M51878	M51888	M51898
M51879	M51889	M51899
M51880	M51890	M51900
M51881	M51891	
M51882	M51892	

Motor Brake Second ■
(TWIN UNITS)

Built by: **Derby Works, B.R.**
Engines: Two B.U.T. (A.E.C.) 6-cyl. horizontal type of 150 b.h.p.
Transmission: **Mechanical.** Cardan shaft and freewheel to four-speed epicyclic gearbox and further cardan shaft to final drive.
Body: 57′ 6″ × 9′ 2″.
Weight: 28 tons 10 cwt.
Seats 2nd: 52.

M51901	M51903	M51904
M51902		

Motor Brake Second ■
(SINGLE UNITS)

Built by: **Gloucester R.C. & W. Co.**
Engines: Two B.U.T. (A.E.C.) 6-cyl. horizontal type of 150 b.h.p.
Transmission: **Mechanical.** Cardan shaft and freewheel to four-speed epicyclic gearbox and further cardan shaft to final drive.
Body: 64′ 6″ × 9′ 3″.
Non-gangwayed, side doors to each seating bay.
Weight: 35 tons.
Seats 2nd: 65.

W55000	W55007	W55014
W55001	W55008	W55015
W55002	W55009	W55016
W55003	W55010	W55017
W55004	W55011	W55018
W55005	W55012	W55019
W55006	W55013	

Motor Parcels Van ■

Built by: **Gloucester R.C. & W. Co.**
Engines: Two B.U.T. (A.E.C.) 6-cyl. horizontal type of 230 b.h.p.
Transmission: **Mechanical.** Cardan shaft and freewheel to four-speed epicyclic gearbox and further cardan shaft to final drive.
Body: 64′ 6″ × 9′ 3″.
Non-gangwayed.
Weight: 40 tons.

M55987	M55988	M55990

Motor Parcels Van ■

Built by: **Gloucester R.C. & W. Co.**
Engines: Two B.U.T. (A.E.C.) 6-cyl. horizontal type of 230 b.h.p.
Transmission: **Mechanical.** Cardan shaft and freewheel to four-speed epicyclic gearbox and further cardan shaft to final drive.
Body: 64′ 6″ × 9′ 3″.
Weight: 41 tons.

W55991	W55993	W55995
W55992	W55994	

Motor Parcels Van ◆

Built by: **Cravens.**
Engines: Two B.U.T. (A.E.C.) 6-cyl. horizontal type of 150 b.h.p.
Transmission. **Mechanical.** Cardan shaft and freewheel to four-speed epicyclic gearbox and further cardan shaft to final drive.
Body: 57′ 6″ × 9′ 3″.
Non-gangwayed.
Weight: 30 tons.

M55997	M55998	M55999

Driving Trailer Composite (L) ■
(TWIN UNITS)

Built by: **Derby Works, B.R.**
Body: 64′ 6″ × 9′ 3″.
Weight: 29 tons 10 cwt.
Seats 1st: 12.
2nd: 62.

E56000	E56012	E56024
E56001	E56013	E56025
E56002	E56014	E56026
E56003	E56015	E56027
E56004	E56016	E56028
E56005	E56017	E56029
E56006	E56018	E56030
E56007	E56019	E56031
E56008	E56020	E56032
E56009	E56021	E56033
E56010	E56022	E56034
E56011	E56023	E56035

E56036	E56041	E56046
E56037	E56042	E56047
E56038	E56043	E56048
E56039	E56044	E56049
E56040	E56045	

Driving Trailer Composite (L) ■
(TWIN UNITS)

Built by: **Metropolitan Cammell.**
Body: 57′ 0″ × 9′ 3″.
Weight: 24 tons 4 cwt.
Seats 1st: 12.
2nd: 53.

E56050	E56065	E56080
E56051	E56066	E56081
E56052	E56067	E56082
E56053	E56068	E56083
E56054	E56069	E56084
E56055	E56070	E56085
E56056	E56071	E56086
E56057	E56072	E56087
E56058	E56073	E56088
E56059	E56074	E56089
E56060	E56075	M56090
E56061	E56076	M56091
E56062	E56077	M56092
E56063	E56078	M56093
E56064	E56079	

Driving Trailer Composite (L) ■
(TWIN UNITS)

Built by: **Gloucester R.C. & W. Co.**
Body: 57′ 6″ × 9′ 3″.
Weight: 24 tons 15 cwt.
Seats 1st: 12.
2nd: 54.

SC56094	SC56101	M56108
SC56095	SC56102	M56109
SC56096	SC56103	M56110
SC56097	SC56104	M56111
SC56098	M56105	M56112
SC56099	M56106	M56113
SC56100	M56107	

Driving Trailer Composite (L) ■
(TWIN UNITS)

Built by: **Cravens.**
Body: 57′ 6″ × 9′ 3″.
Weight: 23 tons.
Seats 1st: 12.
2nd: 51.
54*.

E56114	E56126	E56138
E56115	E56127	E56139
E56116	E56128	E56140
E56117	E56129	E56141
E56118	E56130	E56142
E56119	E56131	E56143
E56120	E56132	E56144
E56121	E56133	M56145*
E56122	E56134	M56146*
E56123	E56135	M56147*
E56124	E56136	M56148*
E56125	E56137	M56149*

Driving Trailer Composite (L) ■
(TWIN UNITS)

Built by: **Park Royal Vehicles.**
Body: 57′ 6″ × 9′ 3″.
Weight: 26 tons 7 cwt.
Seats 1st: 16.
2nd: 48.

M56150	M56157	M56164
M56151	M56158	M56165
M56152	M56159	M56166
M56153	M56160	M56167
M56154	M56161	M56168
M56155	M56162	M56169
M56156	M56163	

Driving Trailer Composite (L) ■
(TWIN UNITS)

Built by: **D. Wickham & Co. Ltd.**
Body: 57′ 0″ × 9′ 3″.
Weight: 20 tons 10 cwt.
Seats 1st: 16.
2nd: 50.

E56170	E56172	E56174
E56171	E56173	

Driving Trailer Composite (L) ■

(TWIN UNITS)

Built by: **Birmingham R.C. & W. Co.**
Body: 57′ 6″ × 9′ 3″.
Weight:
Seats 1st: 12.
2nd: 54.

M56175	M56179	M56183
M56176	M56180	M56184
M56177	M56181	
M56178	M56182	

Driving Trailer Composite (L) ■

(TWIN UNITS)

Built by: **Birmingham R.C. & W. Co.**
Body: 57′ 6″ × 9′ 3″.
Weight: 24 tons.
Seats 1st: 12.
2nd: 51.

E56185	E56187	E56189
E56186	E56188	

Driving Trailer Composite (L) ■

(TWIN UNITS)

Built by: **Derby Works, B.R.**
Body: 57′ 6′ × 9′ 2″.
Weight: 22 tons.
Seats 1st: 12.
2nd: 53.

E56190	E56199	E56208
E56191	E56200	E56209
E56192	E56201	E56210
E56193	E56202	M56211
E56194	E56203	M56212
E56195	E56204	M56213
E56196	E56205	M56214
E56197	E56206	M56215
E56198	E56207	

Driving Trailer Composite (L) ■

(TWIN UNITS)

Built by: **Metropolitan Cammell.**
Body: 57′ 0″ × 9′ 3″.
Weight: 25 tons.
Seats 1st: 12.
2nd: 45.

E56218	E56219	E56220

Driving Trailer Composite (L) ■

(TWIN UNITS)

Built by: **Derby Works, B.R.**
Body: 57′ 6″ × 9′ 2″.
Weight: 23 tons.
Seats 1st: 12.
2nd: 53.

M56221	M56241	M56261
M56222	M56242	M56262
M56223	M56243	M56263
M56224	M56244	M56264
M56225	M56245	M56265
M56226	M56246	M56266
M56227	M56247	M56267
M56228	M56248	M56268
M56229	M56249	M56269
M56230	M56250	M56270
M56231	M56251	M56271
M56232	M56252	M56272
M56233	M56253	M56273
M56234	M56254	M56274
M56235	M56255	M56275
M56236	M56256	M56276
M56237	M56257	M56277
M56238	M56258	M56278
M56239	M56259	M56279
M56240	M56260	

Driving Trailer Second ■

(For use with Single Unit cars Nos. W55000, etc.)

Built by: **Gloucester R.C. & W. Co.**
Body: 64′ 0″ × 9′ 3″.
Non-gangwayed, side doors to each seating bay.
Weight:
Seats 2nd: 95.

W56291	W56294	W56297
W56292	W56295	W56298
W56293	W56296	W56299

Driving Trailer Composite (L) ■

(TWIN UNITS)

For Details see SC56094-M56113

SC56300	SC56307	SC56314
SC56301	SC56308	SC56315
SC56302	SC56309	SC56316
SC56303	SC56310	SC56317
SC56304	SC56311	SC56318
SC56305	SC56312	SC56319
SC56306	SC56313	

Driving Trailer Composite (L) ■

(TWIN UNITS)

Built by: **Metropolitan Cammell.**
Body: 57′ 0″ × 9′ 3″.
Weight: 24 tons 4 cwt.
Seats 1st: 12. *2nd:* 53.

M56332	M56355	E56378
M56333	M56356	E56379
M56334	M56357	E56380
M56335	M56358	E56381
M56336	M56359	SC56382
M56337	M56360	SC56383
M56338	M56361	SC56384
M56339	E56362	SC56385
M56340	E56363	SC56386
M56341	E56364	SC56387
M56342	E56365	SC56388
M56343	E56366	SC56389
M56344	E56367	SC56390
M56345	E56368	SC56391
M56346	E56369	SC56392
M56347	E56370	SC56393
M56348	E56371	SC56394
M56349	E56372	SC56395
M56350	E56373	SC56396
M56351	E56374	SC56397
M56352	E56375	SC56398
M56353	E56376	SC56399
M56354	E56377	SC56400

SC56401	SC56405	SC56409
SC56402	SC56406	SC56410
SC56403	SC56407	SC56411
SC56404	SC56408	

Driving Trailer Composite (L) ■

Built by: **Cravens.**
Body: 57′ 6″ × 9′ 3″.
Weight: 24 tons.
Seats 1st: 12. *2nd:* 51.

E56412	E56436	E56460
E56413	E56437	E56461
E56414	E56438	SC56462
E56415	E56439	SC56463
E56416	E56440	SC56464
E56417	E56441	SC56465
E56418	E56442	SC56466
E56419	E56443	SC56467
E56420	E56444	SC56468
E56421	E56445	SC56469
E56422	E56446	SC56470
E56423	E56447	SC56471
E56424	E56448	SC56472
E56425	E56449	SC56473
E56426	E56450	SC56474
E56427	E56451	SC56475
E56428	E56452	SC56476
E56429	E56453	SC56477
E56430	E56454	SC56478
E56431	E56455	SC56479
E56432	E56456	SC56480
E56433	E56457	SC56481
E56434	E56458	SC56482
E56435	E56459	SC56483

Driving Trailer Composite (L) ■

(TWIN UNITS)

Built by: **Derby Works, B.R.**
Body: 57′ 6″ × 9′ 2″.
Weight: 23 tons.
Seats 1st: 12
2nd: 53.

M56484	M56486	M56487
M56485		

Trailer Composite ■

(THREE-CAR SUBURBAN)

Built by: **Derby Works, B.R.**
Body: 63′ 8¾″ × 9′ 3″. Non-gangwayed, side doors to each seating bay.
Weight: 28 tons 10 cwt.
Seats 1st: 28.
2nd: 74.

W59000	W59011	W59022
W59001	W59012	W59023
W59002	W59013	W59024
W59003	W59014	W59025
W59004	W59015	W59026
W59005	W59016	W59027
W59006	W59017	W59028
W59007	W59018	W59029
W59008	W59019	W59030
W59009	W59020	W59031
W59010	W59021	

Trailer Second ■

(THREE-CAR SUBURBAN)

Built by: **Derby Works, B.R.**
Body: 63′ 8¾″ × 9′ 3″. Non-gangwayed, side doors to each seating bay.
Weight: 28 tons 10 cwt.
Seats 2nd: 106.

W59032	W59036	W59040
W59033	W59037	W59041
W59034	W59038	
W59035	W59039	

Trailer Second (L) ■

(FOUR-CAR UNITS)

Built by: **Metropolitan Cammell.**
Body: 57′ 0″ × 9′ 3″.
Weight: 25 tons.
Seats 2nd: 61.

E59042	E59045	E59048
E59043	E59046	
E59044	E59047	

Trailer Brake Second (L) ■

(FOUR-CAR UNITS)

Built by: **Metropolitan Cammell.**
Body: 57 0″ × 9′ 3″.
Weight: 25 tons.
Seats 2nd: 45.

E59049	E59052	E59055
E59050	E59053	
E59051	E59054	

Trailer Second (L) ■

(FOUR-CAR UNITS)

Built by: **Metropolitan Cammell.**
Body: 57′ 0″ × 9′ 3″.
Weight: 25 tons.
Seats 2nd: 71.

E59060	E59065	E59070
E59061	E59066	E59071
E59062	E59067	E59072
E59063	E59068	
E59064	E59069	

Trailer Brake Second ■

(FOUR-CAR UNITS)

Built by: **Metropolitan Cammell.**
Body: 57′ 0″ × 9′ 3″.
Weight: 25 tons.
Seats 2nd: 53.

E59073	E59078	E59083
E59074	E59079	E59084
E59075	E59080	E59085
E59076	E59081	
E59077	E59082	

Trailer Second (L) ■

(FOUR-CAR UNITS)

For Details see E59042-8

E59086	E59088	E59090
E59087	E59089	E59091

Trailer Brake Second (L) ■

(FOUR-CAR UNITS)

For Details see E59049-55)

E59092	E59094	E59096
E59093	E59095	E59097

Trailer Second (L) ■

(THREE-CAR UNITS)

Built by: **Metropolitan Cammell.**
Body: 57′ 0″ × 9′ 3″.
Weight: 24 tons 10 cwt.
Seats 2nd: 71.

E59100	E59104	E59108
E59101	E59105	E59109
E59102	E59106	
E59103	E59107	

Trailer Brake Second (L) ■
(FOUR-CAR UNITS)

Built by: **Metropolitan Cammell.**
Body: 57′ 0″ × 9′ 3″.
Weight: 25 tons.
Seats 2nd: 53.

E59112 E59113

Trailer Composite (L) ■
(THREE-CAR UNITS)

Built by: **Metropolitan Cammell.**
Body: 57′ 0″ × 9′ 3″.
Weight: 25 tons.
Seats 1st: 12.
2nd: 53.

M59114	M59120	M59126
M59115	M59121	M59127
M59116	M59122	M59128
M59117	M59123	M59129
M59118	M59124	M59130
M59119	M59125	M59131

Trailer Composite (L) ■
(THREE-CAR UNITS)

Built by: **Birmingham R. C. & W. Co.**
Body: 57′ 0″ × 9′ 3″.
Weight: 24 tons.
Seats 2nd: 12.
2nd: 54.

M59132	M59151	M59170
M59133	M59152	M59171
M59134	M59153	M59172
M59135	M59154	M59173
M59136	M59155	M59174
M59137	M59156	M59175
M59138	M59157	M59176
M59139	M59158	M59177
M59140	M59159	M59178
M59141	M59160	M59179
M59142	M59161	M59180
M59143	M59162	M59181
M59144	M59163	M59182
M59145	M59164	M59183
M59146	M59165	M59184
M59147	M59166	M59185
M59148	M59167	M59186
M59149	M59168	M59187
M59150	M59169	

Trailer Second (L) ■
(FOUR-CAR UNITS)

Built by: **Birmingham R.C. & W. Co.**
Body: 57′ 0″ × 9′ 3″.
Weight: 24 tons.
Seats 2nd: 69.

E59188	E59195	E59202
E59189	E59196	E59203
E59190	E59197	E59204
E59191	E59198	E59205
E59192	E59199	E59206
E59193	E59200	E59207
E59194	E59201	E59208

Trailer Brake Second (L) ■
(FOUR-CAR UNITS)

Built by: **Birmingham R. C. & W. Co.**
Body: 57′ 0″ × 9′ 3″.
Weight: 25 tons.
Seats 2nd: 51.

E59209	E59216	E59223
E59210	E59217	E59224
E59211	E59218	E59225
E59212	E59219	E59226
E59213	E59220	E59227
E59214	E59221	E59228
E59215	E59222	E59229

Trailer Second (L) ■
(FOUR-CAR UNITS)

For Details see E59188-E59208

E59230	E59232	E59234
E59231	E59233	

Trailer Brake Second (L) ■
(FOUR-CAR UNITS)

For Details see E59209-29

E59240	E59242	E59244
E59241	E59243	

Trailer Brake Second (L) ■
(FOUR-CAR UNITS)

Built by: **Derby Works, B.R.**
Body: 57′ 6″ × 9′ 2″.
Weight: 22 tons 10 cwt
Seats 2nd: 50.

E59245	E59247	E59249
E59246	E59248	E59250

Trailer Buffet Second (L) ■
(THREE-CAR CROSS-COUNTRY)

Built by: **Swindon Works, B.R.**
Body: 64′ 6″ × 9′ 3″.
Open second with small buffet and counter at one end.
Weight: 30 tons 12 cwt.
Seats 2nd: 60.
Buffet: 4.

W59255	W59271	W59287
W59256	W59272	W59288
W59257	W59273	W59289
W59258	W59274	W59290
W59259	W59275	W59291
W59260	W59276	W59292
W59261	W59277	W59293
W59262	W59278	W59294
W59263	W59279	W59295
W59264	W59280	W59296
W59265	W59281	W59297
W59266	W59282	W59298
W59267	W59283	W59299
W59268	W59284	W59300
W59269	W59285	W59301
W59270	W59286	

Trailer Second (L) ■
(THREE-CAR UNITS)

Built by: **Metropolitan Cammell.**
Body: 57′ 0″ × 9′ 3″.
Weight: 24 tons 10 cwt.
Seats 2nd: 71.

E59302 E59303 E59304

Trailer Second (L) ■
(FOUR-CAR UNITS)

Built by: **Metropolitan Cammell.**
Body: 57′ 0″ × 9′ 3″
Weight: 25 tons.
Seats 2nd: 71.

E59305 E59306

Trailer Second (L) ■ or Trailer Composite (L)*
(THREE-CAR UNITS)

Built by **Cravens.**
Body: 57′ 6″ × 9′ 3″.
Weight: 23 tons.
Seats 2nd: 69.
1st: 12*.
2nd: 51*.

M59307*	M59314	M59321*
M59308	M59315	M59322*
M59309	M59316*	M59323
M59310*	M59317*	M59324
M59311	M59318*	M59325
M59312	M59319	
M59313	M59320*	

Trailer Composite ■
(THREE-CAR SUBURBAN)

For Details see W59000-31

W59326	W59343	W59360
W59327	W59344	W59361
W59328	W59345	W59362
W59329	W59346	W59363
W59330	W59347	W59364
W59331	W59348	W59365
W59332	W59349	W59366
W59333	W59350	W59367
W59334	W59351	W59368
W59335	W59352	W59369
W59336	W59353	W59370
W59337	W59354	W59371
W59338	W59355	W59372
W59339	W59356	W59373
W59340	W59357	W59374
W59341	W59358	W59375
W59342	W59359	W59376

Trailer Second (L) ■
(THREE* AND FOUR-CAR UNITS)

Built by: **Derby Works, B.R.**
Body: 57′ 6″ × 9′ 2″.
Weight: 22 tons. / 22 tons 10 cwt.*
Seats 2nd: 68.

E59380	E59384	E59388*
E59381	E59385	E59389*
E59382	E59386*	E59390*
E59383	E59387*	

Trailer First K ●

(INTER-CITY UNITS)

Built by: **Swindon Works, B.R.**
Body: 64′ 6″ × 9′ 3″.
Weight:
Seats 1st: 42.

SC59391	SC59395	SC59399
SC59392	SC59396	SC59400
SC59393	SC59397	
SC59394	SC59398	

Trailer Composite (L) ●

(INTER CITY UNITS)

Built by: **Swindon Works, B.R.**
Body: 64′ 6″ × 9′ 3″.
Weight:
Seats 1st: 18.
2nd: 32.

SC59402	SC59406	SC59410
SC59403	SC59407	SC59411
SC59404	SC59408	SC59412
SC59405	SC59409	

Trailer Buffet Second (L) ■

(THREE-CAR CROSS COUNTRY)

Built by: **Gloucester R.C. & W. Co.**
Body: 64′ 6″ × 9′ 3″.
Open second with small buffet and counter at one end.
Weight: 31 tons 8 cwt.
Seats 2nd: 60 or 64.

W59413	W59422	W59431
W59414	W59423	W59432
W59415	W59424	W59433
W59416	W59425	W59434
W59417	W59426	W59435
W59418	W59427	W59436
W59419	W59428	W59437
W59420	W59429	
W59421	W59430	

Trailer Composite ■

(THREE-CAR SUBURBAN)

For Details see W59000-31

W59438	W59442	W59446
W59439	W59443	W59447
W59440	W59444	W59448
W59441	W59445	

Trailer Second ★

(THREE-CAR SUBURBAN)

Built by: **Derby Works, B.R.**
Body: 63′ 8¾″ × 9′ 3″. Non-gangwayed, side doors to each seating bay.
Weight: 28 tons 10 cwt.
Seats 2nd: 106.

E59449	E59456	E59463
E59450	E59457	E59464
E59451	E59458	E59465
E59452	E59459	E59466
E59453	E59460	E59467
E59454	E59461	E59468
E59455	E59462	

Trailer Composite (L) ■

(THREE-CAR SUBURBAN)

Built by: **Pressed Steel Co.**
Body:
Weight:
Seats 1st:
2nd:

W59484	W59487	W59490
W59485	W59488	W59491
W59486	W59489	W59492

Trailer Composite (L) ■

(THREE OR *FOUR-CAR UNITS)

Built by: **Metropolitan Cammell.**
Body: 57′ 0″ × 9′ 3″.
Weight: 25 tons.
Seats 1st: 12.
2nd: 53.

E59523*	E59533*	SC59543
E59524*	E59534*	SC59544
E59525*	E59535*	SC59545
E59526*	E59536*	SC59546
E59527*	E59537*	SC59547
E59528*	E59538*	SC59548
E59529*	E59539*	SC59549
E59530*	E59540*	SC59550
E59531*	E59541*	SC59551
E59532*	E59542*	SC59552

SC59553	SC59559	SC59565
SC59554	SC59560	SC59566
SC59555	SC59561	SC59567
SC59556	SC59562	SC59568
SC59557	SC59563	
SC59558	SC59564	

Trailer Second (L) ■

(THREE-CAR UNITS)

Built by: **Metropolitan Cammell.**
Body: 57′ 0″ × 9′ 3″.
Weight: 24 tons 10 cwt.
Seats 2nd: 71.

E59569	E59571
E59570	E59572

Trailer Second (L) ■

(FOUR-CAR SUBURBAN)

Built by: **Derby Works, B.R.**
Body: 63′ 10″ × 9′ 3″. Non-gangwayed, side door to each seating bay. Intermediate lavatories on each side of central passageway.
Weight:
Seats 2nd: 90.

M59589	M59599	M59609
M59590	M59600	M59610
M59591	M59601	M59611
M59592	M59602	M59612
M59593	M59603	M59613
M59594	M59604	M59614
M59595	M59605	M59615
M59596	M59606	M59616
M59597	M59607	M59617
M59598	M59608	M59618

Trailer Second ■

(FOUR-CAR SUBURBAN)

Built by: **Derby Works, B.R.**
Body: 63′ 8¾″ × 9′ 3″. Non-gangwayed, side doors to each seating bay.
Weight: 28 tons 10 cwt.
Seats 2nd: 108.

M59619	M59634	M59649
M59620	M59635	M59650
M59621	M59636	M59651
M59622	M59637	M59652
M59623	M59638	M59653
M59624	M59639	M59654
M59625	M59640	M59655
M59626	M59641	M59656
M59627	M59642	M59657
M59628	M59643	M59658
M59629	M59644	M59659
M59630	M59645	M59660
M59631	M59646	M59661
M59632	M59647	M59662
M59633	M59648	M59663

Trailer Composite ■

(FOUR-CAR SUBURBAN)

Built by: **Derby Works, B.R.**
Body:
Weight:
Seats 1st:
2nd:

M59664	M59669	M59674
M59665	M59670	M59675
M59666	M59671	M59676
M59667	M59672	M59677
M59668	M59673	M59678

Trailer Buffet Second (L) ■

(THREE-CAR CROSS COUNTRY)

Built by: **Swindon Works, B.R.**
Body: 64′ 6″ × 9′ 3″.
Open second with small buffet and counter at one end.
Weight: 30 tons 12 cwt.
Seats 2nd: 60.
Buffet: 4.

SC59679	SC59682	SC59685
SC59680	SC59683	
SC59681	SC59684	

Trailer Composite (L) ■
(THREE-CAR UNITS)

Built by: **Metropolitan Cammell.**
Body: 57′ 0″ × 9′ 3″.
Weight: 25 tons.
Seats 1st: 12.
2nd: 53.

SC59686	SC59689	SC59692
SC59687	SC59690	
SC59688	SC59691	

Trailer Second ■
(FOUR-CAR SUBURBAN)

Built by: **Derby Works, B.R.**
Body:
Weight:
Seats 2nd:

M59713	M59715	M59717
M59714	M59716	M59718

Trailer Composite (L) ■
(FOUR-CAR SUBURBAN)

Built by: **Derby Works, B.R.**
Body:
Weight:
Seats 1st:
2nd:

M59719	M59721	M59723
M59720	M59722	M59724

Trailer Second Suburban ■
(FOUR-CAR SUBURBAN)

For Details see M59713-8

M59725	M59732	M59739
M59726	M59733	M59740
M59727	M59734	M59741
M59728	M59735	M59742
M59729	M59736	M59743
M59730	M59737	M59744
M59731	M59738	

Trailer Composite ■
(FOUR-CAR SUBURBAN)

For Details see M59719-24

M59745	M59752	M59759
M59746	M59753	M59760
M59747	M59754	M59761
M59748	M59755	M59762
M59749	M59756	M59763
M59750	M59757	M59764
M59751	M59758	

Motor Brake Second
(HASTINGS UNITS)

Unit numbers 1001–7*
1011–9†
1031–7‡

Built by: **Eastleigh Works, B.R.**
Engine: English Electric 4-cyl. type 4SRKT Mark II of 500 b.h.p. at 850 r.p.m.
Transmission: **Electric.** Two nose-suspended axle-hung traction motors.
Body: 58′ 0″ × 8′ 2½″*
64′ 6″ × 8′ 2½″†‡
Guard's, luggage compartment, engine room and full width driving compartment at outer end of car.
Weight: 54 tons 2 cwt.*
55 tons 0 cwt.†‡
Seats 2nd: 22*
30†‡

S60000*	S60016†	S60032‡
S60001*	S60017†	S60033‡
S60002*	S60018†	S60034‡
S60003*	S60019†	S60035‡
S60004*	S60020†	S60036‡
S60005*	S60021†	S60037‡
S60006*	S60022†	S60038‡
S60007*	S60023†	S60039‡
S60008*	S60024†	S60040‡
S60009*	S60025†	S60041‡
S60010*	S60026†	S60042‡
S60011*	S60027‡	S60043‡
S60012*	S60028†	S60044‡
S60013*	S60029†	S60045‡
S60014†	S60030†	
S60015†	S60031†	

Motor Brake Cars
PULLMAN UNITS

Built by: **Metropolitan Cammell.**
Engines: One North British/M.A.N. 12-cyl. pressure-charged V-type of 1,000 b.h.p.
Transmission: **Electric.**
Body:
Weight:
Seats:

M60090	M60092	W60094
M60091	M60093	W60095

Motor Brake Second
(TWIN* OR THREE-CAR UNITS)

Unit numbers 1101-18, 1119-22*, 1123-6

Built by: **Eastleigh Works, B.R.**
Engine: English Electric 4-cyl. type 4SRKT Mark II of 600 b.h.p. at 850 r.p.m.
Transmission. **Electric.** Two nose-suspended axle-hung traction motors.
Body: 64′ 0″ × 9′ 3″.
Guard's, luggage compartment, engine room and full width driving compartment at outer end of car. Non-gangwayed, side door to each seating bay.
Weight: 56 tons 0 cwt.
Seats 2nd: 52.

S60100	S60109	S60118*
S60101	S60110	S60119*
S60102	S60111	S60120*
S60103	S60112	S60121*
S60104	S60113	S60122
S60105	S60114	S60123
S60106	S60115	S60124
S60107	S60116	S60125
S60108	S60117	

Trailer Second (L)
(HASTINGS UNITS)

Unit numbers 1001-7*, 1011-9†, 1031-7‡

Built by: **Eastleigh Works, B.R.**
Body: 58′ 0″ × 8′ 2½″.*
64′ 6″ × 8′ 2½″.†‡
Weight: 29 tons.*
30 tons.†‡
Seats 2nd: 52.*
60.†‡

S60500*	S60521†	S60542†
S60501*	S60522†	S60543†
S60502*	S60523†	S60544†
S60503*	S60524†	S60545†
S60504*	S60525†	S60546†
S60505*	S60526†	S60547†
S60506*	S60527†	S60548‡
S60507*	S60528†	S60549‡
S60508*	S60529†	S60550‡
S60509*	S60530†	S60551‡
S60510*	S60531†	S60552‡
S60511*	S60532†	S60553‡
S60512*	S60533†	S60554‡
S60513*	S60534†	S60555‡
S60514*	S60535†	S60556‡
S60515*	S60536†	S60557‡
S60516*	S60537†	S60558‡
S60517*	S60538†	S60559‡
S60518*	S60539†	S60560‡
S60519*	S60540†	S60561‡
S60520*	S60541†	

First
PULLMAN UNITS

Built by: **Metropolitan Cammell.**
Transmission:
Body:
Weight:
Seats:

W60644 W60645

Trailer Second
(THREE-CAR UNITS)

Unit numbers 1101-18/23-26

Built by: **Eastleigh Works, B.R.**
Body: 63′ 6″ × 9′ 3″.
Weight:
Seats 2nd: 104.

S60650	S60658	S60666
S60651	S60659	S60667
S60652	S60660	S60668
S60653	S60661	S60669
S60654	S60662	S60670
S60655	S60663	S60671
S60656	S60664	
S60657	S60665	

Two Birmingham R.C. & W. three-car units on a Manchester-York Excursion [*K. Field*

Metropolitan-Cammell three-car unit [*P. J. Sharpe*

Gloucester R.C. & W. motor brake second No. M50350 [*J. B. Bucknall*

Gloucester R.C. & W. non-gangwayed motor parcels van No. M55989 *[P. J. Sharpe*

Gloucester R.C. & W. gangwayed motor parcels van No. W55992 *[P. J. Sharpe*

Cravens motor parcels van No. M55998 *[M. Mensing*

Wickham four-wheel railbus No. SC79968 [*R. Furness*

A.C. Cars Ltd. four-wheel railbus No. 79975 [*A. Swain*

Ex-G.W.R: A.E.C. diesel railcar No. W21W [*K. L. Cook*

British Thompson-Houston Type A 25kV a.c. Bo-Bo electric locomotive No. E3001 [*A.E.I.*

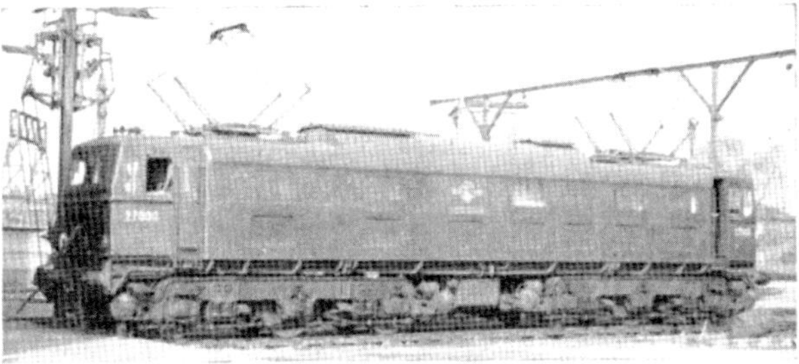

Class EM2 Co-Co No. 27000 *Electra* [*R. A. Panting*

Class EM1 Bo-Bo No. 26002 [*A. Swain*

Motor brake second of Fenchurch Street–Shoeburyness four-car set [T. K. Widd

Motor brake second of Glasgow Suburban three-car set. [T. K. Widd

Trailer brake second of Liverpool Street–Shenfield three-car set. [G. M. Kichenside

Motor brake second No. M28511M of original Manchester–Bury stock [*R. A. Panting*

Driving trailer second of unit No. 01s of Liverpool Street-Southend four-car set. [*P. J. Sharpe*

S.R. 2-NOP unit No. 5658 (new all-steel body on original 2-NOL underframe) [*J. C. Beckett*

2.500 h.p. Bo-Bo electric locomotive No. E5002 [J. H. Ashton

B.R. standard 4-CEP unit No. 7119 arriving at Dover Priory [A. A. Sellman

4-SUB unit No. 4626 [P. J. Sharpe

Trailer First (K)
(HASTINGS UNITS)

Unit numbers 1001-7*
10011-9†
1031-7‡

Built by: **Eastleigh Works, B.R**
Body: 58′ 0″ × 8′ 2½″.*
64′ 6″ × 8′ 2½″.†‡
Side corridor with seven* (eight†‡) first class compartments with side door to each compartment.
Weight: 30 tons.*
31 tons.†‡
Seats 1st: 42.*
48.†‡

S60700*	S60708†	S60716‡
S60701*	S60709†	S60717‡
S60702*	S60710†	S60718‡
S60703*	S60711†	S60719‡
S60704*	S60712†	S60720‡
S60705*	S60713†	S60721‡
S60706*	S60714†	S60722‡
S60707†	S60715†	

First
PULLMAN UNITS

Built by: **Metropolitan Cammell.**
Transmission:
Body:
Weight:
Seats 1st:

M60730	M60732	W60734
M60731	M60733	W60735

First
PULLMAN UNITS

Built by: **Metropolitan Cammell.**
Transmission:
Body:
Weight:
Seats 1st:

M60740	M60742	W60744
M60741	M60743	W60745

Trailer Buffet
(HASTINGS UNITS)

Unit numbers 1031-7
Built by: **Eastleigh Works, B.R**
Body: 64′ 6″ × 8′ 2½″.
Buffet with kitchen and bar; self-contained seating saloon.
Weight: 35 tons.
Seats: 21.

S60750	S60753	S60756
S60751	S60754	
S60752	S60755	

Driving Trailer Composite (L)
(TWIN* OR THREE-CAR UNITS)

Unit numbers 1101–18
1119–22*
1123–6

Built by: **Eastleigh Works, B.R.**
Body: 64′ 0″ × 9′ 3″.
Non-gangwayed, side door to each seating bay or compartment. 5-bay 2nd saloon and 2 1st compartments with intermediate lavatories, also a 2nd class compartment next to driving compartment.
Weight: 32 tons 0 cwt.
Seats 1st: 13.
2nd: 62.

S60800	S60809	S60818*
S60801	S60810	S60819
S60802	S60811	S60820*
S60803	S60812	S60821*
S60804	S60813	S60822
S60805	S60814	S60823
S60806	S60815	S60824
S60807	S60816	S60825
S60808	S60817	

Motor Brake Second ▲
(TWIN UNITS)

Built by: **Derby Works, B.R.**
Engines: Two B.U.T. (Leyland) 6-cyl. horizontal type of 125 b.h.p.
Transmission: **Hydro-Mechanical.** Lysholm Smith (Leyland) torque converter to final drive.
Body: 57′ 6″ × 9′ 2″.
Weight: 26 tons.
Seats 2nd: 61.

E79000	E79003	E79006
E79001	E79004	E79007
E79002	E79005	

Motor Brake Second ◆
(TWIN UNITS)

Built by: **Derby Works, B.R.**
Engines: Two B.U.T. (A.E.C.) 6-cyl. horizontal type of 150 b.h.p.
Transmission: **Mechanical.** Cardan shaft and freewheel to four-speed epicyclic gearbox and further cardan shaft to final drive.
Body: 57′ 6″ × 9′ 2″.
Weight: 27 tons.
Seats 1st: 61.
56*.

M79008	E79021*	E79034*
M79009	E79022*	E79035*
M79010	E79023*	E79036*
M79011	E79024*	E79037*
M79012	E79025*	E79038*
M79013	E79026*	E79039*
M79014	E79027*	E79040*
M79015	E79028*	E79041*
M79016	E79029*	E79042*
M79017	E79030*	E79043*
M79018	E79031*	E79044*
M79019	E79032*	E79045*
M79020	E79033*	E79046*

Motor Brake Second ◆
(TWIN UNITS)

Built by: **Metropolitan Cammell.**
Engines: Two B.U.T. (A.E.C.) 6-cyl. horizontal type of 150 b.h.p.
Transmission: **Mechanical.** Cardan shaft and freewheel to four-speed epicyclic gearbox and further cardan shaft to final drive.
Body: 57′ 0″ × 9′ 3″.
Weight: 26 tons 10 cwt.
Seats 2nd: 57.
53*.

E79047	E79054	E79061
E79048	E79055	E79062
E79049	E79056	E79063
E79050	E79057	E79064
E79051	E79058	E79065
E79052	E79059	E79066
E79053	E79060	E79067

E79068	E79073	M79078*
E79069	E79074	M79079*
E79070	E79075	M79080*
E79071	M79076*	M79081*
E79072	M79077*	M79082*

Motor Brake Second (L) ●
(INTER-CITY UNITS)

Built by: **Swindon Works, B.R.**
Engines: Two B.U.T. (A.E.C.) 6-cyl. horizontal type of 150 b.h.p.
Transmission: **Mechanical.** Cardan shaft and freewheel to four-speed epicyclic gearbox and further cardan shaft to final drive.
Body: 64′ 6″ × 9′ 3″.
Guard's and luggage compartment at outer end. Two types of car; "leading"* with full width driving compartment, gangwayed at inner end only; "intermediate"† with side driving compartment gangwayed at both ends.
Weight: 38 tons.
Seats 2nd: 52.

W79083†	W79093*	SC79103*
W79084†	W79094*	SC79104*
W79085†	SC79095†	SC79105*
W79086†	SC79096*	SC79106*
W79087†	SC79097*	SC79107*
W79088†	SC79098*	SC79108*
W79089†	SC79099*	SC79109*
W79090†	SC79100*	SC79110*
W79091*	SC79101*	SC79111*
W79092*	SC79102*	

Motor Brake Second ◆
(TWIN UNITS)

Built by: **Derby Works, B.R.**
Engines: Two B.U.T. 6-cyl. horizontal type of 150 b.h.p.
Transmission: **Mechanical.** Cardan shaft and freewheel to four-speed epicyclic gearbox and further cardan shaft to final drive.
Body: 57′ 6″ × 9′ 2″.
Weight: 27 tons.
Seats 2nd: 52.

M79118	M79129	M79140
M79119	M79130	M79141
M79120	M79131	M79142
M79121	M79132	M79143
M79122	M79133	M79144
M79123	M79134	M79145
M79124	M79135*	M79146
M79125	M79136	M79147
M79126	M79137	M79148
M79127	M79138	M79149
M79128	M79139	

**Fitted with Self Changing Gears Ltd. automatic four-speed gearbox.*

Motor Second
(FOUR-CAR UNITS)

Built by: **Derby Works, B.R.**
Engines: Two B.U.T. (A.E.C.) 6-cyl. horizontal type of 150 b.h.p.
Transmission: **Mechanical.** Cardan shaft and freewheel to four-speed epicyclic gearbox and further cardan shaft to final drive.
Body: 57′ 6″ × 9′ 2″.
Weight: 26 tons.
Seats 2nd: 64.

E79150	E79152	E79154
E79151	E79153	

Motor Second (L) ●
(INTER-CITY UNITS)

Built by: **Swindon Works, B.R.**
Engines: Two B.U.T. (A.E.C.) 6-cyl. horizontal type of 150 b.h.p.
Transmission: **Mechanical.** Cardan shaft and freewheel to four-speed epicyclic gearbox and further cardan shaft to final drive.
Body: 64′ 6″ × 9′ 3″.
Gangwayed both ends. Side driving compartment at one end.
Weight: 39 tons 3 cwt.
Seats 2nd: 64.

SC79155	SC79160	SC79165
SC79156	SC79161	SC79166
SC79157	SC79162	SC79167
SC79158	SC79163	SC79168
SC79159	SC79164	

Motor Brake Second ◆
(TWIN UNITS)

For Details see M79118-49

M79169	M79174	M79179
M79170	M79175	M79180
M79171	M79176	M79181
M79172	M79177	
M79173	M79178	

Motor Brake Second ◆
(TWIN UNITS)

For Details see M79008-46

M79184	M79186	M79188
M79185	M79187	

Motor Composite (L) ◆
(TWIN UNITS)

Built by: **Derby Works, B.R.**
Engines: Two B.U.T. (A.E.C.) 6-cyl. horizontal type of 150 b.h.p.
Transmission: **Mechanical.** Cardan shaft and freewheel to four-speed epicyclic gearbox and further cardan shaft to final drive.
Body: 57′ 6″ × 9′ 2″.
Weight: 27 tons.
Seats 1st: 12.
2nd: 53.

M79189	M79191	M79193
M79190	M79192	

Driving Trailer Composite (L) ◆
(TWIN UNITS)

Built by: **Derby Works, B.R.**
Body: 57′ 6″ × 9′ 2″.
Weight: 20 tons.
Seats 1st: 16.
2nd: 53.

E79250	E79255	E79260
E79251	E79256	E79261
E79252	E79257	E79262
E79253	E79258	
E79254	E79259	

Driving Trailer Second (L) ◆
(TWIN UNITS)

Built by: **Metropolitan Cammell.**
Body: 57″ 0′ × 9′ 3″.
Weight: 25 tons.
Seats 2nd: 71.

E79263	E79273	E79283
E79264	E79274	E79284
E79265	E79275	E79285
E79266	E79276	E79286
E79267	E79277	E79287
E79268	E79278	E79288
E79269	E79279	E79289
E79270	E79280	E79290
E79271	E79281	E79291
E79272	E79282	

Trailer Brake Second (L) ◆
(FOUR-CAR UNITS)

Built by: **Derby Works, B.R.**
Body: 57′ 6″ × 9′ 2″.
Weight: 20 tons 10 cwt.
Seats 2nd: 45.

E79325	E79327	E79329
E79326	E79328	

Trailer Second (L) ◆
(FOUR-CAR UNITS)

Built by: **Derby Works, B.R.**
Body: 57′ 6″ × 9′ 2″.
Weight: 20 tons 10 cwt.
Seats 2nd: 61.

E79400	E79402	E79404
E79401	E79403	

Trailer Buffet First (K) ●
(INTER-CITY UNITS)

Built by: **Swindon Works, B.R.**
Body: 64′ 6″ × 9′ 3″.
Side corridor with three first class compartments. Buffet with kitchen, bar and saloon.
Weight: 34 tons.
Seats 1st: 18.
Buffet: 12.

W79440	SC79443	SC79446
W79441	SC79444	SC79447
SC79442	SC79445	

Trailer First (K) ●
(INTER-CITY UNITS)

Built by: **Swindon Works, B.R.**
Body: 64′ 6″ × 9′ 3″.
Side corridor with seven first class compartments and end doors.
Weight: 33 tons 9 cwt.
Seats 1st: 42.

W79470	SC79475	SC79480
W79471	SC79476	SC79481
W79472	SC79477	SC79482
W79473	SC79478	
SC79474	SC79479	

Motor Composite (L) ▲
(TWIN UNITS)

Built by: **Derby Works, B.R.**
Engines: Two B.U.T. (Leyland) 6-cyl. horizontal type of 125 b.h.p.
Transmission: **Hydro-Mechanical.** Lysholm Smith (Leyland) torque converter to final drive.
Body: 57′ 6″ × 9′ 2″.
Weight:
Seats 1st: 16.
2nd: 53.

E79500	E79503	E79506
E79501	E79504	E79507
E79502	E79505	

Motor Composite ◆
(FOUR-CAR UNITS)

Built by: **Derby Works, B.R.**
Engines: Two B.U.T. (A.E.C.) 6-cyl. horizontal type of 150 b.h.p.
Transmission: **Mechanical.** Cardan shaft and freewheel to four-speed epicyclic gearbox and further cardan shaft to final drive.
Body: 57′ 6″ × 9′ 2″.
Weight: 26 tons 10 cwt.
Seats 1st: 20.
2nd: 36.

E79508	E79510	E79512
E79509	E79511	

Driving Trailer Composite (L) ◆
(TWIN UNITS)

Built by: **Derby Works, B.R.**
Body: 57′ 6″ × 9′ 2″.
Weight: 21 tons.
Seats 1st: 9.
16*.
2nd: 53.

M79600	M79609	E79618*
M79601	M79610	E79619*
M79602	M79611	E79620*
M79603	M79612	E79621*
M79604	E79613*	E79622*
M79605	E79614*	E79623*
M79606	E79615*	E79624*
M79607	E79616*	E79625*
M79608	E79617*	

Driving Trailer Composite (L) ◆
(TWIN UNITS)

Built by: **Metropolitan Cammell.**
Body: 57′ 0″ × 9′ 3″.
Weight: 25 tons.
Seats 1st: 12.
2nd: 53.

M79626	M79629	M79632
M79627	M79630	
M79628	M79631	

Driving Trailer Composite (L) ◆
(TWIN UNITS)

For Details see M79600-E79625

M79639	M79646	M79653
M79640	M79647	M79654
M79641	M79648	M79655
M79642	M79649†	M79656
M79643	M79650	M79657
M79644	M79651	E79658*
M79645	M79652	E79659*

†This vehicle has been fitted internally for use as an inspection saloon including a pantry, and is not in public service.

E79660*	M79669	M79677
E79661*	M79670	M79678
M79662	M79671	M79679
M79663	M79672	M79680
M79664	M79673	M79681
M79665	M79674	M79682
M79666	M79675	M79683
M79667	M79676	M79684
M79668		

NOTE

For reasons of clarity the 4-wheel units below are not in strict numerical order.

Some of these vehicles are now used by the L.M. Engineers Dept. and are not in public service

Motor Second
(FOUR-WHEEL UNITS)

Built by: **British United Traction Co.**
Engine: B.U.T. (A.E.C.) 6-cyl. horizontal type of 125 b.h.p.
Transmission: **Mechanical.** Cardan shaft and freewheel to four-speed epicyclic gearbox and further cardan shaft to final drive.
Body: 37′ 6″ × 9′ 0″ Non-gangwayed. Driving compartment at each end.
Weight: 15 tons 0 cwt.
Seats 2nd: 34.

M79740 M79745 M79748

Motor Brake Second
(FOUR-WHEEL UNITS)

Built by: **British United Traction Co.**
Engine: B.U.T. (A.E.C.) 6-cyl. horizontal type of 125 b.h.p.
Transmission: **Mechanical.** Cardan shaft and freewheel to four-speed epicyclic gearbox and further cardan shaft to final drive.
Body: 37′ 6″ × 9′ 0″. Non-gangwayed. Driving compartment at each end.
Weight: 15 tons 0 cwt.
Seats 2nd: 28.

M79742	M79744	M79750
M79743		

Trailer Second
(FOUR-WHEEL UNITS)

Built by: **British United Traction Co.**
Body: 37′ 6″ × 9′ 0″. Non-gangwayed.
Weight: 10 tons 10 cwt.
Seats 2nd: 48.

M79741 M79747 M79749
M79746

Motor Brake Second
(SINGLE UNITS)

Built by: **Derby Works, B.R.**
Engine: Two B.U.T. (A.E.C.) 6-cyl. horizontal type of 150 b.h.p.
Transmission: **Mechanical.** Cardan shaft and freewheel to four-speed epicyclic gearbox and further cardan shaft to final drive.
Body: 57′ 6″ × 9′ 2″.
Driving compartment at each end. Non-gangwayed.
Weight: 27 tons.
Seats 2nd: 52.

M79900 M79901

Four-Wheel Railbus

Built by: **Bristol/E.C.W.**
Engine: Gardner 6.H.L.W. 6-cyl. type of 112 b.h.p. at 1,700 r.p.m.
Transmission: **Mechanical.** Cardan shaft and freewheel to Self-Changing Gears Ltd. five-speed epicyclic gearbox and further cardan shaft to final drive.
Body: 42′ 4″ × 9′ 3″ Non-gangwayed.
Weight: 13 tons 10 cwt.
Seats 2nd: 56.

SC79958 SC79959

Four-Wheel Railbus

Built by: **Waggon und Maschinenbau.**
Engine: Buessing 150 b.h.p. at 1,900 r.p.m.
Transmission: **Mechanical.** Cardan shaft to ZF electro-magnetic six-speed gearbox.
Body: 41′ 10″ × 8′ 8$\frac{5}{16}$″. Non-gangwayed.
Weight: 15 tons.
Seats 2nd: 56.

E79960 | E79962 | E79964
E79661 | E79963 |

Four-Wheel Railbus

Built by: **D. Wickham & Co.**
Engine: Meadows 6-cyl. type 6HDT500 of 105 b.h.p. at 1,800 r.p.m.
Transmission: **Mechanical.** Freeborn-Wickham disc and ring coupling driving Self-Changing Gears Ltd. four-speed epicyclic gearbox and cardan shaft to final drive.
Body: 38′ 0″ × 9′ 0″. Non-gangwayed.
Weight: 11 tons 5 cwt.
Seats 2nd: 44.

SC79965 | SC79967 | SC79969
SC79966 | SC79968 |

Four-Wheel Railbus

Built by: **Park Royal Vehicles.**
Engine: B.U.T. (A.E.C.) 6-cyl. horizontal type of 150 b.h.p.
Transmission: **Mechanical.** Cardan shaft and freewheel to Self-Changing Gears Ltd. four-speed epicyclic gearbox and further cardan shaft to final drive.
Body: 42′ 0″ × 9′ 3″. Non-gangwayed.
Weight: 15 tons.
Seats 2nd: 50.

SC79970 | M79972 | SC79974
M79971 | M79973 |

Four-Wheel Railbus

Built by: **A.C. Cars Ltd.**
Engine: B.U.T. (A.E.C.) 6-cyl. horizontal type of 150 b.h.p.
Transmission: **Mechanical.** Cardan shaft and freewheel to four-speed epicyclic gearbox and further cardan shaft to final drive.
Body: 36′ 0″ × 8′ 11″.
Weight: 11 tons.
Seats 2nd: 46.

W79975 | W79977 | W79979
W79976 | W79978 |

For "ex-G.W.R. diesel railcars and Twin-unit Battery-electric railcars see page 256.

ELECTRIC LOCOMOTIVES

British Railways are adopting a new numbering system for all new main-line electric locomotives, using the prefix letter "E" in a series ranging from E1000 for a.c. units, and from E5000 for d.c. units. The first figure of the a.c. series will also give an indication of the locomotive horse-power.

A1A-A1A

Introduced: 1958.
Locomotive manufacturer: Metropolitan-Vickers.
Total h.p.: 2,500.
Equipment: Four 625 h.p. Metropolitan-Vickers nose-suspended traction motors.
Weight: 109 tons.
Driving Wheels: 3′ 8″.
Maximum tractive effort: 40,000 lb.
System: 25 kV. a.c. Overhead.
(Rebuilt from former Gas Turbine Loco. No. 18100.)

E2001 (formerly E1000)

Bo-Bo "A"

Introduced: 1959.
Locomotive manufacturer: British Thomson-Houston.
Total h.p.: 3,300.
Equipment: Four B.T.H. spring-borne d.c. traction motors of 847 h.p. (continuous) driving through Alsthom quill drive.
Weight: 79 tons 12 cwt.
Driving Wheels: 4′ 0″.
Maximum tractive effort: 48,000 lb.
System: 25 kV. a.c. overhead.

E3001	E3007	E3013	E3019
E3002	E3008	E3014	E3020
E3003	E3009	E3015	E3021
E3004	E3010	E3016	E3022
E3005	E3011	E3017	E3023
E3006	E3012	E3018	

Bo-Bo "A"

To be introduced:
Locomotive manufacturer: English Electric.
Total h.p.: 3,300.
Equipment:
Weight:
Driving Wheels:
Maximum tractive effort:
System: 25 kV. a.c. overhead.

E3024	E3027	E3030	E3033
E3025	E3028	E3031	E3034
E3026	E3029	E3032	E3035

Bo-Bo "A"

Introduced: 1960.
Locomotive manufacturer: General Electric.
Total h.p.: 3,300.
Equipment:
Weight:
Driving Wheels:
Maximum tractive effort:
System: 25 kV. a.c. overhead.

E3036	E3039	E3042	E3044
E3037	E3040	E3043	E3045
E3038	E3041		

Bo-Bo "A"

To be introduced:
Locomotive manufacturer: Metropolitan-Vickers.
Total h.p.: 3,300.
Equipment:
Weight:
Driving Wheels:
Maximum tractive effort:
System: 25 kV. a.c. overhead.

E3046	E3049	E3052	E3054
E3047	E3050	E3053	E3055
E3048	E3051		

Bo-Bo "A"

To be introduced:
Locomotive manufacturer: B.R., Doncaster.
Total h.p.: 3,300.
Equipment: B.T.H.
Weight:
Driving Wheels:
Maximum tractive effort:
System: 25 kV. a.c. overhead.

E3056	E3061	E3066	E3071
E3057	E3062	E3067	E3072
E3058	E3063	E3068	E3073
E3059	E3064	E3069	E3074
E3060	E3065	E3070	E3075

Bo-Bo "A"

To be introduced:
Locomotive manufacturer: B.R., Crewe.
Total h.p.: 3,300.
Equipment: B.T.H.
Weight:
Driving Wheels:
Maximum tractive effort:
System: 25 kV. a.c. overhead.

E3076	E3081	E3086	E3091
E3077	E3082	E3087	E3092
E3078	E3083	E3088	E3093
E3079	E3084	E3089	E3094
E3080	E3085	E3090	E3095

Bo-Bo "B"

To be introduced:
Locomotive manufacturer: British Thomson-Houston.
Total h.p.: 3,300.
Equipment:
Weight:
Driving Wheels:
Maximum tractive effort:
System: 25 kV. a.c. overhead.

E3301 E3302

Bo-Bo "B"

To be introduced:
Locomotive manufacturer: English Electric.
Total h.p.: 3,300
Equipment:
Weight:
Driving Wheels:
Maximum tractive effort:
System: 25 kV. a.c. overhead.

E3303 E3304 E3305

Bo-Bo

Introduced: 1958.
Locomotive manufacturer: B.R., Doncaster.
Total h.p.: 2,552.
Equipment: Motor generator booster set and four 638 h.p. English Electric spring-borne traction motors driving through S.L.M. flexible drive.
Weight: 77 tons.
Driving Wheels: 4′ 0″.
Maximum tractive effort: 43,000 lb.
System: 750 V. d.c. 3rd rail and overhead.

E5000	E5006	E5012	E5018
E5001	E5007	E5013	E5019
E5002	E5008	E5014	E5020
E5003	E5009	E5015	E5021
E5004	E5010	E5016	E5022
E5005	E5011	E5017	E5023

Co-Co Class CC

Introduced: 1941. / 1948*.
Locomotive manufacturer: B.R., Ashford.
Total h.p.: 1,470.
Equipment: Motor generator booster set and six 245 h.p. English Electric nose-suspended traction motors.
Weight: 99 tons 14 cwt. / 104 tons 14 cwt.*
Driving Wheels: 3′ 6″.
Maximum tractive effort: 40,000 lb. / 45,000 lb.*
System: 750 V. d.c. 3rd rail and overhead.

20001 20002 20003*

Bo-Bo Class EM1

Introduced: 1941.* / 1950.
Locomotive manufacturer: B.R., Doncaster.
Total h.p.: 1,868.
Equipment: Four 467 h.p. Metropolitan-Vickers nose-suspended traction motors.
Weight: 87 tons 18 cwt.
Driving Wheels: 4′ 2″.
Maximum tractive effort: 45,000 lb.
System: 1,500 V. d.c. overhead.

26000* Tommy

26001	26013	26024	26035
26002	26014	26025	26036
26003	26015	26026	26037
26004	26016	26027	26038
26005	26017	26028	26039
26006	26018	26029	26040
26007	26019	26030	26041
26008	26020	26031	26042
26009	26021	26032	26043
26010	26022	26033	26044
26011	26023	26034	26045
26012			

26046 Archimedes
26047 Diomedes
26048 Hector
26049 Jason
26050 Stentor
26051 Mentor
26052 Nestor
26053 Perseus
26054 Pluto
26055 Prometheus
26056 Triton
26057 Ulysses

Bo-Bo Class ES1

Introduced: 1902.
Locomotive manufacturer: Brush Traction.
Total h.p.:
Equipment: Four B.T.H. nose-suspended traction motors.
Weight: 46 tons.
Driving Wheels:
Maximum tractive effort: 25,000 lb.
System: 630 V. d.c. overhead and 3rd rail.

26500 26501

Co-Co Class EM2

Introduced: 1954.
Locomotive manufacturer: B.R., Gorton.
Total h.p.: 2,490.
Equipment: Six 415 h.p. Metropolitan-Vickers nose-suspended traction motors.
Weight: 102 tons.
Driving Wheels: 4′ 2″.
Maximum tractive effort: 45,000 lb.
System: 1,500 V.d.c. overhead.

27000 Electra
27001 Ariadne
27002 Aurora
27003 Diana
27004 Juno
27005 Minerva
27006 Pandora

Service Locomotives

Eastern Region

Bo-Bo Class EB1

Introduced: 1946.
Locomotive manufacturer:
Total h.p.:
Equipment:
Weight: 74 tons 8 cwt.
Driving Wheels: 4′ 0″.
Maximum tractive effort: 37,600 lb.
System: 1,500 V. d.c. overhead.

100 (formerly 26510)

Southern Region

DS 74 DS 75

ELECTRIC MULTIPLE UNITS

The dimensions shown are length and width over body and width overall.

The letter "L" in the headings indicates an open vehicle fitted with toilet facilities; "K" indicates a side corridor vehicle with toilet.

London Midland Region

SYSTEM: 630 VOLTS D.C.
3rd & 4th RAIL

LONDON DISTRICT THREE-CAR OPEN SETS

Motor Open Brake Second

Body: 57′ 0″ × 8′ 11″ & 9′ 6″.
Weight: 54 tons 15 cwt.
Seats 2nd: 48.
Equipment: Four 260 h.p. Oerlikon Traction Motors.

M28249M M28269M

Trailer Open Second

Body: 57′ 0″ × 8′ 11″ & 9′ 6″.
Weight: 28 tons 4 cwt.
Seats 2nd: 55.

M29733M M29736M

Driving Trailer Open Second

Body: 57′ 0″ × 8′ 11″ & 9′ 6″.
Weight: 29 tons 2 cwt.
Seats 2nd: 60.

M29033M M29036M

LONDON DISTRICT THREE-CAR COMPARTMENT SETS

Motor Brake Second

Body: 59′ 0″ × 8′ 11″ & 9′ 6″.
Weight: 56 tons.
Seats 2nd: 84.
Equipment: Four 280 h.p. G.E.C. or M.V traction motors.

M28001M	M28010M	M28018M
M28002M	M28011M	M28019M
M28003M	M28012M	M28020M
M28004M	M28013M	M28021M
M28005M	M28014M	M28022M
M28006M	M28015M	M28023M
M28007M	M28016M	M28024M
M28008M	M28017M	M28025M
M28009M		

Trailer Second

Body: 57′ 0″ × 8′ 11″ & 9′ 6″.
Weight: 28 tons.
Seats 2nd: 108.

M29400M	M29600M	M29611M
M29401M	M29601M	M29612M
M29402M	M29602M	M29613M
M29403M	M29603M	M29614M
M29404M	M29604M	M29615M
M29405M	M29605M	M29616M
M29406M	M29606M	M29617M
M29407M	M29607M	M29618M
M29408M	M29608M	M29619M
M29409M	M29609M	M29620M
	M29610M	M29621M

Driving Trailer Brake Second

Body: 57′ 0″ × 8′ 11″ & 9′ 6″.
Weight: 30 tons.
Seats 2nd: 96.

M28800M	M28809M	M28817M
M28801M	M28810M	M28818M
M28802M	M28811M	M28819M
M28803M	M28812M	M28820M
M28804M	M28813M	M28821M
M28805M	M28814M	M28822M
M28806M	M28815M	M28823M
M28807M	M28816M	M28824M
M28808M		

LONDON DISTRICT THREE-CAR B.R. SETS

B.R. Standard design

Motor Open Brake Second

Body: 57′ 5″ × 9′ 0″ & 9′ 6″
Weight: 47 tons.
Seats 2nd: 74.
Equipment: Four 185 h.p. G.E.C. traction motors.

M61133	M61152	M61171
M61134	M61153	M61172
M61135	M61154	M61173
M61136	M61155	M61174
M61137	M61156	M61175
M61138	M61157	M61176
M61139	M61158	M61177
M61140	M61159	M61178
M61141	M61160	M61179
M61142	M61161	M61180
M61143	M61162	M61181
M61144	M61163	M61182
M61145	M61164	M61183
M61146	M61165	M61184
M61147	M61166	M61185
M61148	M61167	M61186
M61149	M61168	M61187
M61150	M61169	M61188
M61151	M61170	M61189

Trailer Second

Body: 57′ 1″ × 9′ 0″ & 9′ 6″.
Weight: 29 tons.
Seats 2nd: 108.

M70133	M70152	M70171
M70134	M70153	M70172
M70135	M70154	M70173
M70136	M70155	M70174
M70137	M70156	M70175
M70138	M70157	M70176
M70139	M70158	M70177
M70140	M70159	M70178
M70141	M70160	M70179
M70142	M70161	M70180
M70143	M70162	M70181
M70144	M70163	M70182
M70145	M70164	M70183
M70146	M70165	M70184
M70147	M70166	M70185
M70148	M70167	M70186
M70149	M70168	M70187
M70150	M70169	M70188
M70151	M70170	M70189

Driving Trailer Open Brake Second

Body: 57′ 5″ × 9′ 0″ & 9′ 6″.
Weight: 30 tons.
Seats 2nd: 74.

M75133	M75147	M75161
M75134	M75148	M75162
M75135	M75149	M75163
M75136	M75150	M75164
M75137	M75151	M75165
M75138	M75152	M75166
M75139	M75153	M75167
M75140	M75154	M75168
M75141	M75155	M75169
M75142	M75156	M75170
M75143	M75157	M75171
M75144	M75158	M75172
M75145	M75159	M75173
M75146	M75160	M75174

M75175	M75180	M75185
M75176	M75181	M75186
M75177	M75182	M75187
M75178	M75183	M75188
M75179	M75184	M75189

SYSTEM: 630 VOLTS D.C. 3rd RAIL

LIVERPOOL-SOUTHPORT

TWO- AND THREE-CAR COMPARTMENT SETS

Motor Brake Second

Body: 59′ 0″ × 8′ 11″ & 9′ 3″.
Weight: 56 tons.
Seats 2nd: 84.
Equipment: Four 265 h.p. Metropolitan Vickers traction motors.

M28301M	M28305M	M28308M
M28302M	M28306M	M28309M
M28303M	M28307M	M28310M
M28304M		

Trailer Composite

Body: 57′ 0″ × 8′ 11″ & 9′ 3″.
Weight: 28 tons.
Seats 1st: 24.
2nd: 72.

M29800M	M29804M	M29808M
M29801M	M29805M	M29809M
M29802M	M29806M	M29810M
M29803M	M29807M	M29811M

Driving Trailer Brake Second

Body: 57′ 0″ × 8′ 11″ & 9′ 3″.
Weight: 28 tons.
Seats 2nd: 96.

M29100M	M29104M	M29108M
M29101M	M29105M	M29109M
M29102M	M29106M	M29110M
M29103M	M29107M	

LIVERPOOL-SOUTHPORT
TWO- AND THREE-CAR OPEN SETS
Motor Open Brake Second

Body: 66′ 6″ × 9′ 3″ & 9′ 5″.
Weight: 41 tons.
Seats 2nd: 88.
Equipment: Four 235 h.p. English Electric traction motors.

M28311M	M28331M	M28351M
M28312M	M28332M	M28352M
M28313M	M28333M	M28353M
M28314M	M28334M	M28354M
M28315M	M28335M	M28355M
M28316M	M28336M	M28356M
M28317M	M28337M	M28357M
M28318M	M28338M	M28358M
M28319M	M28339M	M28359M
M28321M	M28340M	M28360M
M28322M	M28341M	M28361M
M28323M	M28342M	M28362M
M28324M	M28343M	M28363M
M28325M	M28344M	M28364M
M28326M	M28345M	M28365M
M28327M	M28347M	M28366M
M28328M	M28348M	M28367M
M28329M	M28349M	M28368M
M28330M	M28350M	M28369M

Trailer Open Second

Body: 66′ 6″ × 9′ 3″ & 9′ 5″.
Weight: 24 tons.
Seats 2nd: 102.

M29545M	M29556M	M29567M
M29546M	M29557M	M29568M
M29547M	M29558M	M29569M
M29548M	M29559M	M29570M
M29549M	M29560M	M29571M
M29550M	M29561M	M29572M
M29551M	M29562M	M29573M
M29552M	M29563M	M29574M
M29553M	M29564M	M29575M
M29554M	M29565M	M29576M
M29555M	M29566M	M29577M

M29578M	M29584M	M29590M
M29579M	M29585M	M29591M
M29580M	M29586M	M29592M
M29581M	M29587M	M29593M
M29582M	M29588M	M29594M
M29583M	M29589M	

Trailer Open Second (Built as Composite)

Body: 66′ 6″ × 9′ 3″ & 9′ 5″.
Weight: 24 tons.
Seats 2nd: 82.

M29812M	M29815M	M29818M
M29813M	M29816M	M29819M
M29814M	M29817M	M29820M

Driving Trailer Open Composite

Body: 66′ 6″ × 9′ 3″ & 9′ 5″.
Weight: 25 tons.
Seats 1st: 53.
2nd: 25.

M29866M	M29878M	M29889M
M29867M	M29879M	M29890M
M29868M	M29880M	M29891M
M29869M	M29881M	M29892M
M29870M	M29882M	M29893M
M29871M	M29883M	M29894M
M29872M	M29884M	M29895M
M29873M	M29885M	M29896M
M29874M	M29886M	M29897M
M29875M	M29887M	M29898M
M29876M	M29888M	M29899M
M29877M		

LIVERPOOL-SOUTHPORT
Motor Parcels Van

Body: { 57′ 0″ × 8′ 11″ & 9′ 3″*.
59′ 0″ × 8′ 11″ & 9′ 3″.
Weight:
Equipment: Two 265 h.p. Metropolitan-Vickers nose-suspended traction motors.

M28496M *M28497M

SYSTEM: 650 VOLTS D.C. 3rd RAIL

WIRRAL & MERSEY

THREE-CAR OPEN SETS

Motor Open Brake Second

Body: 58′ 0″ × 8′ 8″ & 9′ 11″.
Weight: 36 tons.
Seats 2nd: 58.
Equipment: Four 135 h.p. B.T.H. traction motors.

M28371M	M28386M	M28677M
M28372M	M28387M	M28678M
M28373M	M28388M	M28679M
M28374M	M28389M	M28680M
M28375M	M28390M	M28681M
M28376M	M28391M	M28682M
M28377M	M28392M	M28683M
M28378M	M28393M	M28684M
M28379M	M28394M	M28685M
M28380M		M28686M
M28381M	M28672M	M28687M
M28382M	M28673M	M28688M
M28383M	M28674M	M28689M
M28384M	M28675M	M28690M
M28385M	M28676M	

Trailer Open Composite

Body: 56′ 0″ × 8′ 8″ & 9′ 11″.
Weight: 20 tons.
Seats 1st: 40.
2nd: 15.

M29702M	M29718M	M29833M
M29703M	M29719M	M29834M
M29704M	M29720M	M29835M
M29705M		M29836M
M29706M	M29821M	M29837M
M29707M	M29822M	M29838M
M29708M	M29823M	M29839M
M29709M	M29824M	M29840M
M29710M	M29825M	M29841M
M29711M	M29826M	M29842M
M29712M	M29827M	M29843M
M29713M	M29828M	M29844M
M29714M	M29829M	M29845M
M29715M	M29830M	M29846M
M29716M	M29831M	
M29717M	M29832M	

Driving Trailer Open Second

Body: 58′ 0″ × 8′ 8″ & 9′ 11″.
Weight: 21 tons.
Seats 2nd: 68.

M29131M	M29147M	M29276M
M29132M	M29148M	M29277M
M29133M	M29149M	M29278M
M29134M	M29150M	M29279M
M29135M	M29151M	M29280M
M29136M	M29152M	M29281M
M29137M	M29153M	M29282M
M29138M	M29154M	M29283M
M29139M	M29155M	M29284M
M29140M	M29156M	M29285M
M29141M		M29286M
M29142M	M29271M	M29287M
M29143M	M29272M	M29288M
M29144M	M29273M	M29289M
M29145M	M29274M	
M29146M	M29275M	

SYSTEM: 1200 VOLTS D.C. SIDE CONTACT 3rd RAIL

MANCHESTER–BURY

FIVE-CAR OPEN SETS

Gangwayed throughout.

Motor Open Brake Second

Body: 63′ 6″ × 9′ 0″ & 9′ 0″.
Weight: 54 tons.
Seats 2nd: 74.
Equipment: Four 200 h.p. Kerr nose-suspended traction motors.

M28500M	M28512M	M28525M
M28501M	M28513M	M28526M
M28502M	M28514M	M28527M
M28503M	M28515M	M28528M
M28504M	M28516M	M28529M
M28505M	M28517M	M28530M
M28506M	M28518M	M28531M
M28507M	M28519M	M28532M
M28508M	M28521M	M28533M
M28509M	M28522M	M28534M
M28510M	M28523M	M28535M
M28511M	M28524M	M28537M

Driving Trailer Open Second

Body: 63′ 6″ × 9′ 0″ & 9′ 0″.
Weight: 29 tons.
Seats 2nd: 95.

M29200M	M29205M	M29210M
M29201M	M29206M	M29211M
M29202M	M29207M	M29212M
M29203M	M29208M	M29213M
M29204M	M29209M	

Driving Trailer Open Composite

Body: 63′ 6″ × 9′ 0″ & 9′ 0″.
Weight: 29 tons.
Seats 1st: 36.
2nd: 36.

M28700M	M28705M	M28710M
M28701M	M28706M	M28711M
M28702M	M28707M	M28712M
M28703M	M28708M	M28713M
M28704M	M28709M	

MANCHESTER-BURY TWO-CAR B.R. SETS

B.R. Standard design

Motor Open Brake Second

Body: 63′ 11½″ × 9′ 0″ & 9′ 3″.
Weight:
Seats 2nd: 84.
Equipment: Two 141 h.p. English Electric traction motors.

M65436	M65445	M65454
M65437	M65446	M65455
M65438	M65447	M65456
M65439	M65448	M65457
M65440	M65449	M65458
M65441	M65450	M65459
M65442	M65451	M65460
M65443	M65452	M65461
M65444	M65453	

Driving Trailer Composite

Body: 63′ 11½″ × 9′ 0″ & 9′ 3″.
Weight:
Seats 1st: 16.
2nd: 78.

M77157	M77160	M77163
M77158	M77161	M77164
M77159	M77162	M77165

M77166	M77172	M77178
M77167	M77173	M77179
M77168	M77174	M77180
M77169	M77175	M77181
M77170	M77176	M77182
M77171	M77177	

SYSTEM: 1500 VOLTS D.C. OVERHEAD

MANCHESTER–ALTRINCHAM THREE-CAR SETS

Motor Brake Second

Body: 58′ 1″ × 8′ 11″ & 9′ 3″.
Weight: 57 tons.
Seats 2nd: 72.
Equipment: Four 330 h.p. traction motors.

M28571M	M28579M	M28587M
M28572M	M28580M	M28588M
M28573M	M28581M	M28589M
M28574M	M28582M	M28590M
M28575M	M28583M	M28591M
M28576M	M28584M	M28592M
M28577M	M28585M	M28593M
M28578M	M28586M	M28594M

Trailer Composite

Body: 57′ 1″ × 8′ 11″ & 9′ 3″.
Weight: 30 tons.
Seats 1st: 24.
2nd: 72.

M29396M	M29656M	M29664M
	M29657M	M29665M
M29650M	M29658M	M29666M
M29651M	M29659M	M29667M
M29652M	M29660M	M29668M
M29653M	M29661M	M29669M
M29654M	M29662M	M29670M
M29655M	M29663M	M29671M

Driving Trailer Second

Body: 58′ 1″ × 8′ 11″ & 9′ 3″.
Weight: 31 tons.
Seats 2nd: 108.

M29231M	M29235M	M29239M
M29232M	M29236M	M29240M
M29233M	M29237M	M29241M
M29234M	M29238M	M29242M

M29243M	M29247M	M29250M
M29244M	M29248M	M29251M
M29245M	M29249M	M29252M
M29246M		

SYSTEM: 6600 VOLTS A.C. 50 CYCLES OVERHEAD

LANCASTER–MORECAMBE–HEYSHAM THREE-CAR OPEN SETS

Motor Open Brake Second

Body: 57′ 0″ × 8′ 11″ & 9′ 6″.
Weight: 57 tons.
Seats 2nd: {28 38*.
Equipment: Four 215 h.p. English Electric traction motors.

M28219M	M28221M	M28222M*
M28220M		

Trailer Open Second

Body: 57′ 0″ × 8′ 11″ & 9′ 6″.
Weight: 26 tons.
Seats 2nd: 62.

M29719M	M29721M	M29722M
M29720M		

Driving Trailer Open Second

Body: 57′ 0″ × 8′ 11″ & 9′ 6″.
Weight:
Seats 2nd: 56.

M29019M	M29021M	M29022M
M29020M		

SYSTEM: 1500 VOLTS D.C. OVERHEAD

MANCHESTER–GLOSSOP–HADFIELD THREE-CAR OPEN SETS

Motor Open Brake Second

Body: 60′ 4½″ × 9′ 0″ & 9′ 3″.
Weight: 50 tons 12 cwt.
Seats 2nd: 52.
Equipment: Four 185 h.p. GEC traction motors.

M59401E	M59404E	M59407E
M59402E	M59405E	M59408E
M59403E	M59406E	

Trailer Open Second

Body: 55′ 0½″ × 9′ 0″ & 9′ 3″.
Weight: 26 tons 8 cwt.
Seats 2nd :

M59501E	M59504E	M59507E
M59502E	M59505E	M59508E
M59503E	M59506E	

Driving Trailer Open Second

Body: 55′ 4½″ × 9′ 0″ & 9′ 3″.
Weight: 27 tons 9 cwt.
Seats 2nd: 60.

M59601E	M59604E	M59607E
M59602E	M59605E	M59608E
M59603E	M59606E	

Eastern Region

SYSTEM: 1500 VOLTS D.C. OVERHEAD

LIVERPOOL ST.–SOUTHEND FOUR-CAR SETS

These sets are being converted in readiness for working on 25,000 volts a.c. when the Liverpool St.-Chelmsford-Southend lines are altered to this system. Some structural rebuilding will be necessary and sets are renumbered IXX as they are dealt with.

B.R. Standard design

Driving Trailer Second

Body: 63′ 11½″ × 9′ 0″ & 9′ 3″.
Weight: 30 tons 5 cwt.
Seats 2nd: 108.

Trailer Composite (L)

Body: 63′ 6″ × 9′ 0″ & 9′ 3″.
Weight: 30 tons.
Seats 1st: 19.
2nd: 60.

Motor Brake Second

Body: 63′ 6″ × 9′ 0″ & 9′ 3″.
Weight: 48 tons 6 cwt.
Seats 2nd: 96.
Equipment: Four 220 h.p. GEC traction motors.

Driving Trailer Open Second (L)

Body: 63′ 11½″ × 9′ 0″ & 9′ 3″.
Weight: 30 tons 19 cwt.
Seats 2nd: 80.

UNIT Nos.

01s	09s	17s	25s
02s	10s	18s	26s
103	11s	19s	27s
04s	12s	20s	28s
05s	13s	21s	29s
06s	14s	22s	30s
07s	15s	23s	31s
08s	16s	24s	32s

LIVERPOOL ST.–SHENFIELD THREE-CAR OPEN SETS

*These sets are being converted in readiness for working on 25,000 volts a.c. when the Liverpool St.–Chelmsford–Southend lines are altered to this system. The centre trailers are being altered to include the guards compartment and pantograph and part of the passenger saloon thus displaced transferred to the existing motor coach. Ultimately the centre trailer will become the motor coach and the present motor coach will become a driving trailer. Sets are prefixed "0XX" as they are rebuilt.

Motor Open Brake Second

Body: 60′ 4½″ × 9′ 0″ & 9′ 6″.
Weight: 50 tons 17 cwt.
Seats 2nd: { 52. / 62*.
Equipment:

Trailer Open Second

Body: 55′ 0½″ × 9′ 0″ & 9′ 6″.
Weight: 26 tons.
Seats 2nd: { 64. / 46*.

Driving Trailer Open Second

Body: 55′ 4″ × 9′ 0″ & 9′ 6″.
Weight: 27 tons 10 cwt.
Seats 2nd: 60.

UNIT Nos.

001	024	047	070
002	025	048	071
003	026	049	072
004	027	050	073
005	028	051	074
006	029	052	075
007	030	053	076
008	031	054	077
009	032	055	078
010	033	056	079
011	034	057	080
012	035	058	081
013	036	059	082
014	037	060	083
015	038	061	084
016	039	062	085
017	040	063	086
018	041	064	087
019	042	065	088
020	043	066	089
021	044	067	090
022	045	068	091
023	046	069	092

SYSTEM: 25 kV. A.C. OVERHEAD

FENCHURCH ST.–SHOEBURYNESS FOUR-CAR SETS

B.R. Standard design

Driving Trailer Second

Body: 63′ 11½″ × 9′ 0″ & 9′ 3″.
Weight: 32 tons.
Seats 2nd: 108.

Trailer Composite (L)

Body: 63′ 6″ × 9′ 0″ & 9′ 3″.
Weight: 31 tons.
Seats 1st: 19.
2nd: 60.

Motor Brake Second

Body: 63′ 6″ × 9′ 0″ & 9′ 3″.
Weight: 56 tons 10 cwt.
Seats 2nd: 96.
Equipment: Four 240 h.p. English Electric nose-suspended traction motors.

Driving Trailer Open Second (L)

Body: 63′ 11½″ × 9′ 0″ & 9′ 3″.
Weight: 36 tons.
Seats 2nd: 80.

UNIT Nos.

201	220	239	258
202	221	240	259
203	222	241	260
204	223	242	261
205	224	243	262
206	225	244	263
207	226	245	264
208	227	246	265
209	228	247	266
210	229	248	267
211	230	249	268
212	231	250	269
213	232	251	270
214	233	252	271
215	234	253	272
216	235	254	273
217	236	255	274
218	237	256	275
219	238	257	276

277	286	295	304
278	287	296	305
279	288	297	306
280	289	298	307
281	290	299	308
282	291	300	309
283	292	301	310
284	293	302	311
285	294	303	312

UNITS 401-99 and **501-99** are for the Liverpool Street–Enfield –Chingford and Liverpool Street –Bishops Stortford lines. Details of formation are not available at the time of going to press.

SYSTEM: 575 VOLTS D.C. OVERHEAD

GRIMSBY-IMMINGHAM ELECTRIC TRAMS

1	14	19	24	29
3	15	20	25	30
4	16	21	26	31
5	17	22	27	32
11	18	23	28	33
12				

North Eastern Region

SYSTEM: 600 VOLTS D.C. 3rd RAIL

SOUTH TYNESIDE TWO-CAR SETS

B.R. Standard design

Motor Open Brake Second

Body: 63′ 11½″ × 9′ 0″ & 9′ 3″.
Weight: 40 tons.
Seats 2nd : 74.
Equipment: Two 250 h.p. English Electric traction motors.

E65311	E65316	E65321
E65312	E65317	E65322
E65313	E65318	E65323
E65314	E65319	E65324
E65315	E65320	E65325

Driving Trailer Second

Body: 63′ 11½″ × 9′ 0″ & 9′ 3″.
Weight: 30 tons.
Seats 2nd:

E77100	E77105	E77110
E77101	E77106	E77111
E77102	E77107	E77112
E77103	E77108	E77113
E77104	E77109	E77114

SOUTH TYNESIDE Motor Parcels Van

Body: 64′ 5″ × 9′ 0″ & 9′ 3″.
Weight: 49 tons.
Equipment: Four 250 h.p. English Electric traction motors.

E68000

NORTH TYNESIDE ARTICULATED TWIN UNITS

Motor Open Brake Second

Body: 55′ 0″ × 9′ 0½″ & 9′ 3″.
Combined weight with trailer: 54 tons 19 cwt.
Seats 2nd: 52.
Equipment: Two 154 h.p. Crompton Parkinson traction motors.

Driving Trailer Open Second

Body: 55′ 0″ × 9′ 0½″ & 9′ 3″.
Seats 2nd: 76.

Motor Coaches	*Driving Trailers*
E29101E	E29301E
E29102E	E29302E
E29103E	E29303E
E29104E	E29304E
E29105E	E29305E
E29106E	E29306E
E29107E	E29307E
E29108E	E29308E
E29109E	E29309E
E29110E	E29310E
E29111E	E29311E

Motor Open Brake Second

Body: 55′ 0″ × 9′ 0½″ & 9′ 3″.
Combined weight with trailer: 55 tons 7 cwt.
Seats 2nd: 52.
Equipment: Two 154 h.p. Crompton Parkinson traction motors.

Driving Trailer Open Second

Body: 55′ 0″ × 9′ 0½″ & 9′ 3″.
Seats 2nd:

Motor Coaches	*Driving Trailers*
E29113E	E29313E
E29114E	E29314E
E29115E	E29315E
E29116E	E29316E
E29117E	E29317E
E29118E	E29318E
E29119E	E29319E
E29120E	E29320E
E29121E	E29321E
E29122E	E29322E
E29123E	E29323E
E29124E	E29324E
E29125E	E29325E
E29126E	E29326E
E29127E	E29327E
E29128E	E29328E

Motor Open Brake Second

Body: 55′ 0″ × 9′ 0½″ & 9′ 3″.
Combined weight with trailer: 53 tons 12 cwt.
Seats 2nd: 52.
Equipment: Two 154 h.p. Crompton Parkinson traction motors.

Trailer Open Second

Body: 55′ 0″ × 9′ 0½″ & 9′ 3″.
Seats 2nd: 80.

Motor Coaches	*Driving Trailers*
E29129E	E29229E
E29130E	E29230E
E29131E	E29231E
E29132E	E29232E
E29133E	E29233E
E29134E	E29234E
E29135E	E29235E
E29136E	E29236E
E29137E	E29237E
E29138E	E29238E
E29139E	E29239E
E29140E	E29240E
E29141E	E29241E
E29142E	E29242E
E29143E	E29243E
E29144E	E29244E
E29145E	E29245E
E29146E	E29246E

Motor Open Brake Second

Body: 55′ 0″ × 9′ 0½″ & 9′ 3″.
Combined weight with trailer: 54 tons 6 cwt.
Seats 2nd: 52.
Equipment: Two 154 h.p. Crompton Parkinson traction motors.

Trailer Open Second

Body: 55′ 0″ × 9′ 0½″ & 9′ 3″.
Seats 2nd:

Motor Coaches	*Driving Trailers*
E29147E	E29247E
E29148E	E29248E
E29149E	E29249E
E29150E	E29250E
E29151E	E29251E
E29152E	E29252E
E29153E	E29253E
E29154E	E29254E
E29155E	E29255E
E29156E	E29256E
E29157E	E29257E
E29158E	E29258E
E29159E	E29259E
E29160E	E29260E
E29161E	E29261E
E29162E	E29262E
E29163E	E29263E
E29164E	E29264E

Single Motor Open Brake Second

Body: 59′ 0″ × 9′ 0½″ & 9′ 3″.
Weight: 47 tons 5 cwt.
Seats 2nd: 52.
Equipment: Two 154 h.p. Crompton Parkinson traction motors.

E29165E E29166E

Single Driving Trailer Open Second

Body: 56′ 6″ × 9′ 0¾″ & 9′ 3″.
Weight: 26 tons 10 cwt.
Seats 2nd: 68.

E29376E	E29388E
E29387E	E29390E

Motor Parcels Van

Body: 59′ 0″ × 9′ 0½″ & 9′ 3″.
Weight: 38 tons 15 cwt.
Equipment: Four 154 h.p. Crompton Parkinson traction motors.

E29467E E29468E

Scottish Region

SYSTEM: 25 kV. A.C. OVERHEAD

GLASGOW SUBURBAN THREE-CAR SETS

B.R. Standard design

Driving Trailer Open Second

Body: 63′ 11⅝″ × 9′ 3″ & 9′ 3″.
Weight: 34 tons.
Seats 2nd: 83.

SC75566	SC75568	SC75570
SC75567	SC75569	SC75571

SC75572	SC75582	SC75592
SC75573	SC75583	SC75593
SC75574	SC75584	SC75594
SC75575	SC75585	SC75595
SC75576	SC75586	SC75596
SC75577	SC75587	SC75597
SC75578	SC75588	SC75598
SC75579	SC75589	SC75599
SC75580	SC75590	SC75600
SC75581	SC75591	

Motor Open Brake Second

Body: 63′ 6⅛″ × 9′ 3″ & 9′ 3″
Weight: 56 tons.
Seats 2nd: 70.
Equipment: Metropolitan-Vickers.

SC61481	SC61493	SC61505
SC61482	SC61494	SC61506
SC61483	SC61495	SC61507
SC61484	SC61496	SC61508
SC61485	SC61497	SC61509
SC61486	SC61498	SC61510
SC61487	SC61499	SC61511
SC61488	SC61500	SC61512
SC61489	SC61501	SC61513
SC61490	SC61502	SC61514
SC61491	SC61503	SC61515
SC61492	SC61504	

Driving Trailer Open Second

Body: 63′ 11⅝″ × 9′ 3″ & 9′ 3″.
Weight: 38 tons.
Seats 2nd: 83.

SC75601	SC75613	SC75625
SC75602	SC75614	SC75626
SC75603	SC75615	SC75627
SC75604	SC75616	SC75628
SC75605	SC75617	SC75629
SC75606	SC75618	SC75630
SC75607	SC75619	SC75631
SC75608	SC75620	SC75632
SC75609	SC75621	SC75633
SC75610	SC75622	SC75634
SC75611	SC75623	SC75635
SC75612	SC75624	

Southern Region

(Unit numbers to be seen on front and rear of each set)

SYSTEM: 750 VOLTS D.C. 3rd RAIL

TWO-CAR SETS

(2-BIL.)

Motor Brake Second (K)

Body: 62′ 6″ × 9′ 0″ & 9′ 3″.
Weight: 43 tons 10 cwt.
Seats 2nd: 56†.
52.
Equipment: Two 275 h.p. English Electric traction motors.

Driving Trailer Composite (K)

Body: 62′ 6″ × 9′ 0″ & 9′ 3″.
Weight: 31 tons 5 cwt.
Seats 1st: 24.
2nd: 32.

2001†	2008†	2016	2023
2002†	2009†	2017	2024
2003†	2010†	2018	2025
2004†	2011	2019	2026
2005†	2012	2020	2027
2006†	2013	2021	2028
2007†	2015	2022	2029

2030	2054	2078	2103
2031	2055	2079	2104
2032	2056*	2080	2105
2033	2057	2081	2106
2034	2058	2082	2107
2035	2059	2083	2108
2036	2060	2084	2109
2037	2061	2085	2110
2038	2062	2086	2111
2039	2063	2087	2112
2040	2064	2088‡	2113
2041	2065	2089	2114
2042	2066	2090	2115
2043	2067	2091	2116
2044	2068	2092	2117
2045	2069‡	2093	2118
2046	2070	2094	2120
2047	2071	2095	2121
2048	2072	2096	2122
2049	2073	2097	2123
2050	2074	2098	2124
2051	2075	2099	2125
2052	2076	2100‡	2126
2053	2077	2101	2127

2128	2135	2141	2147
2129	2136	2142	2148
2130	2137	2143	2149
2132	2138	2144	2150
2133‡	2139	2145	2151
2134	2140	2146	2152

*BIL Motor Coach and 1939 type HAL Trailer.
‡BIL Motor Coach and post-war all steel HAL Trailer.

TWO-CAR SETS (2-HAL.)

Motor Brake Second

Body: 62′ 6″ × 9′ 0″ & 9′ 3″.
Weight: 45 tons.
Seats 2nd: 70.
Equipment: Two 275 h.p. English Electric nose-suspended traction motors.

Driving Trailer Composite (K)

Body: 62′ 6″ × 9′ 0″ & 9′ 3″.
Weight: 31 tons.
Seats 1st: 18 or 24.
2nd: 40 or 32.

2601	2624	2648	2671
2602	2625	2649	2672
2603	2626	2650	2673
2604	2627	2651	2674
2605	2628	2652	2675
2606	2629	2653*	2676
2607	2630	2654	2677
2608	2631	2655	2678
2609	2632	2656	2679
2610	2633	2657	2681
2611	2634	2658	2682
2612	2635	2659	2683
2613	2636	2660	2684
2614	2637	2661	2685
2615	2638	2662	2686
2616	2639	2663	2687
2617	2640	2664	2688
2618	2641	2665	2689
2619	2642	2666	2690
2620	2643	2667	2691
2621	2644	2668	2692
2622	2645	2669	
2623	2647	2670	

*Post-war all steel Trailer.

TWO-CAR SETS (2-HAL.)

Motor Brake Second

Body: 62′ 6″ × 9′ 0″ & 9′ 3″.
Weight: 43 tons.
Seats 2nd: 84.
Equipment: Two 275 h.p. English Electric nose-suspended traction motors.

Driving Trailer Composite (K)

Body: 62′ 6″ × 9′ 0″ & 9′ 3″.
Weight: 31 tons.
Seats 1st: 18.
2nd: 40.

2693	2695	2697	2699
2694	2696	2698	

TWO-CAR SETS (2-HAL.)

Motor Brake Saloon Second

Body: 62′ 6″ × 9′ 0″ & 9′ 3″.
Weight: 40 tons.
Seats 2nd: 82.
Equipment: Two 275 h.p. English Electric traction motors.

Driving Trailer Composite (K)

Body: 62′ 6″ × 9′ 0″ & 9′ 3″.
Weight: 31 tons.
Seats 1st: 24.
2nd: 32.

2700

FOUR-CAR SETS (4-LAV.)

Motor Brake Second

Body: 62′ 6″ × 9′ 0″ & 9′ 3″.
Weight: 41 tons.
44 tons*.
45 tons†.
Seats 2nd: 70
Equipment: Two 275 h.p. Metropolitan-Vickers traction motors.
†*Two 275 h.p. English Electric traction motors.

Trailer Composite

Body: 62′ 0″ × 9′ 0″ & 9′ 3″.
Weight: 28 tons.
29 tons*.
Seats 1st: 16.
2nd: 70.

Trailer Composite (K)

Body: 62′ 0″ × 9′ 0″ & 9′ 3″.
Weight: 29 tons.
30 tons*.
Seats 1st: 30.
2nd: 24.

Motor Brake Second

(As Above)

2921	2930	2939	2948
2922	2931	2940	2949
2923	2932	2941	2950
2924	2933	2942	2951
2925	2934	2943	2952
2926†	2935	2944	2953
2927	2936	2945	2954*
2928	2937	2946	2955*
2929	2938	2947	

†One motor coach of 1939 2-HAL type.

SIX-CAR SETS (6-PUL.)

Gangwayed within set

Motor Saloon Brake Second

Body: 63′ 6″ × 9′ 0″ & 9′ 5″.
Weight: 59 tons.
Seats 2nd: 52.
Equipment: Four 225 h.p. B.T.H. traction motors.

Trailer Second (K)

Body: 63′ 6″ × 9′ 0″ & 9′ 3″.
Weight: 35 tons.
Seats 2nd: 68.

Trailer Composite (K)

Body: 63′ 6″ × 9′ 0″ & 9′ 3″.
Weight: 35 tons.
Seats 1st: 30.
2nd: 24.

Trailer Composite Pullman (L)

Body: 66′ 0″ × 8′ 11½″ & 8′ 11½″.
Weight: 43 tons.
Seats 1st: 12.
2nd: 16.

Trailer Composite (K)

(As Above)

Motor Saloon Brake Second

(As Above)

3001	3006	3011	3016
3002	3007	3012	3017
3003	3008	3013	3018
3004	3009	3014	3019
3005	3010	3015	3020

SIX-CAR SETS (6-PAN.)

Gangwayed within set

Motor Saloon Brake Second

Body: 63′ 6″ × 9′ 0″ & 9′ 5″.
Weight: 59 tons.
Seats 2nd: 52.
Equipment: Four 225 h.p. English Electric traction motors.

Trailer Second (K)

Body: 63′ 6″ × 9′ 0″ & 9′ 3″.
Weight: 31 tons 10 cwt.
Seats 2nd: 68.

Trailer First (K)

Body: 59′ 0″ × 9′ 0″ & 9′ 3″.
Weight: 31 tons.
Seats 1st: 42.

Trailer Pantry First (K)

Body: 63′ 6″ × 9′ 0″ & 9′ 3″.
Weight: 32 tons.
Seats 1st: 30.

Trailer Second (K)

(As Above)

Motor Saloon Brake Second

(As Above)

3021	3025	3029	3034
3022	3026	3030	3035
3023	3027	3031	3036
3024	3028	3033	3037

SIX-CAR SETS (6-PUL.)

Gangwayed within set

Motor Saloon Brake Second

Body: 63′ 6″ × 9′ 0″ & 9′ 5″
Weight: 57 tons.
59 tons*.
Seats 2nd: 56.
52*.
Equipment: Four 225 h.p. B.T.H. traction motors.

Trailer Second (K)

Body: 59′ 0″ × 9′ 0″ & 9′ 3″.
Weight: 34 tons.
Seats 2nd: 56.

Trailer Composite (K)

Body: 59′ 0″ × 9′ 0″ & 9′ 3″
Weight: 34 tons.
Seats 1st: 30.
2nd: 16.

Trailer Composite Pullman (L)

Body: 66′ 0″ × 8′ 11½″ & 8′ 11½″.
Weight: 43 tons.
Seats 1st: 12.
2nd: 16.

Trailer Composite

(As Above)

Motor Saloon Brake Second

Body: 63′ 6″ × 9′ 0″ & 9′ 3″.
Weight: 59 tons.
Seats 2nd: 52.
Equipment: Four 225 h.p. B.T.H. traction motors.

3041 3042 3043*

FIVE-CAR PULLMAN SETS (5-BEL.)

All-Pullman
Gangwayed within set

Motor Brake Second Pullman (L)

Body: 66′ 0″ × 8′ 11½″ & 8′ 11½″.
Weight: 62 tons.
Seats 2nd: 48.
Equipment: Four 225 h.p. B.T.H. traction motors.

Trailer Second Pullman (L)

Body: 66′ 0″ × 8′ 11½″ & 8′ 11½″.
Weight: 39 tons.
Seats 2nd: 56.

Trailer Kitchen First Pullman (L)

Body: 66′ 0″ × 8′ 11½″ & 8′ 11½″
Weight: 43 tons.
Seats 1st: 20.

Trailer First Pullman (L)

(As Above)

Motor Brake Second Pullman (L)

(As Above)

3051 3052 3053

FOUR-CAR SETS (4-RES.)

Gangwayed throughout

Motor Saloon Brake Second

Body: 63′ 6″ × 9′ 0″ & 9′ 4½″.
Weight: 46 tons 10 cwt.
Seats 2nd: 52.
Equipment: Two 225 h.p. English Electric traction motors.

Trailer First (K)

Body: 63′ 6″ × 9′ 0″ & 9′ 3″.
Weight: 33 tons.
Seats 1st: 30.
1st Dining: 12.

Trailer Kitchen Second (K)

Body: 63′ 6″ × 9′ 0″ & 9′ 4½″.
Weight: 35 tons.
Seats 2nd Dining: 36.

Motor Saloon Brake Second

(As Above)

3054	3059	3065	3069
3055	3061	3066	3070
3056	3062	3067	3071
3057	3064	3068	3072*

*Kitchen Second in this unit converted to Buffet Car, weight 34 tons.

FOUR-CAR SETS (4-BUF.)

Gangwayed throughout

Motor Saloon Brake Second

Body: 63′ 6″ × 9′ 0″ & 9′ 4½″.
Weight: 46 tons 10 cwt.
Seats 2nd: 52.
Equipment: Two 225 h.p. English Electric traction motors.

Trailer Composite (K)

Body: 63′ 6″ × 9′ 0″ & 9′ 3″.
Weight: 32 tons 12 cwt.
Seats 1st: 30.
2nd: 24.

Trailer Buffet (L)

Body: 63′ 6″ × 9′ 0″ & 9′ 3″.
Weight: 37 tons.
Seats Buffet: 26.

Motor Saloon Brake Second

(As Above)

3073	3077	3080	3083
3074	3078	3081	3084
3075	3079	3082	3085
3076			

FOUR-CAR SETS (4-COR.)

Gangwayed throughout

Motor Saloon Brake Second

Body: 63′ 6″ × 9′ 0″ & 9′ 4½″.
Weight: 46 tons 10 cwt.
Seats 2nd: 52.
Equipment: Two 225 h.p. English Electric traction motors.

Trailer Second (K)

Body: 63′ 6″ × 9′ 0″ & 9′ 3″.
Weight: 32 tons 13 cwt.
Seats 2nd: 68.

Trailer Composite (K)

Body: 63′ 6″ × 9′ 0″ & 9′ 3″.
Weight: 32 tons 12 cwt.
Seats 1st: 30.
2nd: 24.

Motor Saloon Brake Second

(As Above)

3101	3116	3131	3146
3102	3117	3132	3147
3103	3118	3133	3148
3104	3119	3134	3149
3105	3120	3135	3150
3106	3121	3136	3151
3107	3122	3137	3152
3108	3123	3138	3153
3109	3124	3139	3154
3110	3125	3140	3155
3111	3126	3141	3156
3112	3127	3142	3157
3113	3128	3143	3158
3114	3129	3144	
3115	3130	3145	

FOUR-CAR SUBURBAN SETS (DOUBLE DECK) (4-DD.)

Motor Brake Second

Body: 62′ 6″ × 9′ 0″ & 9′ 3″.
Weight: 39 tons.
Seats 2nd: Lower deck 55
Upper deck 55 (*plus* 10 tip-up)
Equipment: Two 250 h.p. English Electric traction motors.

Trailer Second

Body: 62′ 0″ × 9′ 0″ & 9′ 3″.
Weight: 28 tons.
Seats 2nd: Lower deck 78.
Upper deck 66 (*plus* 12 tip-up)

Trailer Second

(As Above)

Motor Brake Second

(As Above)

4001 4002

FOUR-CAR SUBURBAN SETS (4-SUB.)

Motor Brake Second

Body: 62′ 6″ × 9′ 0″ & 9′ 3″.
Weight:
Seats 2nd: 102.
Equipment: Two 275 h.p. English Electric traction motors.

Trailer Second

Body: 62′ 0″ × 9′ 0″ & 9′ 3″.
Weight:
Seats 2nd: 132.

Trailer Second

Body: 62′ 0″ × 9′ 0″ & 9′ 3″.
Weight:
Seats 2nd: 120.

Motor Brake Second

(As Above)

4101	4104	4107	4110
4102	4105	4108	
4103	4106	4109	

Motor Brake Second

Body: 62′ 6″ × 9′ 0″ & 9′ 3″.
Weight:
Seats 2nd: 96.
Equipment: Two 275 h.p. English Electric traction motors.

Trailer Second

Body: 62′ 0″ × 9′ 0″ & 9′ 3″.
Weight:
Seats 2nd: 108.

Trailer Second

Body: 62′ 0″ × 9′ 0″ & 9′ 3″.
Weight:
Seats 2nd: 120.

Motor Brake Second

(As Above)

4111	4114	4117	4120
4112	4115	4118	
4113	4116	4119	

Motor Brake Second (Semi-Saloon)

Body: 62′ 6″ × 9′ 0″ & 9′ 3″.
Weight:
Seats 2nd: 84.
Equipment: Two 275 h.p. English Electric traction motors.

Trailer Second

Body: 62′ 0″ × 9′ 0″ & 9′ 3″.
Weight:
Seats 2nd: 108.

Trailer Second (Semi-Saloon)

Body: 62′ 0″ × 9′ 0″ & 9′ 3″
Weight:
Seats 2nd: 106.

Motor Brake Second (Semi-Saloon)

(As Above)

4121	4124	4127	4130
4122	4125	4128	
4123	4126	4129	

Motor Saloon Brake Second

Body: 62′ 6″ × 9′ 0″ & 9′ 3″.
Weight:
Seats 2nd: 82.
Equipment: Two 250 h.p. English Electric traction motors.

Trailer Second

Body: 62′ 0″ × 9′ 0″ & 9′ 3″.
Weight:
Seats 2nd: 120.

Trailer Saloon Second

Body: 62′ 0″ × 9′ 0″ & 9′ 3″.
Weight:
Seats 2nd: 102.

Motor Saloon Brake Second

(As Above)

4277	4283	4289	4295
4278	4284	4290	4296
4279	4285	4291	4297
4280	4286	4292	4298
4281	4287	4293	4299
4282	4288	4294	

Motor Brake Second

Body: 56′ 11″ × 8′ 6″ & 9′ 0″.
Weight: 39 tons.
Seats 2nd: 90.
Equipment: Two 275 h.p. Metropolitan-Vickers traction motors.

Trailer Second

Body: 60′ 0″ × 8′ 6″ & 9′ 0″.
Weight: 27 tons.
Seats 2nd: 90.

Trailer Second

Body: 62′ 0″ × 9′ 0″ & 9′ 3″.
Weight: 28 tons.
Seats 2nd: 120, 108*.

Motor Brake Second

(As Above)

4301	4308	4315	4322
4302	4309†	4316	4323
4303	4310†	4317	4324
4304	4311	4318	4325
4305	4312	4319	
4306	4313*	4320	
4307	4314	4321	

†Unit 4309 has two steel 62-ft. 120-seat trailers. Unit 4310 has two 60-ft. 90-seat trailers.

Motor Brake Second

Body: 62′ 6″ × 8′ 6″ & 9′ 0″.
Weight:
Seats 2nd: 80.
Equipment: Two 275 h.p. English Electric traction motors.

Trailer Second

Body: 62′ 0″ × 8′ 6″ & 9′ 0″.
Weight:
Seats 2nd: 90.

Trailer Second

Body: 62′ 0″ × 9′ 0″ & 9′ 3″.
Weight:
Seats 2nd: 120.

Motor Brake Second

(As Above)

4326	4333	4340	4348
4327	4334	4341	4349
4328	4335	4342	4351†
4329	4336	4343	4352
4330	4337	4344	4353
4331	4338	4346	4354
4332	4339*	4347	

*Unit 4339 has one motor brake second of the 4301-25 type.

†Unit 4351 has two 62-ft. 90 seat trailers.

Motor Brake Second

Body: 62′ 6″ × 9′ 0″ & 9′ 3″.
Weight:
Seats 2nd: 96
Equipment: Two 275 h.p. English Electric traction motors.

Trailer Second

Body: 62′ 0″ × 9′ 0″ & 9′ 3″.
Weight:
Seats 2nd: 120.

Trailer Second

(As Above)

Motor Brake Second

(As Above)

4355	4358	4360	4362
4356	4359	4361	4363
4357			

Motor Brake Second

Body: 62′ 6″ × 9′ 0″ & 9′ 3″.
Weight:
Seats 2nd: 96.
Equipment: Two 275 h.p. English Electric traction motors.

Trailer Second

Body: 62′ 0″ × 9′ 0″ & 9′ 3″.
Weight:
Seats 2nd: 108

Trailer Second

Body: 62′ 0″ × 9′ 0″ & 9′ 3″.
Weight:
Seats 2nd: 120.

Motor Brake Second

(As Above)

4364	4368	4371	4374
4365	4369	4372	4375
4366	4370	4373	4376
4367			

Motor Brake Second

Body: 62′ 6″ × 9′ 0″ & 9′ 3″.
Weight:
Seats 2nd: 96.
Equipment: Two 275 h.p. English Electric traction motors.

Trailer Second

Body: 62′ 0″ × 9′ 0″ & 9′ 3″.
Weight:
Seats 2nd: 108.

Trailer Saloon Second

Body: 62′ 0″ × 9′ 0″ & 9′ 3″.
Weight:
Seats 2nd: 102.

Motor Brake Second

(As Above)

4377

Motor Saloon Brake Second

Body: 62′ 6″ × 9′ 0″ & 9′ 3″.
Weight:
Seats 2nd: 82.
Equipment: Two 275 h.p. English Electric traction motors.

Trailer Second

Body: 62′ 0″ × 9′ 0″ & 9′ 3″.
Weight:
Seats 2nd: 120.

Trailer Saloon Second

Body: 62′ 0″ × 9′ 0″ & 9′ 3″.
Weight:
Seats 2nd: 102.

Motor Saloon Brake Second

(As Above)

4378	4381	4384	4387
4379	4382	4385	
4380	4383	4386	

Motor Saloon Brake Second

Body: 62′ 6″ × 9′ 0″ & 9′ 3″.
Weight:
Seats 2nd: 82.
Equipment: Two 250 h.p. English Electric traction motors.

Trailer Second

Body: 62′ 6″ × 9′ 0″ & 9′ 3″.
Weight:
Seats 2nd: 120.

Trailer Second

(As Above)

Motor Saloon Brake Second

(As Above)

4601	4603	4605	4607
4602	4604	4606	

Motor Saloon Brake Second

Body: 62′ 6″ × 9′ 0″ & 9′ 3″.
Weight:
Seats 2nd: 82.
Equipment: Two 250 h.p. English Electric traction motors.

Trailer Second

Body: 62′ 0″ × 9′ 0 & 9′ 3 .
Weight:
Seats 2nd: 120.
108*.

Trailer Saloon Second

Body: 62′ 0″ × 9′ 0″ & 9′ 3″.
Weight:
Seats 2nd: 102.

Motor Brake Saloon Second

(As Above)

4621	4629	4637	4645
4622	4630	4638	4646
4623	4631	4639	4647
4624	4632	4640	4648
4625	4633	4641	4649
4626	4634	4642	4650
4627	4635	4643	4651
4628	4636	4644	4652

4653	4679	4705	4730
4654	4680	4706	4731
4655	4681	4707	4732
4656	4682	4708	4733*
4657	4683	4709	4734
4658	4684	4710	4735
4659	4685	4711	4736
4660	4686	4712	4737
4661	4687	4713	4738
4662	4688*	4714	4739*
4663	4689	4715	4740
4664	4690	4716	4741
4665	4691	4717	4742
4666	4692	4718	4743
4667	4693	4719	4744
4668	4694	4720	4745
4669	4695	4721	4746
4670	4696*	4722	4747
4671	4697	4723*	4748
4672	4698	4724	4749
4673	4699	4725	4750
4674	4700	4726	4751
4675	4701	4727	4752
4676	4702	4728*	4753
4677	4703	4729	4754
4678	4704		

FOUR-CAR SUBURBAN SETS (4-EPB.)

Motor Saloon Brake Second

Body: 62′ 6″ × 9′ 0″ & 9′ 3″.
Weight:
Seats 2nd: 82.
Equipment: Two 250 h.p. English Electric traction motors.

Trailer Second

Body: 62′ 0″ × 9′ 0″ & 9′ 3″.
Weight:
Seats 2nd: 120.
108*.

Trailer Saloon Second

Body: 62′ 0″ × 9′ 0″ & 9′ 3″.
Weight:
Seats 2nd: 102.

Motor Saloon Brake Second

(As Above)

5001	5039	5122	5158
5002	5040	5123	5159
5003	5041	5124	5160
5004	5042	5125	5161
5005*	5043	5126	5162
5006	5044	5127	5163
5007	5045	5128	5164
5009	5046	5129	5165
5010	5047	5130	5166
5011	5048	5131	5167
5012	5049	5132	5168
5013	5050	5133	5169
5014	5051	5134	5170
5015	5052	5135	5171
5016	5053	5136	5172
5017	5101	5137	5173
5018	5102	5138	5174
5019	5103	5139	5175
5020	5104	5140	5176
5021	5105	5141	5177
5022	5106	5142	5178
5024	5107	5143	5179
5025	5108	5144	5180
5026	5109	5145	5181
5027	5110	5146	5182
5028	5111	5147	5183
5029	5112	5148	5184
5030	5113	5149	5185
5031	5114	5150	5186
5032	5115	5151	5187
5033	5116	5152	5188
5034	5117	5153	5189
5035	5118	5154	5190
5036	5119	5155	5191
5037	5120	5156	5192
5038	5121	5157	5193

5194	5212	5229	5245
5195	5213	5230	5246
5196	5214	5231	5247
5197	5215	5232	5248
5198	5216	5233	5249
5199	5217	5234	5250
5200	5218	5235	5251
5201	5219	5236	5252
5202	5220*	5237	5253
5203	5221	5238	5254
5205	5222	5239	5255
5206	5223	5240	5256
5207	5224	5241	5257
5208	5225	5242	5258
5209	5226	5243	5259
5210	5227	5244	5260
5211	5228		

FOUR-CAR SUBURBAN SETS (4-EPB.)

B.R. Standard design

Motor Saloon Brake Second

Body: 63′ 11½″ × 9′ 0″ & 9′ 3″.
Weight:
Seats 2nd:
Equipment:

Trailer Second (semi-saloon)

Body: 63′ 6″ × 9′ 0″ & 9′ 3″.
Weight:
Seats 2nd:

Trailer Second (semi-saloon)

Body: 63′ 6″ × 9′ 0″ & 9′ 3″.
Weight:
Seats 2nd:

Motor Saloon Brake Second

(As Above)

5301*	5315	5329	5343
5302*	5316	5330	5344
5303	5317	5331	5345
5304	5318	5332	5346
5305	5319	5333	5347
5306	5320	5334	5348
5307	5321	5335	5349
5308	5322	5336	5350
5309	5323	5337	5351
5310	5324	5338	5352
5311	5325	5339	5353
5312	5326	5340	5354
5313	5327	5341	5355
5314	5328	5342	5356

*Formed partly of S.R. type vehicles on 62′ underframes.

TWO-CAR SETS (2-HAP.)

Motor Brake Second (Semi-Saloon)

Body: 62′ 6″ × 9′ 0″ & 9′ 3″.
Weight: 40. tons.
Seats 2nd: 84.
Equipment: Two 250 h.p. English Electric traction motors.

Driving Trailer Composite (K)

Body: 62′ 6″ × 9′ 0″ & 9′ 3″.
Weight: 32 tons.
Seats 1st 18.
2nd: 38.

5601	5610	5619	5628
5602	5611	5620	5629
5603	5612	5621	5630
5604	5613	5622	5631
5605	5614	5623	5632
5606	5615	5624	5633
5607	5616	5625	5634
5608	5617	5626	5635
5609	5618	5627	5636

TWO-CAR SUBURBAN SETS (2-NOP.)

Motor Brake Second (Semi-Saloon)

Body: 62′ 6″ × 9′ 0″ & 9′ 3″.
Weight:
Seats 2nd:
Equipment: Two 250 h.p. English Electric traction motors.

Driving Trailer Second (Semi-Saloon)

Body: 62′ 6″ × 9′ 0″ & 9′ 3″.
Weight:
Seats 2nd:

5651	5660	5669	5677
5652	5661	5670	5678
5653	5662	5671	5679
5654	5663	5672	5680
5655	5664	5673	5681
5656	5665	5674	5682
5657	5666	5675	5683
5658	5667	5676	5684
5659	5668		

TWO-CAR SUBURBAN SETS (2-EPB.)

B.R. Standard design

Motor Brake Second (Semi-Saloon)

Body: 63′ 11½″ × 9′ 0″ & 9′ 3″.
Weight: 41 tons.
Seats 2nd: 84.
Equipment: Two 250 h.p. English Electric traction motors.

Driving Trailer Second (Semi-Saloon)

Body: 63′ 11½″ × 9′ 0″ & 9′ 3″.
Weight: 30 tons.
Seats 2nd: 102.

5701	5721	5741	5761
5702	5722	5742	5762
5703	5723	5743	5763
5704	5724	5744	5764
5705	5725	5745	5765
5706	5726	5746	5767
5707	5727	5747	5768
5708	5728	5748	5769
5709	5729	5749	5770
5710	5730	5750	5771
5711	5731	5751	5772
5712	5732	5752	5773
5713	5733	5753	5774
5714	5734	5754	5775
5715	5735	5755	5776
5716	5736	5756	5777
5717	5737	5757	5778
5718	5738	5758	5779
5719	5739	5759	5800
5720	5740	5760	

TWO-CAR SETS (2-HAP.)

B.R. Standard design

Motor Brake Second (Semi-Saloon)

Body: 63′ 11½″ × 9′ 0″ & 9′ 3″
Weight: 41 tons.
Seats 2nd: 84.
Equipment: Two 250 h.p. English Electric traction motors.

Driving Trailer Composite (L)

Body: 63′ 11½″ × 9′ 0″ & 9′ 3″.
Weight: 30 tons.
Seats 1st: 19.
2nd: 50.

6001	6028	6054	6080
6002	6029	6055	6081
6003	6030	6056	6082
6004	6031	6057	6083
6005	6032	6058	6084
6006	6033	6059	6085
6007	6034	6060	6086
6008	6035	6061	6087
6009	6036	6062	6088
6010	6037	6063	6089
6011	6038	6064	6090
6012	6039	6065	6091
6013	6040	6066	6092
6014	6041	6067	6093
6015	6042	6068	6094
6016	6043	6069	6095
6017	6044	6070	6096
6018	6045	6071	6097
6019	6046	6072	6098
6020	6047	6073	6099
6021	6048	6074	6100
6022	6049	6075	6101
6023	6050	6076	6102
6024	6051	6077	6103
6025	6052	6078	6104
6026	6053	6079	6105
6027			

FOUR-CAR SETS (4-BEP.)

B.R. Standard design

Gangwayed throughout

Motor Saloon Brake Second

Body: 64′ 6″ × 9′ 0″ & 9′ 3″.
Weight: 40 tons*.
41 tons.
Seats 2nd: 36.
Equipment: Two 250 h.p. English Electric traction motors.

Trailer Composite (K)

Body: 64′ 6″ × 9′ 0″ & 9′ 3″.
Weight: 31 tons*.
33 tons.
Seats 1st : 24
2nd: 24

Trailer Buffet

Body: 64′ 6″ × 9′ 0″ & 9′ 3″.
Weight: 35 tons*.
36 tons.
Seats Buffet: 21.

Motor Saloon Brake Second

(As Above)

7001*	7004	7007	7010
7002*	7005	7008	7011
7003	7006	7009	7012

FOUR-CAR SETS (4 CEP.)

B.R. Standard design

Gangwayed throughout

Motor Saloon Brake Second

Body: 64′ 6″ × 9′ 0″ & 9′ 3″.
Weight: 40 tons*.
41 tons.
Seats 2nd: 56.
Equipment: Two 250 h.p. English Electric traction motors.

Trailer Composite (K)

Body: 64′ 6″ × 9′ 0″ & 9′ 3″.
Weight: 31 tons*.
33 tons.
Seats 1st: 24.
2nd: 24.

Trailer Second (K)

Body: 64′ 6″ × 9′ 0″ & 9′ 3″.
Weight: 31 tons*.
32 tons.
Seats 2nd: 64.

Motor Saloon Brake Second

(As Above)

7101*	7104*	7107	7110
7102*	7105	7108	7111
7103*	7106	7109	7112

7113	7124	7134	7144
7114	7125	7135	7145
7115	7126	7136	7146
7116	7127	7137	7147
7117	7128	7138	7148
7118	7129	7139	7149
7119	7130	7140	7150
7120	7131	7141	7151
7121	7132	7142	7152
7122	7133	7143	7153
7123			

Motor Luggage Van

Body: 64′ 6″ × 9′ 0″ & 9′ 3″.
Weight:
Equipment: Two 250 h.p. English Electric traction motors.
Note: These vehicles can work singly, hauling a limited load, or in multiple with CEP type stock. They are equipped with traction batteries for working on non-electrified lines at Dover and Folkestone.

COACH Nos.
S68001 S68002

WATERLOO & CITY ONE- OR FIVE-CAR SETS

Motor Saloon Brake Second

Body: 47′ 0″ × 8′ 7¾″.
Weight:
Seats 2nd: 40.
Equipment: Two 190 h.p. English Electric traction motors.

51	54	57	60
52	55	58	61
53	56	59	62

Trailer Saloon Second

Body: 47′ 0″ × 8′ 7¾″.
Weight: 18 tons 14 cwt.
Seats 2nd: 52.

71	75	79	83
72	76	80	84
73	77	81	85
74	78	82	86

Trains are formed of a single motor car or up to five-car units comprising two motor cars and three trailers.

G.W.R. Railcars

Car No.	*Date*	*Engines*	*Total b.h.p.*	*Seats 2nd.*
5/7	1935	2	242	70
8	1936	2	242	70
13/4§	1936	2	242	—
15	1936	2	242	70
17*	1936	2	242	—
19-32†	1940	2	210	48
33, 38‡	1942	4	420	92
34*	1941	2	210	—
‖1096	—	-	—	64

*Parcels cars.
‡Twin-coach unit with buffet facilities. Adjoining statistics apply per 2-car unit. These cars work and a three-car set with corridor second W1096W.
†These cars may work in pairs with an additional ordinary coach between.
§Rebuilt as Parcels Cars.
‖This is an ordinary 60 ft. ex-G.W. Corridor Second adapted for use between two diesel railcars, and is painted green.

W5W	W14W	W20W	W24W
W7W	W15W	W21W	W25W
W8W	W17W	W22W	W26W
W13W	W19W	W23W	W27W
W28W	W30W	W32W	W34W
W29W	W31W	W33W	W38W
			W1096W

Battery Electric Railcar Motor Brake Second
(TWIN UNIT)

Built by: **Derby/Cowlairs Works, B.R.**
Electrical Equipment: Two 100 kW Siemens-Schuckert nose-suspended traction motors powered by 216 lead-acid cell batteries of 1070 amp/hour capacity.
Body: 57′ 6″ × 9′ 2″.
Weight: 37 tons 10 cwt.
Seats 2nd: 52.

SC79998

Battery Electric Railcar Driving Trailer Composite
(TWIN UNIT)

Built by: **Derby/Cowlairs Works, B.R.**
Body: 57′ 6″ × 9′ 2″.
Weight: 32 tons 10 cwt.
Seats 1st: 12. *2nd:* 53.

SC79999

abc
LOCOSHED BOOK

Summer
1960

LONDON:
Ian Allan Ltd

NOTES ON THE USE OF THIS BOOK

The *ABC Locoshed Book* is not designed to be used on its own, but as a companion to the *ABC of British Railways Locomotives*. As it is difficult to include shed allocations in the latter without harm to the format which has proved popular with *ABC* users, this all-in-one *Locoshed Book* was instituted wherein the number of each British Railways locomotive is listed with the code number of the shed to which it is allocated.

1. No details of wheel arrangements, dimensions or locomotive names are provided in the *Locoshed Book*. All these details are readily ascertained from the *ABC of British Railways Locomotives*, as follows:

PART I	**Locomotives Nos.**	**1–9999**
PART II	,,	**10000–39999**
PART III	,,	**40000–59999**
PART IV	,,	**60000–99999**

Each 2/6

and the *ABC of British Railways Diesels* **2/6.**
ABC of British Railways Electrics **2/6.**

In this publication named locomotives are indicated by an asterisk.

2. Against each locomotive in this booklet is shown the code of its home shed, which the locomotive carries on a small plate at the bottom of the smokebox door; in the case of Diesel and Electric locomotives the plate is affixed to the cab side or the information is painted on the buffer beam. A key to the British Railways shed code is found on pp. 4–9.

3. Sub-sheds, which are not given a special code number by British Railways are included in this list, but locomotives allocated to them carry the shed code of the parent depot, whose number appears immediately above them in the list of shed codes. Sheds listed in bold type are chief sheds of a motive power district.

4. Locomotives not given a shed code were on order, under construction or not yet allocated at the time of compilation.

5. All locomotives solely employed on service or departmental work, whether numbered in the British Railways or in individual departmental series, are listed on pages 89 and 90.

6. **The shed allocations given in this booklet are as they were reported to the following dates:—E.R. to May 21st, 1960; L.M.R. to April 23rd, 1960; N.E.R. to May 28th, 1960; Sc.R. to April 9th, 1960; S.R. to May 6th, 1960; W.R. to April 23rd, 1960. To enable the user to keep the booklet up to date, full details of all alterations in shed allocations are published each month in the Ian Allan periodical, *Trains Illustrated*, price 2s. 0d., obtainable from any bookstall or newsagent.**

BRITISH RAILWAYS LOCOMOTIVE SHEDS AND SHED CODES

(INCLUDING PRINCIPAL SIGNING-ON POINTS)

ALL B.R. STEAM LOCOMOTIVES CARRY THE CODE OF THEIR HOME DEPOT ON A SMALL PLATE AFFIXED TO THE SMOKEBOX DOOR. DIESEL AND ELECTRIC LOCOMOTIVES CARRY THE PLATE ON THE CAB SIDE OR HAVE THE DEPOT NAME PAINTED ON THE BUFFER BEAM.

Some locomotives have been transferred from one Region to another but the receiving Region has not yet announced an allocation. In such cases, the initials of the receiving Region are shown.

LONDON MIDLAND REGION

1A **Willesden**
1B Camden
1C Watford
1D Devons Road (Bow)
1E Bletchley
Leighton Buzzard

2A **Rugby**
2B Nuneaton
2E Northampton
2F Woodford Halse

3A **Bescot**
3B Bushbury
3C Walsall
3D Aston
3E Monument Lane

5A **Crewe North**
5B Crewe South
5C Stafford
5D Stoke
5E Alsager
5F Uttoxeter

6A **Chester (Midland)**
6B Mold Junction
6C Birkenhead
6F Bidston
6G Llandudno Junction
6H Bangor
6J Holyhead
6K Rhyl

8A **Edge Hill**
8B Warrington (Dallam)
8C Speke Junction
8D Widnes
8E Northwich
8F Springs Branch (Wigan)
8G Sutton Oak

9A **Longsight (Manchester)**
9B Stockport (Edgeley)
9C Macclesfield
9D Buxton
9E Trafford Park
Glazebrook
9F Heaton Mersey
Gowhole
9G Gorton
Dinting
Reddish

NOTE

Since this edition was prepared for press, the L.M. Region have notified the following alterations in Shed Codes:

3A	Bescot	renumbered **21B**	**11A**	Barrow	renumbered **12E**
3B	Bushbury	renumbered **21C**	**11B**	Workington	renumbered **12F**
3C	Walsall	renumbered **21F**	**11C**	Oxenholme	renumbered **12G**
3D	Aston	renumbered **21D**	**11D**	Tebay	renumbered **12H**
3E	Monument Lane	renumbered **21E**			

The codes shown in this book against the engines involved in these changes are the old numbers, and require to be amended.

11A **Barrow**
11B Workington
11C Oxenholme
11D Tebay

12A **Carlisle (Kingmoor)**
12B Carlisle (Upperby)
Penrith
12C Carlisle (Canal)
12D Kirkby Stephen

14A **Cricklewood**
14B Kentish Town
14D Neasden
Aylesbury
14E Bedford

15A **Wellingborough**
15B Kettering
15C Leicester (Midland)
15D Coalville
15E Leicester (Central)
15F Market Harborough

16A **Nottingham**
16B Kirkby-in-Ashfield
16D Annesley

17A **Derby**
17B Burton
Horninglow
Overseal
17C Rowsley
Cromford
Middleton
Sheep Pasture

18A **Toton (Stapleford & Sandiacre)**
18B Westhouses
18C Hasland

21A **Saltley**

24A **Accrington**
24B Rose Grove
24C Lostock Hall
24D Lower Darwen
24E Blackpool
24F Fleetwood
24G Skipton
24H Hellifield
24J Lancaster (Green Ayre)
24K Preston
24L Carnforth

26A **Newton Heath**
26B Agecroft
26C Bolton
26D Bury
26E Lees (Oldham)
26F Patricroft

27A **Bank Hall**
27B Aintree
27C Southport
27D Wigan
27E Walton-on-the-Hill
27F Brunswick (Liverpool)
Warrington (Central)

EASTERN REGION

FP **Finsbury Park Diesel Depot**

30A **Stratford**
Bishops Stortford
Chelmsford
Enfield Town
Hertford East
Southend (Victoria)
Wood St. (Walthamstow)
30E Colchester
Clacton
Maldon
Walton-on-Naze
30F Parkeston

31A **Cambridge**
Ely
31B March
31C Kings Lynn

32A **Norwich Thorpe**
Cromer Beach
32B Ipswich
32C Lowestoft Central
32D Yarmouth South Town

33B Tilbury
33C Shoeburyness

34A **Kings Cross**
34B Hornsey
34C Hatfield
34D Hitchin
34E New England
34F Grantham

36A **Doncaster**
36C Frodingham
36E Retford

40A **Lincoln**
40B Immingham
Grimsby
New Holland
40E Colwick
40F Boston
Sleaford

41A **Sheffield (Darnall)**
41B Sheffield (Grimesthorpe)
41C Millhouses
41D Canklow
41E Staveley (Barrow Hill)
41F Mexborough
41H Staveley (G.C.)
41J Langwith

NORTH EASTERN REGION

50A **York**
50B Hull (Dairycoates)
Hull (Alexandra Dock)
50C Hull (Botanic Gardens)
50D Goole
50E Scarborough
50F Malton

51A **Darlington**
51C West Hartlepool
51F West Auckland
51J Northallerton
51L Thornaby

52A **Gateshead**
Bowes Bridge
52B Heaton
52C Blaydon
Alston
52D Tweedmouth
Alnmouth
52E Percy Main
52F North and South Blyth

52G Sunderland
52H Tyne Dock
Pelton Level
52K Consett

55A **Leeds (Holbeck)**
55B Stourton
55C Farnley
55D Royston
55E Normanton
55F Bradford (Manningham)
Keighley
55G Huddersfield
55H Leeds (Neville Hill)

56A **Wakefield**
Knottingley
56B Ardsley
56C Copley Hill
56D Mirfield
56E Sowerby Bridge
56F Low Moor
56G Bradford (Hammerton St.)

SCOTTISH REGION

60A **Inverness**
Dingwall
Kyle of Lochalsh
60B Aviemore
Boat of Garten
60C Helmsdale
Tain
60D Wick
Thurso

61A **Kittybrewster**
Ballater
Fraserburgh
Inverurie
Peterhead
61B Aberdeen (Ferryhill)
61C Keith
Banff
Elgin

62A **Thornton**
Anstruther
Burntisland
Kirkcaldy
Ladybank
Methil
62B Dundee (Tay Bridge)
Arbroath
Montrose
St. Andrews
62C Dunfermline
Alloa
Kelty

63A **Perth**
Aberfeldy
Blair Atholl
Crieff
Forfar
63B Fort William
Mallaig
63C Oban
Ballachulish

64A **St. Margarets (Edinburgh)**
Dunbar
Galashiels
Hardengreen
Longniddry
North Berwick
Seafield
South Leith
64B Haymarket
64C Dalry Road
64F Bathgate
64G Hawick
64H Leith Central

65A **Eastfield (Glasgow)**
Arrochar
65B St. Rollox
65C Parkhead
65D Dawsholm
Dumbarton
65E Kipps
65F Grangemouth
65G Yoker
65H Helensburgh
65I Balloch
65J Stirling
Killin
65K Polmont

66A **Polmadie (Glasgow)**
66B Motherwell
66C Hamilton
66D Greenock (Ladyburn)
66E Carstairs

67A **Corkerhill (Glasgow)**
67B Hurlford
Beith
Muirkirk
67C Ayr
67D Ardrossan

68B Dumfries
68C Stranraer
68D Beattock

SOUTHERN REGION

70A **Nine Elms**
70B Feltham
70C Guildford
    Reading South
70D Basingstoke
70H Ryde (I.O.W.)

71A **Eastleigh**
    Andover Junction
    Lymington
    Southampton Terminus
    Winchester
71B Bournemouth
    Branksome
71G Weymouth
    Bridport
71I Southampton Docks

72A **Exmouth Junction**
    Bude
    Callington
    Exmouth
    Lyme Regis
    Okehampton
    Seaton

72B Salisbury
72C Yeovil
72E Barnstaple Junction
    Ilfracombe
    Torrington
72F Wadebridge

73A **Stewarts Lane**
73B Bricklayers Arms
73C Hither Green
73E Faversham
73F Ashford (Kent)
    Gillingham (Kent)
    Ramsgate
73H Dover
    Folkestone
73J Tonbridge

75A **Brighton**
75B Redhill
75C Norwood Junction
75E Three Bridges
    Horsham
75F Tunbridge Wells West

WESTERN REGION

81A **Old Oak Common**
81B Slough
    Marlow
81C Southall
81D Reading
81E Didcot
81F Oxford
    Fairford

82A **Bristol (Bath Road)**
    Bath
    Wells
    Weston-super-Mare
    Yatton
82B St. Philip's Marsh
82C Swindon
    Chippenham
82D Westbury
    Frome
82E Bristol (Barrow Road)

82F Bath (Green Park)
    Radstock West
82G Templecombe

83A **Newton Abbot**
    Kingsbridge
83B Taunton
    Bridgwater
83C Exeter
    Tiverton Junction
83D Laira (Plymouth)
    Launceston
83E St. Blazey
    Bodmin
    Moorswater
83F Truro
83G Penzance
    Helston
    St. Ives
83H Plymouth (Friary)

84A **Wolverhampton (Stafford Road)**
84B Oxley
84C Banbury
84D Leamington Spa
84E Tyseley
  Stratford-on-Avon
84F Stourbridge Junction
84G Shrewsbury
  Craven Arms
  Knighton
  Builth Road
84H Wellington (Salop)
84J Croes Newydd
  Bala
  Penmaenpool
  Trawsfynydd

85A **Worcester**
  Evesham
  Kingham
85B Gloucester
  Brimscombe
  Cheltenham (Malvern Road)
  Lydney
85C Hereford
  Leominster
  Ross
85D Kidderminster
85E Gloucester (Barnwood)
  Dursley
  Tewkesbury
85F Bromsgrove
  Redditch

86A **Newport (Ebbw Junction)**
86B Newport (Pill)
86C Cardiff (Canton)
86D Llantrisant
86E Severn Tunnel Junction
86F Tondu
86G Pontypool Road
86H Aberbeeg
86J Aberdare
86K Tredegar

87A **Neath**
  Glyn Neath
  Neath (N. & B.)
87B Duffryn Yard
87C Danygraig
87D Swansea East Dock
  Gurnos
  Upper Bank
87E Landore
87F Llanelly
  Burry Port
  Llandovery
  Pantyffynnon
87G Carmarthen
87H Neyland
  Cardigan
  Milford Haven
  Pembroke Dock
  Whitland
87J Goodwick

88A **Cardiff (Radyr)**
  Cathays
88B Cardiff East Dock
88C Barry
88D Merthyr
  Dowlais Cae Harris
  Dowlais Central
  Rhymney
88E Abercynon
88F Treherbert
  Ferndale

89A **Oswestry**
  Llanidloes
  Moat Lane
89B Brecon
89C Machynlleth
  Aberystwyth
  Aberystwyth (V. of R.)
  Portmadoc
  Pwllheli

ABBREVIATIONS USED

CW —Crewe Works
HW —Horwich Works
RW —St. Rollox Works
RTS —Rugby Testing Station
STS —Swindon Testing Station
WW—Wolverton Works

SHED ALLOCATIONS OF BRITISH RAILWAYS LOCOMOTIVES

IN NUMERICAL ORDER

7 *	89C
8 *	89C
9 *	89C
822	89A
823	89A
1000 *	82A
1001 *	87H
1002 *	83G
1003 *	84G
1004 *	82C
1005 *	82A
1006 *	83G
1007 *	83C
1008 *	83G
1009 *	82A
1010 *	82C
1011 *	82A
1012 *	82C
1013 *	84G
1014 *	82A
1015 *	82C
1016 *	84G
1017 *	84G
1018 *	83G
1019 *	82C
1020 *	87H
1021 *	82C
1022 *	84G
1023 *	83C
1024 *	82A
1025 *	84G
1026 *	84G
1027 *	82A
1028 *	82A
1029 *	87H
1143	84G
1151	87D
1152	87D
1338	83B
1361	71G
1362	83B
1363	83D
1364	82C
1365	82C
1366	83B
1367	71G
1368	71G
1369	71G
1371	82C
1407	81C
1409	85B
1410	82C
1412	82A
1419	83E
1420	83D
1421	83D
1424	85B
1426	85B
1427	85B
1431	85B
1432	89A
1433	85B
1434	83D
1435	81F
1438	89A
1440	83C
1441	85B
1442	81F
1444	81B
1445	85C
1447	81B
1448	81B
1449	89C
1450	81F
1451	83C
1452	83C
1453	81B
1454	85B
1455	85C
1458	89A
1462	83C
1463	82A
1464	82C
1466	83A
1468	83C
1470	83A
1471	83C
1472	85B
1473	14D
1474	81D
1500	81A
1501	81C
1502	81E
1503	81A
1504	81A
1505	81A
1506	86A
1507	81A
1508	86C
1601	87H
1602	89A
1604	89A
1605	85B
1606	87F
1607	87F
1608	83C
1609	87F
1611	87F
1612	88E
1613	87H
1614	87F
1615	87F
1617	85C
1618	84J
1619	84F
1620	88E
1621	84F
1622	87F
1623	85B
1624	83E
1625	85C
1626	83E
1627	85B
1628	89A
1629	85A
1630	85B
1631	85B
1632	85B
1633	87F
1634	82C
1636	89A
1637	87H
1638	87F
1639	85B
1640	82C
1641	88E
1642	85B
1643	87F
1645	87A
1646	60C
1647	85A
1648	87G
1649	60C
1650	83D
1651	87F
1653	86A
1654	87F
1655	87F
1656	86A
1657	85C
1658	82C
1659	84J
1660	84J
1661	85A
1662	85C
1663	84F
1664	83E
1665	87F
1666	87F
1667	85C
1668	83B
1669	81C
2200	81E
2201	81E
2202	89C
2203	82B
2204	89C
2206	81D
2207	85B
2209	85A
2210	81D
2211	84E
2212	81D
2213	82B
2214	81E
2215	82B
2216	87G
2217	89C
2218	86A
2219	86A
2220	87H
2221	81E
2222	81A
2223	86A

2224	82B
2227	86A
2229	82E
2230	81E
2231	86E
2232	89C
2233	89C
2234	85A
2236	86A
2239	89A
2240	81E
2241	85C
2242	85C
2243	85A
2244	89C
2245	85B
2246	81E
2247	86A
2248	85B
2249	85C
2250	82C
2251	87H
2253	85B
2255	89C
2256	84C
2257	84E
2260	89C
2261	82B
2264	89C
2265	82B
2267	84E
2268	82D
2271	87J
2273	85A
2274	87G
2276	81A
2277	82B
2282	81A
2283	87H
2286	89C
2287	89A
2288	82B
2289	85A
2291	82C
2292	86E
2294	89C
2295	85C
2297	84C
2298	89C
2805	83A
2807	83A
2813	86J
2818	86A
2819	81E
2821	86C
2822	83B
2834	86C
2835	82C
2836	81E
2837	86E
2839	86G
2841	81D
2842	81D
2845	86G
2846	83A
2849	81E
2851	83B
2852	82C
2853	81D
2854	85B
2855	84J
2856	84F
2857	86G
2858	86A
2859	86G
2860	86E
2861	86E
2862	86E
2865	86C
2866	86G
2867	86G
2871	84J
2872	86E
2873	86J
2874	86C
2875	83A
2876	86J
2879	82C
2882	83B
2883	86G
2884	86A
2885	84F
2886	86J
2887	86E
2888	84F
2889	86C
2890	82C
2891	86C
2892	86E
2893	81E
2894	86A
2895	86E
2896	86E
2897	84F
2898	86A
2899	83D
3200	89A
3201	84J
3202	89A
3203	85B
3204	85A
3205	85A
3206	81E
3207	84G
3208	89A
3209	89A
3210	81E
3211	81E
3212	82D
3213	85A
3214	85A
3215	82B
3216	85A
3217	84C
3218	82G
3219	81D
3400	84G
3401	88A
3402	88A
3403	88A
3404	88A
3405	88A
3406	88A
3407	88A
3408	88A
3409	88A
3440 *	82C
3600	89A
3601	85D
3602	84G
3603	86J
3604	82A
3605	85A
3606	82E
3607	85A
3608	81B
3609	85B
3610	86J
3611	87A
3612	86D
3613	87B
3614	82D
3615	84A
3616	86F
3617	86D
3618	81C
3619	84D
3620	81C
3621	87A
3622	81E
3623	82A
3624	84D
3625	84E
3626	84H
3627	86J
3628	86G
3629	82D
3630	6A
3631	84D
3632	82B
3633	73H
3634	86A
3635	83E
3636	86A
3637	87J
3638	86A
3639	87H
3640	86G
3641	87D
3642	87F
3643	82B
3644	86D
3645	82C
3646	84C
3647	86H
3648	81A
3649	84F
3650	82B
3651	86G
3652	86B
3653	81E
3654	87H
3655	86J
3656	86D
3657	84E
3658	84F
3659	83A
3660	84E
3661	87D
3662	86A
3663	86D
3664	84A
3665	6A
3666	82C
3667	84F
3668	86F
3669	83B
3670	86C
3671	72C
3672	88A
3673	84E
3674	86B
3675	83D
3676	6A
3677	82A
3678	87E
3679	72A
3680	86D
3681	88A
3682	82C
3683	86H
3684	82C
3685	86G
3686	83D
3687	87A
3688	81A
3689	84J
3690	86F

3691-4130

3691 86A
3692 82B
3693 84E
3694 86A
3695 86J
3696 82D
3697 81B
3698 84B
3699 86J
3700 86K
3701 87E
3702 83F
3703 86G
3704 81C
3705 83E
3706 86A
3707 88E
3708 86G
3709 81E
3710 84F
3711 82C
3712 86K
3713 86A
3714 86A
3715 84A
3716 86J
3717 86G
3718 87B
3719 87F
3720 82G
3721 81E
3722 81F
3723 81D
3724 82C
3725 85A
3726 82B
3727 88C
3728 85C
3729 84F
3730 88E
3731 82B
3732 84H
3733 72C
3734 88E
3735 82D
3736 83B
3737 71G
3738 81D
3739 82C
3741 87A
3742 82F
3743 84F
3744 84H
3745 84F
3746 82C
3747 86A
3748 82A
3749 84J
3750 81C
3751 81E
3752 82E
3753 86J
3754 81A
3755 86C
3756 84A
3757 87A
3758 82C
3759 71G
3760 84J
3761 87F
3762 87B
3763 82C
3764 82B
3765 82B
3766 87A
3767 86A
3768 87E
3769 84G
3770 89A
3771 87F
3772 86A
3773 82B
3774 87A
3775 85A
3776 82B
3777 87F
3778 84A
3779 86G
3780 82C
3781 86F
3782 84G
3783 88E
3784 82B
3785 87E
3786 6A
3787 83D
3788 84G
3789 89A
3790 83D
3791 87B
3792 84A
3794 83C
3795 82B
3796 83A
3797 87E
3798 86A
3799 81C
3800 86E
3801 86E
3802 84B
3803 85B
3804 86G
3805 86A
3806 86A
3807 86A
3808 86A
3809 86C
3810 86C
3811 87F
3812 86E
3813 84B
3814 81F
3815 84J
3816 84F
3817 86C
3818 86G
3819 82D
3820 84B
3821 84F
3822 86G
3823 81F
3824 86A
3825 84F
3826 86G
3827 86A
3828 84J
3829 84B
3830 86A
3831 84F
3832 86A
3833 86A
3834 87F
3835 86C
3836 84G
3837 86A
3838 86E
3839 84F
3840 83A
3841 83A
3842 84B
3843 81D
3844 86G
3845 86C
3846 84F
3847 86E
3848 85B
3849 86C
3850 86J
3851 87F
3852 86E
3853 86A
3854 84B
3855 86C
3856 86E
3857 81F
3858 81D
3859 86G
3860 86C
3861 84B
3862 83D
3863 86E
3864 83A
3865 84B
3866 86J
4037 * 83A
4073 * 86C
4074 * 87E
4075 * 81A
4076 * 87E
4077 * 82A
4078 * 81A
4079 * 82A
4080 * 83A
4081 * 82A
4082 * 81A
4083 * 83A
4084 * 86C
4085 * 85A
4086 * 86C
4087 * 83D
4088 * 85A
4089 * 85A
4090 * 87G
4092 * 81D
4093 * 87E
4094 * 87E
4095 * 83G
4096 * 81A
4097 * 87E
4098 * 83A
4099 * 87E
4100 85B
4101 85B
4102 82C
4103 81F
4104 84F
4105 83A
4106 87E
4107 87E
4108 83F
4109 85A
4110 84F
4111 84E
4112 84D
4113 85A
4114 85D
4115 85C
4116 85B
4117 83C
4118 84D
4119 86E
4120 84H
4121 86F
4122 87H
4123 85B
4124 85A
4125 81F
4126 84E
4127 86E
4128 83B
4129 82A
4130 86E

4131	82B
4132	87H
4133	71G
4134	87G
4135	86G
4136	83G
4137	86E
4140	84F
4141	85B
4142	85A
4143	88A
4144	86F
4145	83A
4146	86A
4147	81F
4148	81F
4149	84C
4150	83A
4151	86E
4152	86E
4153	85D
4154	84C
4155	84E
4156	86E
4157	83B
4158	84H
4159	83B
4160	88A
4161	84F
4162	84D
4163	88A
4165	85B
4166	71G
4167	83E
4168	84F
4169	87A
4170	84E
4171	84D
4172	84E
4173	84F
4174	83A
4175	85D
4176	83A
4177	83A
4178	83A
4179	83A
4203	86A
4207	86C
4213	87B
4214	86B
4218	86F
4222	86F
4225	86C
4227	86A
4228	86J
4229	86E
4230	86C
4232	87D
4233	86B
4235	86B
4236	86F
4237	86H
4238	86B
4241	86E
4242	87A
4243	86F
4246	86A
4247	86A
4248	86A
4250	86H
4251	86F
4252	86D
4253	86B
4254	86C
4255	87A
4256	87B
4257	86J
4258	86B
4259	86B
4262	86J
4263	86F
4264	87A
4265	87B
4266	86C
4267	86D
4268	86D
4269	86F
4270	86C
4271	87D
4272	87F
4273	86D
4274	86F
4275	87A
4276	86B
4277	86H
4278	87B
4279	87A
4280	86B
4281	87A
4282	87A
4283	86A
4284	87A
4285	86H
4286	87F
4287	86H
4288	87A
4289	86E
4290	86A
4291	86H
4292	87F
4293	87B
4294	83E
4295	87A
4296	87B
4297	86A
4298	86C
4299	87B
4507	72C
4549	83D
4550	87H
4552	83E
4555	83A
4556	87H
4557	87H
4558	87H
4559	83E
4561	83A
4563	83G
4564	83G
4565	83E
4566	83G
4567	82D
4569	83E
4570	83G
4571	83G
4573	85B
4574	83F
4575	82A
4587	83F
4588	83G
4589	83C
4591	83D
4593	83F
4594	87H
4600	86G
4601	73H
4602	6A
4603	82B
4604	83B
4605	84H
4606	81B
4607	82D
4608	81C
4609	81D
4610	73H
4611	86A
4612	82C
4613	85A
4614	85A
4615	81A
4616	73H
4617	84J
4618	88C
4619	82A
4620	86D
4621	87A
4622	83F
4623	84G
4624	71G
4625	85A
4626	73H
4627	86H
4628	85B
4629	85D
4630	73H
4631	73H
4632	88D
4633	86C
4634	70A
4635	88D
4636	82D
4637	86D
4638	81B
4639	86G
4640	87B
4641	81D
4642	86G
4643	86B
4644	81A
4645	84J
4646	84F
4647	82D
4648	84E
4649	81E
4650	81B
4651	82C
4652	86H
4653	87A
4654	87H
4655	82B
4656	72C
4657	85C
4658	83D
4659	85C
4660	82B
4661	81D
4662	86D
4663	83B
4664	85A
4665	81D
4666	72F
4667	88C
4668	86G
4669	86F
4670	81D
4671	86A
4672	70A
4673	81C
4674	86D
4675	86F
4676	87F
4677	87J
4678	85C
4679	83D
4680	85B
4681	70A
4682	86B
4683	84J
4684	87B
4685	86H
4687	84F
4688	82B

4689	71G
4690	88D
4691	81B
4692	70A
4693	84G
4694	72F
4695	87B
4696	84F
4697	82C
4698	70A
4699	87H
4700	81A
4701	81A
4702	81A
4703	82B
4704	81A
4705	83D
4706	82B
4707	81C
4708	81A
4901 *	84A
4902 *	81E
4903 *	81D
4904 *	83B
4905 *	83A
4906 *	83E
4907 *	85A
4908 *	81D
4909 *	82B
4910 *	84C
4912 *	84B
4913 *	85C
4914 *	82B
4915 *	81E
4916 *	86G
4917 *	82D
4918 *	84A
4919 *	81A
4920 *	83A
4921 *	81D
4922 *	82B
4923 *	84C
4924 *	83B
4925 *	81C
4926 *	86G
4927 *	86E
4928 *	86C
4929 *	85B
4930 *	83B
4931 *	86C
4932 *	83B
4933 *	82D
4934 *	81C
4935 *	87G
4936 *	83A
4937 *	86G
4938 *	84A
4939 *	81E
4941 *	87F
4942 *	84C
4943 *	86G
4944 *	83C
4945 *	82D
4946 *	84G
4947 *	82B
4948 *	83C
4949 *	82B
4950 *	83D
4951 *	84B
4952 *	86C
4953 *	82C
4954 *	84A
4955 *	83B
4956 *	86C
4957 *	84G
4958 *	86G
4959 *	81E
4960 *	82B
4961 *	81D
4962 *	81D
4963 *	84B
4964 *	84C
4965 *	81E
4966 *	84B
4967 *	83D
4968 *	82B
4969 *	81E
4970 *	83B
4971 *	83B
4972 *	82C
4973 *	86C
4974 *	84F
4975 *	83A
4976 *	83D
4977 *	81D
4978 *	83B
4979 *	81F
4980 *	82B
4981 *	87J
4982 *	84E
4983 *	86G
4984 *	84B
4985 *	83B
4986 *	84A
4987 *	81D
4988 *	86E
4989 *	85B
4990 *	85C
4991 *	83B
4992 *	83C
4993 *	85A
4994 *	81E
4995 *	81C
4996 *	85A
4997 *	84B
4998 *	81D
4999 *	86C
5000 *	82C
5001 *	84G
5002 *	82C
5003 *	83A
5004 *	87E
5006 *	87G
5007 *	82C
5008 *	81A
5009 *	82C
5011 *	83A
5012 *	81F
5013 *	87E
5014 *	81A
5015 *	82A
5016 *	87E
5017 *	85B
5018 *	81D
5019 *	84A
5020 *	83G
5021 *	86C
5022 *	84A
5023 *	82C
5024 *	83A
5025 *	81F
5026 *	84A
5027 *	81A
5028 *	83D
5029 *	83D
5030 *	87G
5031 *	84A
5032 *	81A
5033 *	81F
5034 *	81A
5035 *	81A
5036 *	81D
5037 *	85A
5038 *	84G
5039 *	87E
5040 *	81A
5041 *	87E
5042 *	81A
5043 *	81A
5044 *	81A
5045 *	84A
5046 *	84A
5047 *	84A
5048 *	82A
5049 *	83A
5050 *	84G
5051 *	87E
5052 *	81A
5053 *	83D
5054 *	81A
5055 *	83A
5056 *	81A
5057 *	81A
5058 *	83D
5059 *	84G
5060 *	81A
5061 *	86C
5062 *	82A
5063 *	84A
5064 *	82C
5065 *	81A
5066 *	81A
5067 *	87G
5068 *	82C
5069 *	83D
5070 *	84G
5071 *	85A
5072 *	84A
5073 *	82A
5074 *	81A
5075 *	83C
5076 *	81D
5077 *	87E
5078 *	82A
5079 *	83A
5080 *	87G
5081 *	85A
5082 *	81A
5084 *	81A
5085 *	82A
5087 *	81A
5088 *	84A
5089 *	84A
5090 *	82A
5091 *	87E
5092 *	82A
5093 *	81A
5094 *	85B
5095 *	86C
5096 *	82A
5097 *	82A
5098 *	83D
5099 *	86C
5101	84D
5103	86G
5104	82B
5110	86E
5150	83A
5151	84A
5152	84C
5153	83A
5154	83A
5158	83A
5164	83A
5166	86E
5167	84C
5169	86E
5173	85B

5174	83C	5237	86J	5418	85B	5573	83A
5175	83D	5238	86A	5420	84C	5600	88F
5176	84F	5239	87A	5421	85B	5601	88E
5177	84D	5240	87F	5422	89A	5602	86C
5179	85A	5241	86H	5503	83B	5603	88D
5180	87G	5242	87A	5504	83B	5604	87B
5181	86E	5243	85B	5508	82D	5605	88D
5182	85B	5244	86B	5509	83F	5606	84J
5183	83A	5245	85A	5510	82C	5607	88F
5184	84D	5246	87D	5511	83D	5608	88F
5187	84A	5247	87F	5514	85B	5609	88C
5188	86A	5248	87F	5515	83F	5610	88D
5190	81F	5249	86J	5516	86H	5611	88F
5191	86E	5250	86B	5518	85D	5612	87F
5192	84E	5251	86A	5519	83D	5613	88F
5193	83E	5252	86B	5520	87H	5614	88C
5194	84D	5253	86E	5521	83B	5615	88A
5195	83A	5254	87B	5523	83E	5616	87D
5197	82B	5255	86A	5524	83C	5617	88E
5198	85B	5256	86B	5525	83B	5618	88A
5199	84F	5257	86H	5526	82D	5619	88C
5200	86B	5258	86J	5527	87H	5620	86E
5201	86A	5259	86A	5529	82A	5621	88C
5202	86B	5260	86C	5531	83D	5622	88D
5203	87F	5261	86C	5532	83D	5623	88E
5204	87B	5262	87F	5534	83E	5624	86J
5205	86A	5263	86J	5536	82C	5625	86G
5206	86H	5264	87B	5537	83F	5626	88D
5207	86C	5306	86G	5538	83F	5627	88E
5208	86F	5311	82B	5539	83E	5628	87D
5209	87F	5318	86G	5540	89C	5629	86F
5210	87D	5322	86G	5541	83G	5630	88D
5211	87D	5324	84G	5542	82D	5631	87E
5212	86E	5326	82B	5543	83B	5632	88F
5213	87F	5330	86G	5544	86H	5633	86J
5214	86E	5331	84G	5545	86F	5634	84G
5215	83E	5332	87F	5546	83F	5635	88D
5216	87B	5333	85D	5547	82C	5636	88C
5217	86A	5336	86E	5548	72C	5637	88C
5218	86C	5337	81E	5549	87H	5638	86G
5219	87F	5339	82B	5550	87H	5639	81E
5220	87B	5351	81E	5552	83F	5640	88A
5221	87B	5353	87G	5553	89C	5641	88E
5222	87A	5357	87H	5554	83B	5642	86J
5223	87F	5358	82D	5555	86F	5643	88E
5224	86E	5369	84E	5557	83E	5644	88E
5225	86C	5370	87F	5558	83A	5645	86G
5226	85A	5376	82B	5560	87H	5646	88F
5227	86A	5380	81E	5561	82A	5647	81E
5228	86A	5384	71G	5562	83F	5648	88A
5229	86A	5385	82B	5563	72C	5649	86J
5230	87B	5396	85A	5564	83E	5650	88D
5231	86B	5399	6A	5565	89C	5651	84J
5232	87D	5407	84C	5568	86H	5652	88D
5233	86A	5410	82D	5569	83D	5653	88F
5234	86A	5412	83C	5570	83E	5654	88F
5235	86B	5416	82D	5571	83B	5655	88D
5236	86E	5417	84C	5572	83D	5656	87F

5657 86A
5658 84E
5659 86G
5660 88D
5661 88D
5662 88D
5663 88A
5664 88C
5665 88F
5666 88D
5667 88C
5668 88F
5669 88A
5670 87B
5671 88D
5672 88D
5673 87E
5674 88D
5675 87D
5676 88F
5677 88D
5678 88F
5679 86G
5680 88E
5681 88D
5682 88E
5683 88A
5684 88F
5685 86C
5686 88E
5687 88F
5688 87B
5689 82D
5690 84G
5691 88F
5692 88A
5693 88F
5694 88F
5695 88F
5696 88D
5697 82B
5698 86J
5699 88E
5702 87F
5704 87D
5706 86H
5717 81A
5720 87A
5727 86C
5728 87B
5731 86H
5744 81E
5746 81E
5748 87H
5749 86C
5750 86G
5754 84F
5755 81B
5756 86G
5757 82D
5758 86B
5759 86G
5761 87A
5763 85B
5764 81A
5766 81B
5768 86B
5769 82B
5770 87B
5771 82B
5773 87A
5774 84J
5775 86G
5776 86C
5778 87A
5779 83B
5780 83B
5783 81E
5787 87B
5789 86G
5791 85D
5793 83B
5798 83B
5815 82C
5900 * 84A
5901 * 81D
5902 * 87F
5903 * 87F
5904 * 82D
5905 * 87J
5906 * 81D
5907 * 81D
5908 * 87J
5909 * 87F
5910 * 86C
5911 * 86C
5912 * 84F
5913 * 87E
5914 * 85B
5916 * 84B
5917 * 85A
5918 * 81E
5919 * 84B
5920 * 83A
5921 * 84C
5922 * 82C
5923 * 81A
5924 * 82B
5925 * 81C
5926 * 84A
5927 * 84E
5928 * 87J
5929 * 81A
5930 * 84F
5931 * 81A
5932 * 81A
5933 * 81F
5934 * 82A
5935 * 82D
5936 * 81D
5937 * 87G
5938 * 87G
5939 * 81A
5940 * 82A
5941 * 82A
5942 * 84G
5943 * 81E
5944 * 84B
5945 * 82C
5946 * 83C
5947 * 84C
5948 * 86G
5949 * 82A
5950 * 82B
5951 * 85B
5952 * 85C
5953 * 87G
5954 * 82B
5955 * 87E
5956 * 85A
5957 * 81F
5958 * 81A
5959 * 84E
5960 * 81F
5961 * 87F
5962 * 86C
5963 * 82D
5964 * 82C
5965 * 84B
5966 * 81F
5967 * 82D
5968 * 84G
5969 * 87J
5970 * 86G
5971 * 84G
5972 * 86E
5973 * 81D
5974 * 82D
5975 * 82D
5976 * 81A
5977 * 81D
5978 * 82C
5979 * 81D
5980 * 86E
5981 * 82C
5982 * 81D
5983 * 82C
5984 * 87F
5985 * 84B
5986 * 82C
5987 * 81E
5988 * 84C
5989 * 84C
5990 * 84C
5991 * 84B
5992 * 83B
5993 * 81D
5994 * 85A
5995 * 84B
5996 * 85A
5997 * 82C
5998 * 85C
5999 * 83B

6000 * 81A
6001 * 84A
6002 * 83D
6003 * 81A
6004 * 81A
6005 * 84A
6006 * 84A
6007 * 84A
6008 * 84A
6009 * 81A
6010 * 81A
6011 * 84A
6012 * 81A
6013 * 81A
6014 * 84A
6015 * 81A
6016 * 83D
6017 * 84A
6018 * 81A
6019 * 81A
6020 * 84A
6021 * 81A
6022 * 84A
6023 * 81A
6024 * 81A
6025 * 81A
6026 * 81A
6027 * 84A
6028 * 81A
6029 * 81A
6101 81D
6103 81D
6104 81D
6106 81F
6107 81D
6108 81A
6109 81B
6110 81C
6111 81F
6112 81D
6113 81A
6114 87E
6115 81B
6116 84E
6117 81B

6118	86E	6309	82C	6380	6A	6615	84J
6119	81D	6310	87F	6381	85B	6616	87G
6120	81A	6312	82B	6382	85D	6617	84J
6121	81A	6313	81E	6384	86E	6618	88A
6122	81D	6314	85D	6385	81D	6619	88F
6123	81B	6316	87G	6386	86E	6620	87B
6124	81E	6317	84F	6387	84C	6621	86H
6125	81D	6319	82B	6388	85D	6622	86J
6126	81B	6320	82D	6389	87H	6623	87B
6127	81B	6323	82E	6390	83B	6624	88A
6128	81C	6324	81D	6391	82C	6625	82D
6129	81D	6326	86C	6392	89C	6626	88A
6130	81D	6327	82C	6394	85B	6627	87H
6131	81D	6329	87G	6395	84G	6628	86J
6132	81A	6330	85B	6398	83B	6629	86H
6133	81C	6332	84F	6400	83D	6630	82B
6134	81D	6333	81E	6401	84F	6631	84E
6135	81A	6335	84C	6403	84C	6632	84J
6136	81B	6336	82C	6406	83D	6633	88A
6137	85B	6337	83B	6408	83D	6634	86G
6138	81F	6338	86E	6410	83D	6635	88A
6139	81E	6339	84J	6411	88A	6636	86G
6140	86E	6340	84F	6412	86A	6637	88C
6141	81C	6341	82B	6413	83D	6638	88A
6142	81A	6342	89A	6415	85B	6639	82C
6143	81B	6343	83B	6416	88D	6640	84B
6144	81C	6344	71G	6418	84A	6641	87A
6145	81A	6345	87F	6419	83D	6642	86E
6146	81B	6346	82E	6421	83D	6643	88C
6147	81C	6347	87J	6422	84A	6644	86H
6148	81C	6348	86A	6424	86E	6645	84B
6149	81C	6349	84F	6425	86A	6646	84F
6150	81B	6350	82E	6426	86A	6647	88A
6151	81B	6351	82B	6429	84C	6648	88A
6152	81B	6352	86C	6430	86E	6649	87E
6153	81D	6353	84B	6431	86J	6650	87A
6154	81B	6356	82B	6433	88D	6651	86J
6155	86E	6357	84J	6434	88A	6652	86J
6156	81C	6360	82B	6435	88E	6653	87F
6157	81A	6361	86J	6436	88D	6654	81D
6158	81A	6362	86E	6437	86J	6655	88C
6159	81C	6363	85B	6438	88E	6656	86A
6160	84E	6364	84E	6439	86K	6657	88A
6161	81D	6365	85B	6600	86D	6658	88C
6162	81D	6366	86K	6601	82B	6659	88A
6163	81A	6367	84F	6602	87B	6660	88A
6164	81E	6368	85B	6603	88A	6661	86J
6165	81C	6369	86E	6604	84F	6662	87D
6166	83D	6370	86A	6605	86J	6663	86H
6167	81B	6371	89C	6606	88A	6664	81E
6168	81A	6372	83B	6607	88A	6665	88A
6169	81C	6373	85B	6608	88A	6666	86E
6300	86G	6374	82B	6609	84F	6667	84F
6301	83D	6375	83B	6610	84J	6668	84E
6302	81E	6376	82E	6611	84J	6669	85B
6304	85B	6377	87G	6612	88A	6670	82B
6306	87H	6378	89C	6613	87D	6671	82B
6307	84J	6379	81E	6614	88A	6672	86E

6673		86F
6674		84J
6675		86G
6676		86G
6677		84F
6678		84F
6679		85D
6680		87E
6681		82B
6682		88A
6683		84F
6684		88A
6685		86G
6686		87B
6687		86J
6688		87E
6689		88A
6690		85B
6691		87B
6692		84F
6693		86G
6694		84J
6695		87E
6696		84J
6697		88C
6698		84G
6699		88A
6700		87D
6702		87D
6712		87D
6714		87D
6719		87D
6720		87D
6724		86B
6728		86B
6738		87D
6739		86B
6741		82C
6742		86B
6749		87D
6751		86B
6752		88C
6753		87D
6754		88C
6755		84B
6756		86B
6757		86B
6758		82C
6760		86B
6761		87B
6762		87D
6763		87D
6764		86B
6765		88C
6766		87B
6767		87D
6768		87D
6769		82C
6770		83F
6772		86B
6775		88C
6776		87D
6777		87D
6778		87D
6800	*	83G
6801	*	83G
6802	*	86G
6803	*	84F
6804	*	82B
6805	*	83F
6806	*	84B
6807	*	85A
6808	*	83G
6809	*	82B
6810	*	87F
6811	*	82B
6812	*	86G
6813	*	83A
6814	*	83E
6815	*	83B
6816	*	83G
6817	*	84B
6818	*	87F
6819	*	86G
6820	*	85A
6821	*	86G
6822	*	86C
6823	*	83F
6824	*	83G
6825	*	83G
6826	*	83G
6827	*	82B
6828	*	83F
6829	*	83A
6830	*	82B
6831	*	82B
6832	*	86C
6833	*	86C
6834	*	82B
6835	*	82B
6836	*	83A
6837	*	83G
6838	*	86A
6839	*	84B
6840	*	86G
6841	*	82B
6842	*	82B
6843	*	87F
6844	*	87F
6845	*	83G
6846	*	82B
6847	*	86C
6848	*	86G
6849	*	83G
6850	*	86A
6851	*	85A
6852	*	82B
6853	*	84E
6854	*	83D
6855	*	84E
6856	*	85A
6857	*	84B
6858	*	86C
6859	*	86C
6860	*	83G
6861	*	84E
6862	*	84B
6863	*	83D
6864	*	86C
6865	*	82B
6866	*	84E
6867	*	86G
6868	*	83B
6869	*	83G
6870	*	83G
6871	*	83B
6872	*	86G
6873	*	83D
6874	*	83B
6875	*	83G
6876	*	86A
6877	*	85A
6878	*	82B
6879	*	84E
6900	*	82B
6901	*	86G
6902	*	82C
6903	*	86G
6904	*	84G
6905	*	86E
6906	*	84C
6907	*	84B
6908	*	82B
6909	*	87J
6910	*	81E
6911	*	84C
6912	*	86E
6913	*	83D
6914	*	83B
6915	*	81E
6916	*	84G
6917	*	85B
6918	*	87E
6919	*	82A
6920	*	81A
6921	*	83D
6922	*	84G
6923	*	81D
6924	*	81D
6925	*	84B
6926	*	84A
6927	*	81F
6928	*	86G
6929	*	84C
6930	*	84A
6931	*	83E
6932	*	86C
6933	*	84A
6934	*	84B
6935	*	86C
6936	*	86C
6937	*	81E
6938	*	83D
6939	*	86C
6940	*	83A
6941	*	83D
6942	*	81A
6943	*	86C
6944	*	84G
6945	*	84A
6946	*	86G
6947	*	85A
6948	*	85A
6949	*	84G
6950	*	85A
6951	*	82D
6952	*	81F
6953	*	81D
6954	*	82B
6955	*	82D
6956	*	84G
6957	*	81E
6958	*	86G
6959	*	81A
6960	*	81D
6961	*	81A
6962	*	81A
6963	*	86C
6964	*	84G
6965	*	83C
6966	*	81A
6967	*	81C
6968	*	81D
6969	*	81E
6970	*	81F
6971	*	84E
6972	*	82A
6973	*	81A
6974	*	81A
6975	*	84B
6976	*	84C
6977	*	82B
6978	*	81A
6979	*	84C
6980	*	84B
6981	*	82A
6982	*	82A
6983	*	81E
6984	*	85A
6985	*	85B
6986	*	82B
6987	*	84A

6988	* 82A
6989	* 85A
6990	* 81A
6991	* 81C
6992	* 85A
6993	* 82C
6994	* 82D
6995	* 83B
6996	* 81E
6997	* 82A
6998	* 84G
6999	* 86C
7000	* 85B
7001	* 81A
7002	* 85A
7003	* 82A
7004	* 81A
7005	* 85A
7006	* 86C
7007	* 85A
7008	* 81A
7009	* 87E
7010	* 81A
7011	* 86C
7012	* 87G
7013	* 81A
7014	* 82A
7015	* 84G
7016	* 87G
7017	* 81A
7018	* 82A
7019	* 82A
7020	* 81A
7021	* 87E
7022	* 83D
7023	* 86C
7024	* 81A
7025	* 81A
7026	* 84A
7027	* 81A
7028	* 87E
7029	* 83A
7030	* 81A
7031	* 82C
7032	* 81A
7033	* 81A
7034	* 82A
7035	* 85B
7036	* 81A
7037	* 82C
7200	87E
7201	86G
7202	88A
7203	86J
7204	86A
7205	88A
7206	86E
7207	87E
7208	86E
7209	87E
7210	86G
7211	86A
7212	86A
7213	86G
7214	86J
7215	87D
7216	86J
7217	86A
7218	81F
7219	86A
7220	86G
7221	86J
7222	86A
7223	86E
7224	86J
7225	87D
7226	87D
7227	86G
7228	84C
7229	86A
7230	84J
7231	86A
7232	87F
7233	86A
7234	86A
7235	87B
7236	87E
7237	86J
7238	81F
7239	81F
7240	86A
7241	88C
7242	88A
7243	86A
7244	84C
7245	86A
7246	86G
7247	84C
7248	87D
7249	87B
7250	86A
7251	86G
7252	88A
7253	86A
7300	84J
7301	82B
7302	82D
7303	71G
7304	83B
7305	84C
7306	87H
7307	87F
7308	86E
7309	84G
7310	84J
7311	83C
7312	85B
7313	84J
7314	87F
7315	84C
7316	83C
7317	84E
7318	87H
7319	85B
7320	87H
7321	87F
7322	86E
7323	82B
7324	81E
7325	86G
7326	85C
7327	81E
7328	86E
7329	84G
7330	84G
7331	81D
7332	86C
7333	83D
7334	86G
7335	83D
7336	84G
7337	82C
7338	85B
7339	84B
7340	87H
7341	84J
7400	87G
7402	87G
7403	84J
7404	81F
7405	89A
7406	89C
7407	87G
7408	87D
7409	84J
7410	89A
7412	81F
7413	82C
7414	84J
7417	89C
7418	85C
7419	87G
7421	82C
7422	87G
7423	86J
7424	84E
7425	87G
7426	85C
7427	82C
7428	84J
7429	84F
7430	84F
7431	84J
7432	84F
7433	84J
7434	89C
7435	84F
7436	83B
7437	85C
7439	87G
7440	84J
7441	84F
7442	84J
7443	84J
7444	87G
7445	81F
7446	83E
7448	84F
7449	84F
7700	85B
7702	84D
7704	87D
7707	85A
7708	81D
7709	83E
7712	86G
7713	83B
7715	83E
7718	87F
7719	85C
7720	86J
7721	86K
7722	84F
7723	85E
7724	86G
7725	86F
7726	88E
7728	82B
7729	82B
7732	86F
7733	88E
7736	86K
7739	87A
7740	86G
7741	85B
7744	88E
7745	87F
7747	87J
7748	82D
7749	82B
7753	86F
7755	86H
7756	85E
7757	87A
7758	87B
7760	81F
7761	84C
7762	6A

7764	86E
7765	87F
7766	88C
7771	86K
7772	81E
7775	86C
7776	87F
7777	85A
7780	71G
7781	86A
7782	71G
7783	82B
7784	82D
7785	87F
7786	87A
7787	86K
7788	81D
7790	82B
7794	86A
7796	86G
7798	86F
7799	87A
7800 *	89A
7801 *	89A
7802 *	89C
7803 *	89C
7804 *	87G
7805 *	86C
7806 *	83E
7807 *	89A
7808 *	83A
7809 *	89A
7810 *	89A
7811 *	84G
7812 *	83F
7813 *	83F
7814 *	89C
7815 *	89C
7816 *	83E
7817 *	84J
7818 *	89C
7819 *	89A
7820 *	83F
7821 *	83A
7822 *	89A
7823 *	89C
7824 *	84E
7825 *	87G
7826 *	87G
7827 *	89A
7828 *	84G
7829 *	87G
7900 *	81F
7901 *	82A
7902 *	81A
7903 *	81A
7904 *	81A
7905 *	84C
7906 *	81D
7907 *	82B
7908 *	84E
7909 *	82D
7910 *	81C
7911 *	81F
7912 *	84E
7913 *	86C
7914 *	81D
7915 *	84B
7916 *	83A
7917 *	82D
7918 *	84E
7919 *	81D
7920 *	85A
7921 *	83D
7922 *	84G
7923 *	81C
7924 *	83B
7925 *	86C
7926 *	85B
7927 *	81A
7928 *	85A
7929 *	83E
8100	84D
8101	85D
8102	87G
8103	87G
8104	87A
8106	85A
8107	87H
8108	84E
8109	84D
8400	85F
8401	85F
8402	85F
8403	85F
8404	85F
8405	85F
8406	85F
8407	87B
8409	85B
8411	84A
8413	81C
8414	87D
8415	84E
8416	87B
8418	87A
8420	88A
8422	83D
8424	81F
8425	84A
8426	84A
8427	85A
8428	84B
8430	81D
8431	87D
8433	82C
8435	81E
8436	86H
8437	86H
8438	88A
8439	87E
8440	86B
8441	86C
8444	86H
8445	86J
8446	88C
8449	84G
8451	81C
8452	84C
8453	86F
8454	87B
8456	81C
8457	86C
8458	81E
8459	81A
8460	85A
8461	84A
8464	84B
8465	82C
8466	86C
8467	87F
8468	84E
8469	88A
8470	88A
8471	88A
8472	82C
8473	83G
8474	87F
8475	87D
8476	87D
8477	87F
8478	88A
8479	82B
8480	85A
8481	88C
8482	82D
8483	87D
8484	86C
8486	83F
8487	85B
8488	85B
8489	86H
8490	87B
8491	85B
8493	86G
8494	81F
8495	86G
8496	85A
8497	86F
8498	84C
8499	86B
8700	84E
8701	85B
8702	83E
8705	86H
8706	87F
8707	86G
8708	87F
8709	6A
8710	86F
8711	86K
8712	86F
8713	84E
8714	82B
8715	87A
8716	86G
8717	85B
8718	85D
8719	83E
8720	81E
8721	86F
8722	85C
8723	86C
8724	87B
8725	82E
8726	84A
8727	84J
8728	86C
8729	6A
8730	6A
8731	85B
8732	87A
8733	83E
8734	84J
8735	88E
8736	87F
8737	83E
8738	87H
8739	87H
8740	86F
8741	82A
8742	84F
8743	85B
8744	82D
8745	72C
8746	82B
8747	82B
8748	86F
8749	87F
8750	81C
8751	86A
8752	81C
8753	81A
8754	81A
8756	81A
8757	81A
8759	81A
8760	87A

8761	81F
8762	81A
8763	81A
8764	88C
8765	81A
8766	86A
8767	81A
8768	81A
8769	81C
8770	81A
8771	81A
8772	81A
8773	81A
8774	81C
8775	87A
8776	86C
8777	87G
8778	86H
8779	82C
8780	88A
8781	85C
8782	87A
8783	82C
8784	87A
8785	87F
8786	86H
8787	85C
8788	87E
8789	87E
8790	82B
8791	84J
8792	84F
8793	82C
8794	87E
8795	82B
8796	84A
8797	84F
8798	84A
8799	71G
9004	84J
9014	84J
9015	89C
9017	89C
9018	89A
9401	85A
9404	81D
9405	81A
9406	81B
9407	81E
9408	84B
9409	81C
9410	81A
9411	81A
9412	81A
9413	81C
9414	81A
9415	81B
9416	81A
9418	81A
9419	81A
9420	81A
9421	81B
9422	81C
9423	81A
9424	81B
9425	88C
9426	86C
9428	84A
9429	85A
9430	87A
9431	87D
9433	83D
9434	83G
9435	84A
9436	87E
9437	86C
9440	83A
9441	85B
9442	87B
9444	87B
9446	87A
9447	81D
9448	87A
9449	84C
9450	81F
9451	86F
9452	87A
9453	85B
9454	87B
9455	85A
9456	87B
9457	87B
9458	86H
9460	86H
9461	86C
9462	83A
9463	84G
9464	85B
9465	87F
9466	85A
9467	83D
9468	86A
9469	81A
9470	84G
9471	85B
9472	84G
9473	87A
9474	83C
9475	85B
9476	82C
9477	85B
9478	87A
9479	81A
9480	83C
9481	82A
9482	86A
9483	87B
9484	87E
9485	87F
9486	85A
9487	83A
9488	82B
9489	87D
9490	85A
9493	86C
9494	86C
9495	82B
9497	83C
9498	84G
9600	82C
9601	82B
9602	87J
9603	86C
9604	82C
9605	82C
9606	87G
9607	86J
9608	83B
9609	86F
9610	84J
9611	81F
9612	82D
9613	84F
9614	84E
9615	82D
9616	86A
9617	87B
9618	88D
9619	86E
9620	71G
9621	84H
9622	88E
9623	82A
9624	84F
9625	87D
9626	82A
9627	87A
9628	82D
9629	83C
9630	84H
9631	88D
9632	72C
9633	83A
9634	87B
9635	84E
9636	84F
9637	87E
9638	88D
9639	84H
9640	81F
9641	81C
9642	81C
9643	88D
9644	86A
9645	87J
9646	83B
9647	83B
9648	86C
9649	86F
9650	86G
9651	82B
9652	87F
9653	81F
9654	81F
9655	83E
9656	84G
9657	84G
9658	81A
9659	81A
9660	86F
9661	81A
9662	86K
9663	83B
9664	86A
9665	85C
9666	87J
9667	86A
9668	82D
9669	84J
9670	83B
9671	83B
9672	82C
9673	83E
9674	86A
9675	88D
9676	88D
9677	87J
9678	83A
9679	88A
9680	84E
9681	89A
9682	84E
9700	81A
9701	81A
9702	81A
9703	81A
9704	81A
9705	81A
9706	81A
9707	81A
9709	81A
9710	81A
9711	83D
9712	86J
9713	86C
9714	87H
9715	87E
9716	83D

9717-9799

9717	85C	9738	86F	9759	86C	9781	81B
9718	83B	9739	84B	9760	87J	9782	84F
9719	84F	9740	82C	9761	87A	9783	87A
9720	82C	9741	84H	9762	82D	9784	81A
9721	82C	9742	87B	9763	81D	9785	87B
9722	81B	9743	87F	9764	72C	9786	87A
9723	86C	9744	87D	9765	83C	9787	87G
9724	84E	9745	86A	9766	87B	9788	87F
9725	81A	9746	86A	9767	84F	9789	81C
9726	81C	9747	88D	9768	84B	9790	82C
9727	84E	9748	83G	9769	82B	9791	81C
9728	6A	9749	81D	9770	70A	9792	87A
9729	82B	9750	87A	9771	82A	9793	84J
9730	86G	9751	81A	9773	82C	9794	6A
9731	86J	9752	84B	9774	84H	9795	82C
9732	72C	9753	84E	9775	86C	9796	86G
9733	84E	9754	81A	9776	88D	9797	86G
9734	87A	9755	83E	9777	87E	9798	84E
9735	87B	9756	71G	9778	86C	9799	87B
9736	87B	9757	83B	9779	87A		
9737	87B	9758	81A	9780	86D		

W.R. Diesel Railcars

5	85A	17	84D	24	82B	30	81D
7	84F	19	85B	25	81C	31	81C
8	84F	20	85A	26	85A	32	85A
13	84D	21	81C	27	81C	33	81D
14	84D	22	85A	28	82B	34	81C
15	84F	23	85A	29	85A	38	81D

Diesel Locomotives at present numbered **11100-11719** and **13000-13336** are being re-numbered as under.

Present No.	New No.
11100–3	D2200–3
11105–15	D2204–14
11116–20	D2500–4
11121–35	D2215–29
11136–43	D2550–7
11144–8	D2505–9
11149–60	D2230–41
11161–76	D2558–73
11177–86	D2400–9
11187–11209	D2000–22
11212–29	D2242–59
11500–8	D2950–8
11700–19	D2700–19
13000–13336	D3000–D3336

D1 * 1B
D2 * 17A
D3 * 1B
D4 * 1B
D5 * 1B
D6 * 17A
D7 * 1B
D8 * 17A
D9 * 1B
D10 * 1B
D11
D12
D13
D14
D15
D16
D17
D18
D19
D20
D21
D22
D23
D24
D25
D26
D27
D28
D29
D30
D31
D32
D33
D34
D35
D36
D37
D38
D39
D40
D41
D42
D43
D44
D45
D46
D47
D48
D49
D50
D51
D52
D53
D54
D55
D56
D57
D58
D59
D60
D61
D62
D63
D64
D65
D66
D67
D68
D69
D70
D71
D72
D73
D74
D75
D76
D77
D78
D79
D80
D81
D82
D83
D84
D85
D86
D87
D88
D89
D90
D91
D92
D93
D94
D95
D96
D97
D98
D99
D100
D101
D102
D103
D104
D105
D106
D107
D108
D109
D110
D111
D112
D113
D114
D115
D116
D117
D118
D119
D120
D121
D122
D123
D124
D125
D126
D127
D128
D129
D130
D131
D132
D133
D134
D135
D136
D137
D138
D139
D140
D141
D142
D143
D144
D145
D146
D147
D148
D149
D150
D151
D152
D153
D154
D155
D156
D157
D158
D159
D160
D161
D162
D163
D164
D165
D166
D167
D168
D169
D170
D171
D172
D173
D174
D175
D176
D177
D178
D179
D180
D181
D182
D183
D184
D185
D186
D187
D188
D189
D190
D191
D192
D193
D194
D195
D196
D197
D198
D199
D200 30A
D201 FP
D202 30A
D203 30A
D204 30A
D205 30A
D206 FP
D207 FP
D208 FP
D209 FP
D210 * 1B
D211 1B
D212 12B
D213 12B
D214 9A
D215 8A
D216 12B
D217 9A
D218 8A
D219 1B
D220 8A
D221 9A
D222 8A
D223 8A
D224 1B

D225-D838

D225 12B
D226 1B
D227 5A
D228 9A
D229 1B
D230 5A
D231 8A
D232 1B
D233 5A
D234 8A
D235 5A
D236 8A
D237 52A
D238 52A
D239 52A
D240 52A
D241 52A
D242 52A
D243 52A
D244 52A
D245 52A
D246 52A
D247 52A
D248 FP
D249 52A
D250 50A
D251 50A
D252 50A
D253 50A
D254 50A
D255 1B
D256 52A
D257 52A
D258 50A
D259 50A
D260 64B
D261 64B
D262 64B
D263 64B
D264 64B
D265 64B
D266 64B
D267 1B
D268 5A
D269 1B
D270 52A
D271 52A
D272 52A
D273 52A
D274 52A
D275 50A
D276 50A
D277
D278
D279
D280
D281
D282

D283
D284
D285
D286
D287
D288
D289
D290
D291
D292
D293
D294
D295
D296
D297
D298
D299

D300
D301
D302
D303
D304
D305
D306
D307
D308
D309
D310
D311
D312
D313
D314
D315
D316
D317
D318
D319
D320
D321
D322
D323
D324
D325
D326
D327
D328
D329
D330
D331
D332
D333
D334
D335
D336

D337
D338
D339
D340
D341
D342
D343
D344
D345
D346
D347
D348
D349
D350
D351
D352
D353
D354
D355
D356
D357
D358
D359
D360
D361
D362
D363
D364
D365
D366
D367
D368
D369
D370
D371
D372
D373
D374
D375
D376
D377
D378
D379
D380
D381
D382
D383
D384
D385
D386
D387
D388
D389
D390
D391
D392
D393
D394

D395
D396
D397
D398
D399

D600 * 83D
D601 * 83D
D602 * 83D
D603 * 83D
D604 * 83D

D800 * 83D
D801 * 83D
D802 * 83D
D803 * 83D
D804 * 83D
D805 * 83D
D806 * 83D
D807 * 83D
D808 * 83D
D809 * 83D
D810 * 83D
D811 * 83D
D812 * 83D
D813 * 83D
D814 * 83D
D815 * 83D
D816 * 83D
D817 * 83D
D818 * 83D
D819 *
D820 *
D821 *
D822 *
D823 *
D824 *
D825 *
D826 *
D827 *
D828 *
D829 *
D830 *
D831 *
D832 *
D833 *
D834 *
D835 *
D836 *
D837 *
D838 *

D839 *
D840 *
D841 *
D842 *
D843 *
D844 *
D845 *
D846 *
D847 *
D848 *
D849 *
D850 *
D851 *
D852 *
D853 *
D854 *
D855 *
D856 *
D857 *
D858 *
D859 *
D860 *
D861 *
D862 *
D863 *
D864 *
D865 *
D866 *
D867 *
D868 *
D869 *
D870 *

D1000
D1001
D1002
D1003
D1004
D1005
D1006
D1007
D1008
D1009
D1010
D1011
D1012
D1013
D1014
D1015
D1016
D1017
D1018
D1019
D1020
D1021
D1022
D1023
D1024
D1025
D1026
D1027
D1028
D1029
D1030
D1031
D1032
D1033
D1034
D1035
D1036
D1037
D1038
D1039
D1040
D1041
D1042
D1043
D1044
D1045
D1046
D1047
D1048
D1049
D1050
D1051
D1052
D1053
D1054
D1055
D1056
D1057
D1058
D1059
D1060
D1061
D1062
D1063
D1064
D1065
D1066
D1067
D1068
D1069
D1070
D1071
D1072
D1073

D1500
D1501
D1502
D1503
D1504
D1505
D1506
D1507
D1508
D1509
D1510
D1511
D1512

D2000 34D
D2001 34D
D2002 34D
D2003 34D
D2004 31A
D2005 31A
D2006 31A
D2007 31A
D2008 31A
D2009 31A
D2010 31C
D2011 31C
D2012 31C
D2013 31C
D2014 31C
D2015 31C
D2016 31A
D2017 31A
D2018 34D
D2019 34D
D2020 40B
D2021 40B
D2022 40B
D2023 40F
D2024 40F
D2025 40F
D2026 40A
D2027 40A
D2028 31A
D2029 34D
D2030 31C
D2031 31B
D2032 32A
D2033 32A
D2034 32A
D2035 32A
D2036 32A
D2037 32A
D2038 32A
D2039 32C
D2040 32B
D2041 32B
D2042 32B
D2043 32B
D2044 52F
D2045 52F
D2046 50A
D2047 52G
D2048 52C
D2049 52C
D2050 52G
D2051 50B
D2052 50B
D2053 50B
D2054 50B
D2055 52A
D2056 52A
D2057 52A
D2058 52A
D2059 52A
D2060 52A
D2061 52A
D2062 50A
D2063 50A
D2064 50A
D2065 50A
D2066 50A
D2067 51L
D2068 51C
D2069 51C
D2070 51C
D2071 56G
D2072 56G
D2073 56G
D2074 56G
D2075 56G
D2076 51C
D2077 51C
D2078 51L
D2079 51A
D2080 51A
D2081 56G
D2082 75A
D2083 73C
D2084 73F
D2085 71A
D2086 82C
D2087 82C
D2088 82C
D2089 56G
D2090 56G
D2091 56G
D2092 52E
D2093 52E
D2094
D2095
D2096
D2097
D2098
D2099

D2100	
D2101	
D2102	
D2103	
D2104	
D2105	
D2106	
D2107	
D2108	
D2109	
D2110	
D2111	
D2112	
D2113	
D2114	87C
D2115	87C
D2116	87C
D2117	87C
D2118	87C
D2119	87C
D2120	87C
D2121	87C
D2122	87C
D2123	85B
D2124	87C
D2125	87C
D2126	87C
D2127	83D
D2128	83D
D2129	83A
D2130	83A
D2131	83C
D2132	83C
D2133	83B
D2134	83B
D2135	82E
D2136	85B
D2137	85B
D2138	85B
D2139	85B
D2140	83B
D2141	
D2142	
D2143	
D2144	
D2145	
D2146	
D2147	50A
D2148	50A
D2149	
D2150	
D2151	
D2152	
D2153	
D2154	
D2155	
D2156	
D2157	
D2158	
D2159	
D2160	
D2161	
D2162	
D2163	
D2164	
D2165	
D2166	
D2167	
D2168	
D2169	
D2170	
D2171	
D2172	
D2173	
D2174	
D2200	30A
D2201	31B
D2202	31B
D2203	32A
D2204	51C
D2205	51C
D2206	51C
D2207	40B
D2208	30F
D2209	30F
D2210	32D
D2211	30F
D2212	32D
D2213	6A
D2214	32A
D2215	30A
D2216	30A
D2217	30A
D2218	6B
D2219	32A
D2220	6B
D2221	5B
D2222	32B
D2223	30A
D2224	30A
D2225	30A
D2226	30A
D2227	30A
D2228	30A
D2229	30A
D2230	51C
D2231	51C
D2232	51C
D2233	40B
D2234	40B
D2235	40B
D2236	5B
D2237	31B
D2238	31B
D2239	31B
D2240	31B
D2241	40F
D2242	55H
D2243	55H
D2244	55H
D2245	50A
D2246	55H
D2247	52F
D2248	52F
D2249	52F
D2250	73H
D2251	73C
D2252	71A
D2253	73F
D2254	71A
D2255	83H
D2256	73C
D2257	83H
D2258	83H
D2259	83H
D2260	56G
D2261	56G
D2262	55G
D2263	55G
D2264	56G
D2265	56G
D2266	55D
D2267	56G
D2268	50A
D2269	50A
D2270	50A
D2271	55A
D2272	55A
D2273	55A
D2274	71B
D2275	71B
D2276	73F
D2277	73E
D2278	75C
D2279	75C
D2280	75C
D2281	75A
D2282	75A
D2283	73C
D2284	73C
D2285	73F
D2286	75A
D2287	73H
D2288	75C
D2289	71A
D2290	70C
D2400	40B
D2401	40F
D2402	40F
D2403	40B
D2404	40A
D2405	40A
D2406	40A
D2407	40A
D2408	40A
D2409	40F
D2410	60A
D2411	60A
D2412	60A
D2413	60A
D2414	61C
D2415	61C
D2416	61A
D2417	61A
D2418	61A
D2419	61A
D2420	61A
D2421	61A
D2422	61A
D2423	60A
D2424	61A
D2425	66A
D2426	66B
D2427	66D
D2428	66A
D2429	66B
D2430	66C
D2431	66C
D2432	66A
D2433	66C
D2434	67C
D2435	67C
D2436	
D2437	
D2438	
D2439	
D2440	
D2441	
D2442	
D2443	
D2444	
D2500	6C
D2501	6C
D2502	6C
D2503	6C
D2504	6C
D2505	6C
D2506	6C
D2507	6C
D2508	6C

D2509	6C
D2550	30F
D2551	30F
D2552	30F
D2553	32A
D2554	30F
D2555	32C
D2556	32B
D2557	32B
D2558	32A
D2559	32A
D2560	32B
D2561	32B
D2562	32A
D2563	32A
D2564	32B
D2565	32A
D2566	32A
D2567	32A
D2568	32C
D2569	32A
D2570	32C
D2571	32D
D2572	32B
D2573	32C
D2574	68C
D2575	68C
D2576	62A
D2577	62A
D2578	62A
D2579	62A
D2580	62A
D2581	62A
D2582	62A
D2583	62A
D2584	62A
D2585	62A
D2586	56B
D2587	56A
D2588	56A
D2589	56A
D2590	56A
D2591	56A
D2592	56A
D2593	56A
D2594	52D
D2595	50A
D2596	55A
D2597	
D2598	
D2599	
D2600	
D2601	
D2602	
D2603	
D2604	
D2605	
D2606	
D2607	
D2608	
D2609	
D2610	
D2611	
D2612	
D2613	
D2614	
D2615	
D2616	
D2617	
D2618	
D2700	51C
D2701	51C
D2702	51C
D2703	65K
D2704	62C
D2705	64A
D2706	64A
D2707	62C
D2708	62B
D2709	62B
D2710	62B
D2711	62B
D2712	62B
D2713	62B
D2714	62B
D2715	62B
D2716	62B
D2717	62C
D2718	62C
D2719	64A
D2720	64A
D2721	64A
D2722	64A
D2723	64A
D2724	65F
D2725	64A
D2726	64A
D2727	64A
D2728	64A
D2729	64A
D2730	64A
D2731	64A
D2732	64A
D2733	65G
D2734	65G
D2735	65G
D2736	65G
D2737	65G
D2738	65G
D2739	65J
D2740	65J
D2741	65J
D2742	65J
D2743	62C
D2744	62C
D2745	64A
D2746	64A
D2747	64A
D2748	64A
D2749	64A
D2750	64A
D2751	64A
D2752	64B
D2753	
D2754	
D2755	
D2756	
D2757	
D2758	
D2759	
D2760	
D2761	
D2762	
D2763	
D2764	
D2765	
D2766	
D2767	
D2768	
D2769	
D2770	
D2771	
D2772	
D2773	
D2774	
D2775	
D2776	
D2777	
D2778	
D2779	
D2900	1D
D2901	1D
D2902	1D
D2903	1D
D2904	1D
D2905	1D
D2906	1D
D2907	1D
D2908	2A
D2909	2A
D2910	2A
D2911	
D2912	
D2913	
D2914	
D2915	
D2916	
D2917	
D2918	
D2919	
D2920	
D2950	32B
D2951	32B
D2952	32B
D2953	30A
D2954	30A
D2955	30A
D2956	30A
D2957	30A
D2958	30A
D3000	82B
D3001	82B
D3002	82B
D3003	82B
D3004	84E
D3005	67C
D3006	67C
D3007	67B
D3008	67B
D3009	67B
D3010	71A
D3011	71A
D3012	71A
D3013	71A
D3014	71A
D3015	1A
D3016	1A
D3017	1B
D3018	1A
D3019	8C
D3020	3D
D3021	3C
D3022	14A
D3023	14A
D3024	14A
D3025	84E
D3026	84E
D3027	84E
D3028	84E
D3029	84E
D3030	81A
D3031	81A
D3032	81A
D3033	81A
D3034	84B
D3035	84B
D3036	84B

D3037-D3260

D3037	84B
D3038	84B
D3039	84B
D3040	70B
D3041	70B
D3042	70B
D3043	73F
D3044	73F
D3045	73F
D3046	75C
D3047	75C
D3048	75C
D3049	75C
D3050	1A
D3051	1A
D3052	1A
D3053	2A
D3054	2A
D3055	2A
D3056	15A
D3057	15A
D3058	15A
D3059	15A
D3060	41F
D3061	41F
D3062	41F
D3063	41F
D3064	41F
D3065	31B
D3066	2F
D3067	2F
D3068	2F
D3069	2F
D3070	50B
D3071	50B
D3072	50B
D3073	50B
D3074	50B
D3075	50B
D3076	50B
D3077	50B
D3078	50B
D3079	50B
D3080	50B
D3081	50B
D3082	21A
D3083	16A
D3084	16A
D3085	16A
D3086	41B
D3087	12B
D3088	12B
D3089	5B
D3090	3B
D3091	3C
D3092	70C
D3093	75A
D3094	75A
D3095	73C
D3096	73C
D3097	73C
D3098	73C
D3099	73C
D3100	70B
D3101	73F
D3102	86E
D3103	86E
D3104	86E
D3105	84C
D3106	84C
D3107	84C
D3108	84C
D3109	84C
D3110	84C
D3111	84G
D3112	84F
D3113	84F
D3114	84G
D3115	84F
D3116	84F
D3117	18A
D3118	18A
D3119	18A
D3120	18A
D3121	18A
D3122	18A
D3123	9D
D3124	18A
D3125	18A
D3126	18A
D3127	41A
D3128	41A
D3129	41B
D3130	31B
D3131	41A
D3132	65F
D3133	65F
D3134	65F
D3135	65F
D3136	65F
D3137	51L
D3138	51L
D3139	51L
D3140	51L
D3141	51L
D3142	51L
D3143	51L
D3144	51L
D3145	51L
D3146	51L
D3147	51L
D3148	51L
D3149	51L
D3150	51L
D3151	51L
D3152	40B
D3153	40B
D3154	40B
D3155	40B
D3156	40B
D3157	40B
D3158	40B
D3159	40B
D3160	40B
D3161	40B
D3162	40B
D3163	40B
D3164	40B
D3165	40B
D3166	40B
D3167	21A
D3168	21A
D3169	2A
D3170	12B
D3171	12C
D3172	24K
D3173	1A
D3174	1A
D3175	5B
D3176	5B
D3177	1A
D3178	1A
D3179	14A
D3180	14A
D3181	14A
D3182	82B
D3183	82B
D3184	82B
D3185	82B
D3186	82B
D3187	82B
D3188	86E
D3189	86E
D3190	86E
D3191	84B
D3192	84E
D3193	84G
D3194	84G
D3195	81D
D3196	81C
D3197	66A
D3198	66A
D3199	66A
D3200	66A
D3201	66A
D3202	66B
D3203	66B
D3204	66B
D3205	66B
D3206	66B
D3207	65A
D3208	65A
D3209	65A
D3210	65A
D3211	65A
D3212	65C
D3213	65C
D3214	65C
D3215	65B
D3216	65B
D3217	75A
D3218	75A
D3219	75A
D3220	75A
D3221	75A
D3222	75C
D3223	75C
D3224	75C
D3225	75C
D3226	75C
D3227	51A
D3228	51A
D3229	51A
D3230	50B
D3231	50B
D3232	50B
D3233	50D
D3234	NE
D3235	NE
D3236	NE
D3237	50A
D3238	50A
D3239	50A
D3240	50A
D3241	52B
D3242	52B
D3243	52B
D3244	52B
D3245	5B
D3246	16A
D3247	16A
D3248	21A
D3249	14A
D3250	21A
D3251	41B
D3252	41B
D3253	41B
D3254	41B
D3255	82B
D3256	82B
D3257	82B
D3258	88B
D3259	88B
D3260	88B

D3261	88B
D3262	88B
D3263	88B
D3264	88B
D3265	88B
D3266	88B
D3267	88B
D3268	81D
D3269	81D
D3270	70C
D3271	70C
D3272	70C
D3273	70C
D3274	70C
D3275	62A
D3276	65F
D3277	65C
D3278	65B
D3279	65B
D3280	65B
D3281	65F
D3282	66B
D3283	66A
D3284	66B
D3285	66A
D3286	66B
D3287	66B
D3288	41B
D3289	41B
D3290	16A
D3291	5B
D3292	5B
D3293	41B
D3294	55B
D3295	55B
D3296	55B
D3297	55B
D3298	30F
D3299	30F
D3300	30A
D3301	30A
D3302	30F
D3303	30A
D3304	14A
D3305	14A
D3306	14A
D3307	34A
D3308	34A
D3309	34A
D3310	34A
D3311	34A
D3312	34A
D3313	50A
D3314	50A
D3315	50A
D3316	52B
D3317	52B
D3318	50A
D3319	50A
D3320	50A
D3321	52B
D3322	52B
D3323	50B
D3324	52A
D3325	41A
D3326	41A
D3327	31B
D3328	31B
D3329	41F
D3330	41A
D3331	FP
D3332	FP
D3333	41F
D3334	34A
D3335	41A
D3336	41A
D3337	62A
D3338	62A
D3339	62A
D3340	62A
D3341	62A
D3342	62C
D3343	62C
D3344	62C
D3345	62C
D3346	62C
D3347	62B
D3348	66B
D3349	66B
D3350	66B
D3351	66B
D3352	87F
D3353	87F
D3354	87F
D3355	87F
D3356	87F
D3357	87F
D3358	87F
D3359	87F
D3360	87F
D3661	87F
D3362	88B
D3363	88B
D3364	88B
D3365	88B
D3366	88B
D3367	5B
D3368	24K
D3369	24K
D3370	8C
D3371	24K
D3372	26A
D3373	26A
D3374	24C
D3375	55G
D3376	55D
D3377	55D
D3378	55D
D3379	55D
D3380	55E
D3381	55E
D3382	66B
D3383	66B
D3384	66B
D3385	66B
D3386	65B
D3387	65B
D3388	65A
D3389	65A
D3390	65A
D3391	65A
D3392	65A
D3393	65A
D3394	65E
D3395	65E
D3396	65A
D3397	88B
D3398	88B
D3399	88B
D3400	88B
D3401	88B
D3402	88B
D3403	88B
D3404	88B
D3405	88B
D3406	81A
D3407	88B
D3408	65B
D3409	65E
D3410	65C
D3411	65G
D3412	65G
D3413	65D
D3414	65D
D3415	65D
D3416	65E
D3417	65B
D3418	65A
D3419	88B
D3420	88B
D3421	88B
D3422	88B
D3423	88B
D3424	88B
D3425	88B
D3426	88B
D3427	88B
D3428	88B
D3429	87C
D3430	87C
D3431	87C
D3432	87B
D3433	87B
D3434	87B
D3435	87B
D3436	87B
D3437	87B
D3438	87B
D3439	36A
D3440	34E
D3441	34E
D3442	34C
D3443	36A
D3444	36A
D3445	34E
D3446	34E
D3447	34E
D3448	34E
D3449	34E
D3450	34E
D3451	34E
D3452	34E
D3453	34E
D3454	55B
D3455	52A
D3456	51A
D3457	55F
D3458	55D
D3459	73C
D3460	73C
D3461	75C
D3462	73C
D3463	73C
D3464	75C
D3465	75C
D3466	73F
D3467	73F
D3468	73C
D3469	73F
D3470	73F
D3471	73C
D3472	73C
D3473	36A
D3474	36A
D3475	34C
D3476	34C
D3477	34C
D3478	34C
D3479	36A
D3480	36A
D3481	36A
D3482	36A
D3483	36A
D3484	36A

D3485	34E
D3486	34E
D3487	34E
D3488	34E
D3489	40F
D3490	40F
D3491	31B
D3492	31B
D3493	31B
D3494	31B
D3495	30F
D3496	30F
D3497	30A
D3498	30A
D3499	30A
D3500	30A
D3501	30A
D3502	30A
D3503	82B
D3504	82B
D3505	82B
D3506	82B
D3507	82B
D3508	82B
D3509	83F
D3510	83F
D3511	83A
D3512	81A
D3513	83A
D3514	83G
D3515	83A
D3516	83D
D3517	83A
D3518	84E
D3519	83A
D3520	83D
D3521	83C
D3522	83C
D3523	83D
D3524	83D
D3525	83D
D3526	83D
D3527	88B
D3528	66B
D3529	66A
D3530	65E
D3531	65E
D3532	65C
D3533	65E
D3534	65I
D3535	63A
D3536	65J
D3537	65J
D3538	65J
D3539	65J
D3540	65J
D3541	63A
D3542	63A
D3543	63A
D3544	63A
D3545	63A
D3546	61B
D3547	61B
D3548	61B
D3549	61B
D3550	61B
D3551	61B
D3552	61A
D3553	61A
D3554	64F
D3555	64F
D3556	65K
D3557	65K
D3558	64A
D3559	65K
D3560	64C
D3561	64C
D3562	65C
D3563	67C
D3564	67C
D3565	12A
D3566	12A
D3567	12A
D3568	17B
D3569	17B
D3570	17B
D3571	17B
D3572	17B
D3573	14A
D3574	41B
D3575	41B
D3576	18A
D3577	18A
D3578	8A
D3579	8A
D3580	11B
D3581	24K
D3582	21A
D3583	5B
D3584	5B
D3585	17B
D3586	17B
D3587	17B
D3588	26A
D3589	26A
D3590	26A
D3591	26A
D3592	26A
D3593	88B
D3594	88B
D3595	88B
D3596	88B
D3597	81A
D3598	81A
D3599	81A
D3600	81A
D3601	81A
D3602	81A
D3603	88B
D3604	81A
D3605	88B
D3606	88B
D3607	88B
D3608	30A
D3609	30A
D3610	31A
D3611	31A
D3612	36E
D3613	36E
D3614	36E
D3615	36E
D3616	36E
D3617	36E
D3618	36E
D3619	36E
D3620	36E
D3621	36A
D3622	36A
D3623	36A
D3624	40E
D3625	40E
D3626	40E
D3627	40E
D3628	40E
D3629	34E
D3630	34E
D3631	30A
D3632	30A
D3633	30A
D3634	30A
D3635	30A
D3636	30A
D3637	36A
D3638	36C
D3639	36C
D3640	36C
D3641	36C
D3642	36C
D3643	36C
D3644	36C
D3645	36C
D3646	36C
D3647	36C
D3648	36A
D3649	36A
D3650	36A
D3651	36A
D3652	55C
D3653	55C
D3654	55B
D3655	55B
D3656	55F
D3657	55F
D3658	55F
D3659	41A
D3660	41A
D3661	41A
D3662	41B
D3663	41A
D3664	41A
D3665	71A
D3666	71A
D3667	71A
D3668	75C
D3669	75C
D3670	73E
D3671	73E
D3672	51C
D3673	52B
D3674	52C
D3675	50D
D3676	50D
D3677	51A
D3678	52C
D3679	52F
D3680	30F
D3681	30A
D3682	30A
D3683	30A
D3684	30A
D3685	41A
D3686	41A
D3687	34A
D3688	34A
D3689	34C
D3690	34C
D3691	FP
D3692	FP
D3693	FP
D3694	41A
D3695	41A
D3696	41A
D3697	41F
D3698	41A
D3699	41A
D3700	41A
D3701	41A
D3702	41A
D3703	41A
D3704	FP

D3705	FP
D3706	FP
D3707	41A
D3708	40B
D3709	40B
D3710	FP
D3711	FP
D3712	FP
D3713	FP
D3714	34A
D3715	34A
D3716	34A
D3717	34A
D3718	34A
D3719	73E
D3720	75C
D3721	73E
D3722	34A
D3723	34A
D3724	34A
D3725	34A
D3726	41A
D3727	41A
D3728	64A
D3729	64A
D3730	64A
D3731	64A
D3732	64A
D3733	64A
D3734	64A
D3735	60E
D3736	64B
D3737	64C
D3738	64B
D3739	64B
D3740	64A
D3741	64C
D3742	64A
D3743	86A
D3744	86A
D3745	86A
D3746	86A
D3747	86A
D3748	86A
D3749	86A
D3750	82B
D3751	82B
D3752	84B
D3753	81C
D3754	81C
D3755	84B
D3756	87C
D3757	84B
D3758	81A
D3759	81A
D3760	81A
D3761	81C
D3762	81C
D3763	5B
D3764	6A
D3765	9A
D3766	9A
D3767	9A
D3768	9A
D3769	9A
D3770	9A
D3771	9B
D3772	9B
D3773	17B
D3774	17C
D3775	17C
D3776	15B
D3777	15B
D3778	15B
D3779	26A
D3780	24D
D3781	24D
D3782	24B
D3783	24B
D3784	26A
D3785	15E
D3786	15C
D3787	15C
D3788	15C
D3789	15C
D3790	15C
D3791	15C
D3792	18C
D3793	8D
D3794	8D
D3795	8B
D3796	8B
D3797	8B
D3798	5D
D3799	5D
D3800	5D
D3801	5D
D3802	5D
D3803	82B
D3804	82C
D3805	82B
D3806	82B
D3807	86B
D3808	86B
D3809	86B
D3810	86B
D3811	86B
D3812	86B
D3813	86B
D3814	86B
D3815	86B
D3816	86B
D3817	86A
D3818	86B
D3819	86B
D3820	86A
D3821	86B
D3822	86A
D3823	86A
D3824	86A
D3825	87C
D3826	87C
D3827	87C
D3828	87C
D3829	87C
D3830	87C
D3831	87C
D3832	6B
D3833	6B
D3834	8B
D3835	8B
D3836	8F
D3837	8F
D3838	24L
D3839	24L
D3840	24L
D3841	24L
D3842	26A
D3843	26A
D3844	26A
D3845	26A
D3846	24K
D3847	1B
D3848	1B
D3849	1B
D3850	1B
D3851	8B
D3852	9F
D3853	9F
D3854	9F
D3855	27F
D3856	27F
D3857	27F
D3858	27E
D3859	16D
D3860	16D
D3861	16D
D3862	17A
D3863	17A
D3864	17A
D3865	17A
D3866	5D
D3867	24J
D3868	26A
D3869	14A
D3870	8C
D3871	24J
D3872	50A
D3873	51L
D3874	50A
D3875	51L
D3876	51L
D3877	
D3878	
D3879	
D3880	
D3881	
D3882	
D3883	
D3884	
D3885	
D3886	
D3887	
D3888	
D3889	
D3890	
D3891	
D3892	
D3893	
D3894	
D3895	
D3896	
D3897	
D3898	
D3899	
D3900	
D3901	
D3902	
D3903	
D3904	
D3905	
D3906	
D3907	
D3908	
D3909	
D3910	
D3911	
D3912	
D3913	
D3914	
D3915	
D3916	
D3917	
D3918	
D3919	
D3920	
D3921	
D3922	
D3923	
D3924	
D3925	
D3926	
D3927	
D3928	

D3929	
D3930	
D3931	
D3932	
D3933	
D3934	
D3935	
D3936	
D3937	55D
D3938	52E
D3939	52E
D3940	50A
D3941	55D
D3942	52E
D3943	52E
D3944	50B
D3945	50B
D3946	50A
D3947	81A
D3948	81A
D3949	81A
D3950	81A
D3951	81A
D3952	81A
D3953	81A
D3954	
D3955	81A
D3956	
D3957	
D3958	
D3959	
D3960	
D3961	
D3962	
D3963	
D3964	
D3965	
D3966	
D3967	
D3968	
D3969	
D3970	
D3971	
D3972	
D3973	
D3974	
D3975	
D3976	
D3977	
D3978	
D3979	
D3980	
D3981	
D3982	
D3983	
D3984	
D3985	
D3986	
D3987	
D3988	
D3989	
D3990	
D3991	
D3992	
D3993	
D3994	
D3995	
D3996	
D3997	
D3998	
D3999	
D4000	
D4001	
D4002	
D4003	
D4004	
D4005	
D4006	
D4007	
D4008	
D4009	
D4010	
D4011	
D4012	
D4013	
D4014	
D4015	
D4016	
D4017	
D4018	
D4019	
D4020	
D4021	
D4022	
D4023	
D4024	
D4025	
D4026	
D4027	
D4028	
D4029	
D4030	
D4031	
D4032	
D4033	
D4034	
D4035	
D4036	
D4037	
D4038	
D4039	
D4040	
D4041	
D4042	
D4043	
D4044	
D4045	
D4046	
D4047	
D4048	
D4049	
D4050	
D4051	
D4052	
D4053	
D4054	
D4055	
D4056	
D4057	
D4058	
D4059	
D4060	
D4061	
D4062	
D4063	
D4064	
D4065	
D4066	
D4067	
D4068	
D4069	
D4070	
D4071	
D4072	
D4073	
D4074	
D4075	
D4076	
D4077	
D4078	
D4079	
D4080	
D4081	
D4082	
D4083	
D4084	
D4085	
D4086	
D4087	
D4088	
D4089	
D4090	
D4091	
D4092	
D4093	
D4094	
D5000	73C
D5001	73C
D5002	73C
D5003	5B
D5004	73C
D5005	73C
D5006	73C
D5007	73C
D5008	SR
D5009	73C
D5010	73C
D5011	73C
D5012	73C
D5013	73C
D5014	73C
D5015	1B
D5016	1B
D5017	73C
D5018	1B
D5019	1B
D5020	32B
D5021	32B
D5022	32B
D5023	32B
D5024	32B
D5025	32B
D5026	32B
D5027	32B
D5028	32B
D5029	32B
D5030	30A
D5031	30A
D5032	30A
D5033	30A
D5034	30A
D5035	30A
D5036	32B
D5037	32B
D5038	31B
D5039	31B
D5040	32B
D5041	32B
D5042	31B
D5043	31B
D5044	31B
D5045	31B
D5046	31B
D5047	31B
D5048	31B
D5049	31B
D5050	31B
D5051	31B
D5052	31B
D5053	31B
D5054	31B
D5055	31B
D5056	31B
D5057	31B

D5058	31B
D5059	31B
D5060	31B
D5061	31B
D5062	31B
D5063	31B
D5064	31B
D5065	31B
D5066	31B
D5067	31B
D5068	31B
D5069	31B
D5070	31B
D5071	31B
D5072	1A
D5073	1A
D5074	1A
D5075	1A
D5076	31B
D5077	31B
D5078	1A
D5079	1A
D5080	2A
D5081	1A
D5082	1A
D5083	1A
D5084	1A
D5085	
D5086	
D5087	
D5088	
D5089	
D5090	
D5091	
D5092	
D5093	
D5094	31B
D5095	31B
D5096	52A
D5097	52A
D5098	52A
D5099	
D5100	
D5101	
D5102	
D5103	
D5104	
D5105	
D5106	
D5107	
D5108	
D5109	
D5110	
D5111	
D5112	
D5113	
D5114	
D5115	
D5116	
D5117	
D5118	
D5119	
D5120	
D5121	
D5122	
D5123	
D5124	
D5125	
D5126	
D5127	
D5128	
D5129	
D5130	
D5131	
D5132	
D5133	
D5134	
D5135	
D5136	
D5137	
D5138	
D5139	
D5140	
D5141	
D5142	
D5143	
D5144	
D5145	
D5146	
D5147	
D5148	
D5149	
D5150	
D5300	ScR
D5301	ScR
D5302	ScR
D5303	ScR
D5304	ScR
D5305	ScR
D5306	ScR
D5307	ScR
D5308	ScR
D5309	ScR
D5310	ScR
D5311	FP
D5312	ScR
D5313	ScR
D5314	FP
D5315	FP
D5316	FP
D5317	FP
D5318	FP
D5319	FP
D5320	64H
D5321	64H
D5322	64H
D5323	64H
D5324	64H
D5325	64H
D5326	64H
D5327	64H
D5328	64H
D5329	64H
D5330	64H
D5331	64H
D5332	64H
D5333	64H
D5334	64H
D5335	64H
D5336	64H
D5337	64H
D5338	60A
D5339	60A
D5340	61A
D5341	61A
D5342	62B
D5343	62B
D5344	64H
D5345	64H
D5346	60A
D5347	
D5348	
D5349	
D5350	
D5351	
D5352	
D5353	
D5354	
D5355	
D5356	
D5357	
D5358	
D5359	
D5360	
D5361	
D5362	
D5363	
D5364	
D5365	
D5366	
D5367	
D5368	
D5369	
D5370	
D5371	
D5372	
D5373	
D5374	
D5375	
D5376	
D5377	
D5378	
D5379	
D5380	
D5381	
D5382	
D5383	
D5384	
D5385	
D5386	
D5387	
D5388	
D5389	
D5390	
D5391	
D5392	
D5393	
D5394	
D5395	
D5396	
D5397	
D5398	
D5399	
D5400	
D5401	
D5402	
D5403	
D5404	
D5405	
D5406	
D5407	
D5408	
D5409	
D5410	
D5411	
D5412	
D5413	
D5414	
D5415	
D5500	32A
D5501	30A
D5502	30A
D5503	30A
D5504	30A
D5505	30A
D5506	30A

D5507-D5806

D5507	30A
D5508	30A
D5509	30A
D5510	30A
D5511	30A
D5512	30A
D5513	30A
D5514	30A
D5515	32B
D5516	30A
D5517	30A
D5518	31B
D5519	31B
D5520	32B
D5521	32B
D5522	32B
D5523	32B
D5524	30A
D5525	31B
D5526	32B
D5527	32B
D5528	32A
D5529	32A
D5530	32A
D5531	32B
D5532	32A
D5533	32A
D5534	32A
D5535	32A
D5536	32B
D5537	32B
D5538	32B
D5539	32B
D5540	32B
D5541	32B
D5542	32B
D5543	32B
D5544	32B
D5545	30A
D5546	31B
D5547	31B
D5548	32B
D5549	32B
D5550	32B
D5551	32B
D5552	32B
D5553	32B
D5554	32B
D5555	32B
D5556	32B
D5557	32B
D5558	32B
D5559	32B
D5560	32B
D5561	32B
D5562	32B
D5563	32B
D5564	32B
D5565	32A
D5566	32A
D5567	32A
D5568	32A
D5569	32A
D5570	31B
D5571	31B
D5572	31B
D5573	31B
D5574	32A
D5575	32A
D5576	32A
D5577	32A
D5578	30A
D5579	30A
D5580	32A
D5581	32A
D5582	32A
D5583	30A
D5584	31B
D5585	31B
D5586	FP
D5587	FP
D5588	FP
D5589	FP
D5590	FP
D5591	FP
D5592	FP
D5593	FP
D5594	FP
D5595	FP
D5596	FP
D5597	FP
D5598	FP
D5599	FP
D5600	FP
D5601	FP
D5602	FP
D5603	FP
D5604	FP
D5605	FP
D5606	FP
D5607	FP
D5608	FP
D5609	FP
D5610	FP
D5611	FP
D5612	FP
D5613	FP
D5614	FP
D5615	FP
D5616	30A
D5617	30A
D5618	
D5619	
D5620	
D5621	
D5622	
D5623	
D5624	
D5625	
D5626	
D5627	
D5628	
D5629	
D5630	
D5631	
D5632	
D5633	
D5634	
D5635	
D5636	
D5637	
D5638	
D5639	
D5640	
D5641	
D5642	
D5643	
D5644	
D5645	
D5646	
D5647	
D5648	
D5649	
D5650	
D5651	
D5652	
D5653	
D5654	
D5655	
D5656	
D5657	
D5658	
D5659	
D5660	
D5661	
D5662	
D5663	
D5664	
D5665	
D5666	
D5667	
D5668	
D5669	
D5670	
D5671	
D5672	
D5673	
D5674	
D5675	
D5676	
D5677	
D5678	
D5679	
D5680	
D5681	
D5682	
D5683	
D5684	
D5685	
D5686	
D5687	
D5688	
D5689	
D5690	
D5691	
D5692	
D5693	
D5694	
D5695	
D5696	
D5697	
D5698	
D5699	
D5700	17A
D5701	17A
D5702	17A
D5703	17A
D5704	17A
D5705	17A
D5706	17A
D5707	17A
D5708	17A
D5709	17A
D5710	17A
D5711	17A
D5712	14A
D5713	14A
D5714	14A
D5715	14A
D5716	14A
D5717	14A
D5718	14A
D5719	14A
D5800	
D5801	
D5802	
D5803	
D5804	
D5805	
D5806	

D5807	
D5808	
D5809	
D5810	
D5811	
D5812	
D5813	
D5814	
D5815	
D5816	
D5817	
D5818	
D5819	
D5820	
D5821	
D5822	
D5823	
D5824	
D5825	
D5900	FP
D5901	FP
D5902	FP
D5903	FP
D5904	FP
D5905	FP
D5906	FP
D5907	FP
D5908	FP
D5909	FP
D6100	ScR
D6101	ScR
D6102	65A
D6103	ScR
D6104	65A
D6105	ScR
D6106	ScR
D6107	65A
D6108	ScR
D6109	65A
D6110	30A
D6111	30A
D6112	30A
D6113	ScR
D6114	30A
D6115	30A
D6116	30A
D6117	32B
D6118	30A
D6119	32B
D6120	32B
D6121	32B
D6122	32B
D6123	ScR
D6124	ScR
D6125	ScR
D6126	ScR
D6127	ScR
D6128	ScR
D6129	32B
D6130	63A
D6131	32B
D6132	ScR
D6133	ScR
D6134	32B
D6135	32B
D6136	32B
D6137	32B
D6138	61A
D6139	61A
D6140	61A
D6141	61A
D6142	61A
D6143	61A
D6144	61A
D6145	
D6146	
D6147	
D6148	
D6149	
D6150	
D6151	
D6152	
D6153	
D6154	
D6155	
D6156	
D6157	
D6300	83D
D6301	83D
D6302	83D
D6303	83D
D6304	83D
D6305	83D
D6306	83D
D6307	83D
D6308	83D
D6309	83D
D6310	83D
D6311	83D
D6312	83D
D6313	83D
D6314	83D
D6315	83D
D6316	83D
D6317	83D
D6318	83D
D6319	83D
D6320	83D
D6321	83D
D6322	83D
D6323	
D6324	
D6325	
D6326	
D6327	
D6328	
D6329	
D6330	
D6331	
D6332	
D6333	
D6334	
D6335	
D6336	
D6337	
D6338	
D6339	
D6340	
D6341	
D6342	
D6343	
D6344	
D6345	
D6346	
D6347	
D6348	
D6349	
D6350	
D6351	
D6352	
D6353	
D6354	
D6355	
D6356	
D6357	
D6500	73C
D6501	73C
D6502	73C
D6503	73C
D6504	73C
D6505	73C
D6506	73C
D6507	73C
D6508	
D6509	
D6510	
D6511	
D6512	
D6513	
D6514	
D6515	
D6516	
D6517	
D6518	
D6519	
D6520	
D6521	
D6522	
D6523	
D6524	
D6525	
D6526	
D6527	
D6528	
D6529	
D6530	
D6531	
D6532	
D6533	
D6534	
D6535	
D6536	
D6537	
D6538	
D6539	
D6540	
D6541	
D6542	
D6543	
D6544	
D6545	
D6546	
D6547	
D6548	
D6549	
D6550	
D6551	
D6552	
D6553	
D6554	
D6555	
D6556	
D6557	
D6558	
D6559	
D6560	
D6561	
D6562	
D6563	
D6564	
D6565	
D6566	
D6567	
D6568	
D6569	
D6570	
D6571	

D6572-D8021

D6572
D6573
D6574
D6575
D6576
D6577
D6578
D6579
D6580
D6581
D6582
D6583
D6584
D6585
D6586
D6587
D6588
D6589
D6590
D6591
D6592
D6593
D6594
D6595
D6596
D6597

D6700
D6701
D6702
D6703
D6704
D6705
D6706
D6707
D6708
D6709
D6710
D6711
D6712
D6713
D6714
D6715
D6716
D6717
D6718
D6719
D6720
D6721
D6722
D6723
D6724
D6725
D6726
D6727
D6728
D6729
D6730
D6731
D6732
D6733
D6734
D6735
D6736
D6737
D6738
D6739
D6740
D6741
D6742
D6743
D6744
D6745
D6746
D6747
D6748
D6749
D6750
D6751
D6752
D6753
D6754
D6755
D6756
D6757
D6758
D6759
D6760
D6761
D6762
D6763
D6764
D6765
D6766
D6767
D6768
D6769
D6770
D6771
D6772
D6773
D6774
D6775
D6776
D6777
D6778

D7000
D7001
D7002
D7003
D7004
D7005
D7006
D7007
D7008
D7009
D7010
D7011
D7012
D7013
D7014
D7015
D7016
D7017
D7018
D7019
D7020
D7021
D7022
D7023
D7024
D7025
D7026
D7027
D7028
D7029
D7030
D7031
D7032
D7033
D7034
D7035
D7036
D7037
D7038
D7039
D7040
D7041
D7042
D7043
D7044
D7045
D7046
D7047
D7048
D7049
D7050
D7051
D7052
D7053
D7054
D7055
D7056
D7057
D7058
D7059
D7060
D7061
D7062
D7063
D7064
D7065
D7066
D7067
D7068
D7069
D7070
D7071
D7072
D7073
D7074
D7075
D7076
D7077
D7078
D7079
D7080
D7081
D7082
D7083
D7084
D7085
D7086
D7087
D7088
D7089
D7090
D7091
D7092
D7093
D7094

D8000 5B
D8001 5B
D8002 5B
D8003 5B
D8004 5B
D8005 ID
D8006 ID
D8007 ID
D8008 ID
D8009 ID
D8010 ID
D8011 ID
D8012 ID
D8013 ID
D8014 ID
D8015 ID
D8016 ID
D8017 ID
D8018 ID
D8019 ID
D8020 FP
D8021 FP

D8022	FP
D8023	FP
D8024	FP
D8025	FP
D8026	FP
D8027	FP
D8028	61A
D8029	61A
D8030	61A
D8031	61A
D8032	60A
D8033	60A
D8034	60A
D8035	1A
D8036	1A
D8037	1B
D8038	1D
D8039	1B
D8040	1D
D8041	1D
D8042	1D
D8043	1D
D8044	1D
D8045	FP
D8046	FP
D8047	FP
D8048	FP
D8049	FP
D8050	
D8051	
D8052	
D8053	
D8054	
D8055	
D8056	
D8057	
D8058	
D8059	
D8060	
D8061	
D8062	
D8063	
D8064	
D8065	
D8066	
D8067	
D8068	
D8069	
D8070	
D8071	
D8072	
D8073	
D8074	
D8075	
D8076	
D8077	
D8078	
D8079	
D8080	
D8081	
D8082	
D8083	
D8084	
D8085	
D8086	
D8087	
D8088	
D8089	
D8090	
D8091	
D8092	
D8093	
D8094	
D8095	
D8096	
D8097	
D8098	
D8099	
D8100	
D8101	
D8102	
D8103	
D8104	
D8105	
D8106	
D8107	
D8108	
D8109	
D8110	
D8111	
D8112	
D8113	
D8114	
D8115	
D8116	
D8117	
D8118	
D8119	
D8120	
D8121	
D8122	
D8123	
D8124	
D8125	
D8126	
D8127	
D8200	32A
D8201	32A
D8202	32A
D8203	32A
D8204	32A
D8205	32A
D8206	32A
D8207	32A
D8208	30A
D8209	30A
D8210	30A
D8211	30A
D8212	31B
D8213	31B
D8214	31B
D8215	31B
D8216	31B
D8217	31B
D8218	31B
D8219	
D8220	30A
D8221	30A
D8222	30A
D8223	32B
D8224	32B
D8225	32B
D8226	32B
D8227	
D8228	
D8229	
D8230	
D8231	
D8232	
D8233	
D8234	
D8235	
D8236	
D8237	
D8238	
D8239	
D8240	
D8241	
D8242	
D8400	30A
D8401	30A
D8402	30A
D8403	30A
D8404	30A
D8405	30A
D8406	30A
D8407	30A
D8408	30A
D8409	30A
D9000	
D9001	
D9002	
D9003	
D9004	
D9005	
D9006	
D9007	
D9008	
D9009	
D9010	
D9011	
D9012	
D9013	
D9014	
D9015	
D9016	
D9017	
D9018	
D9019	
D9020	
D9021	
10000	1A
10001	1A
10201	1A
10202	1A
10203	1A
12000	5B
12001	5B
12003	8F
12004	5B
12005	5B
12006	8C
12007	8C
12008	8C
12009	5B
12010	5B
12011	5B
12012	5B
12013	5B
12014	8C
12015	8C
12016	8C
12017	8C
12018	8C
12019	8F
12020	5B
12021	5B
12022	8G

12023	8G
12024	8C
12025	5B
12026	8C
12027	8C
12028	8C
12029	8C
12030	5B
12031	5B
12032	5B
12033	17A
12034	17A
12035	21A
12036	6A
12037	6A
12038	18A
12039	21A
12040	21A
12041	21A
12042	21A
12043	21A
12044	21A
12045	2A
12046	2A
12047	2A
12048	6A
12049	21A
12050	16A
12051	16A
12052	16A
12053	6A
12054	6A
12055	18A
12056	3C
12057	6A
12058	14A
12059	21A
12060	21A
12061	21A
12062	21A
12063	14A
12064	14A
12065	14A
12066	21A
12067	14A
12068	14A
12069	14A
12070	1A
12071	8F
12072	17A
12073	1A
12074	1A
12075	1A
12076	1A
12077	21A
12078	1A
12079	12A
12080	12A
12081	8C
12082	18A
12083	12A
12084	12C
12085	12C
12086	12C
12087	12A
12088	3D
12089	3D
12090	3D
12091	3A
12092	3A
12093	3B
12094	3B
12095	3D
12096	16A
12097	16A
12098	16A
12099	8F
12100	1A
12101	1A
12102	8F
12103	30A
12104	30A
12105	30A
12106	30A
12107	30A
12108	30A
12109	30A
12110	30A
12111	30A
12112	FP
12113	NE
12114	NE
12115	NE
12116	NE
12117	NE
12118	NE
12119	NE
12120	NE
12121	NE
12122	NE
12123	40B
12124	40B
12125	40B
12126	40B
12127	30A
12128	30A
12129	FP
12130	30A
12131	FP
12132	30A
12133	40B
12134	31B
12135	40B
12136	31B
12137	FP
12138	FP
15000	31B
15001	31B
15002	31B
15003	31B
15004	34E
15100	82C
15101	88B
15102	88B
15103	88B
15104	88B
15105	88B
15106	88B
15201	75C
15202	73C
15203	75C
15211	75C
15212	75C
15213	75C
15214	71A
15215	75C
15216	73C
15217	73C
15218	73C
15219	73C
15220	73F
15221	73C
15222	73C
15223	73C
15224	73F
15225	73C
15226	73C
15227	73F
15228	73F
15229	73F
15230	71A
15231	71A
15232	71A
15233	71A
15234	71A
15235	71A
15236	71A
18000	81A
E2001	
E3001	9A
E3002	9A
E3003	9A
E3004	9A
E3005	
E3006	
E3007	
E3008	
E3009	
E3010	
E3011	
E3012	
E3013	
E3014	
E3015	
E3016	
E3017	
E3018	
E3019	
E3020	
E3021	
E3022	
E3023	
E3024	
E3025	
E3026	
E3027	
E3028	
E3029	
E3030	
E3031	
E3032	
E3033	
E3034	
E3035	
E3036	9A
E3037	
E3038	
E3039	
E3040	
E3041	
E3042	
E3043	
E3044	
E3045	
E3046	
E3047	
E3048	
E3049	
E3050	
E3051	
E3052	
E3053	
E3054	
E3055	
E3056	
E3057	
E3058	

E3059		E5008	73A	26031	Reddish	30043	70B
E3060		E5009	73A	26032	Reddish	30044	72A
E3061		E5010	73A	26033	Reddish	30045	72A
E3062		E5011	73A	26034	Reddish	30048	72A
E3063		E5012	73A	26035	Reddish	30049	75A
E3064		E5013	73A	26036	Reddish	30050	75A
E3065		E5014	73A	26037	Reddish	30051	75A
E3066		E5015	73A	26038	Reddish	30052	75E
E3067		E5016	73A	26039	Reddish	30053	75A
E3068		E5017	73A	26040	Reddish	30055	75E
E3069		E5018	73A	26041	Reddish	30056	75A
E3070		E5019		26042	Reddish	30057	71B
E3071		E5020		26043	Reddish	30058	71B
E3072		E5021		26044	Reddish	30059	71B
E3073		E5022		26045	Reddish	30060	71B
E3074		E5023		26046 *	Reddish	30061	71I
E3075				26047 *	Reddish	30062	71I
E3076				26048 *	Reddish	30063	71I
E3077				26049 *	Reddish	30064	71I
E3078				26050 *	Reddish	30065	71I
E3079		20001	73A	26051 *	Reddish	30066	71I
E3080		20002	73A	26052 *	Reddish	30067	71I
E3081		20003	73A	26053 *	Reddish	30068	71I
E3082				26054 *	Reddish	30069	71I
E3083				26055 *	Reddish	30070	71I
E3084				26056 *	Reddish	30071	71I
E3085				26057 *	Reddish	30072	71I
E3086		26000 *	Reddish			30073	71I
E3087		26001	Reddish			30074	71I
E3088		26002	Reddish	26500	52B	30089	70C
E3089		26003	Reddish	26501	52B	30096	71A
E3090		26004	Reddish			30102	71B
E3091		26005	Reddish			30104	71B
E3092		26006	Reddish			30105	71B
E3093		26007	Reddish	27000 *	Reddish	30106	71B
E3094		26008	Reddish	27001 *	Reddish	30107	71B
E3095		26009	Reddish	27002 *	Reddish	30108	71B
		26010	Reddish	27003 *	Reddish	30109	75E
		26011	Reddish	27004 *	Reddish	30110	75A
		26012	Reddish	27005 *	Reddish	30111	71B
		26013	Reddish	27006 *	Reddish	30112	71B
E3301		26014	Reddish			30117	71A
E3302		26015	Reddish			30120	71A
E3303		26016	Reddish			30124	70C
E3304		26017	Reddish	30021	72A	30125	71A
E3305		26018	Reddish	30023	72A	30127	71B
		26019	Reddish	30024	72A	30128	71B
		26020	Reddish	30025	72A	30129	72C
		26021	Reddish	30028	71A	30131	72C
		26022	Reddish	30029	71A	30132	70C
E5000	73A	26023	Reddish	30031	70B	30133	71A
E5001	73A	26024	Reddish	30032	70B	30183	83H
E5002	73A	26025	Reddish	30033	72E	30192	83H
E5003	73A	26026	Reddish	30034	83H	30193	83H
E5004	73A	26027	Reddish	30035	71A	30199	72A
E5005	73A	26028	Reddish	30036	83H	30200	72F
E5006	73A	26029	Reddish	30039	70A	30223	71A
E5007	73A	26030	Reddish	30040	71B	30225	83H

30229	71A	30379	73J	30524	72B	30698	70C
30238	70C	30448	* 72B	30530	71A	30699	70A
30241	70A	30450	* 72B	30531	71A	30700	70C
30245	70A	30451	* 72B	30532	71A	30701	70A
30246	70C	30453	* 72B	30533	75C	30707	71B
30247	72E	30456	* 70D	30534	75C	30709	72A
30248	70A	30457	* 70A	30535	71A	30715	72A
30249	70A	30474	71A	30536	71A	30717	72A
30251	72E	30475	71A	30537	75C	30718	72A
30253	72E	30476	71A	30538	75C	30719	72A
30254	72E	30479	71A	30539	71B	30729	72A
30255	72E	30480	71A	30540	75C	30763	* 70A
30258	70D	30489	70A	30541	71B	30764	* 71B
30266	72B	30491	70A	30542	71A	30765	* 70D
30274	71B	30494	70B	30543	71A	30768	* 71A
30277	70C	30495	70B	30544	75E	30770	* 71A
30287	71A	30496	70B	30545	75E	30771	* 71B
30288	71A	30497	70B	30546	75E	30772	* 71B
30300	71A	30498	70B	30547	75E	30773	* 71A
30306	71A	30499	70B	30548	71B	30777	* 70B
30308	70C	30500	70B	30549	75C	30781	* 71B
30309	72B	30501	70B	30582	72A	30782	* 71B
30313	72A	30502	70B	30583	72A	30783	* 71B
30315	72B	30503	70B	30584	72A	30788	* 71A
30316	71A	30504	70B	30585	72F	30790	* 71A
30317	72A	30505	70B	30586	72F	30791	* 71A
30320	70A	30506	70B	30587	72F	30793	* 70B
30321	70A	30507	70B	30667	72A	30794	* 70D
30325	70C	30508	70B	30668	72A	30795	* 70B
30326	70C	30509	70B	30669	72A	30796	* 72B
30327	72A	30510	70B	30670	72A	30798	* 72B
30328	73J	30511	70B	30673	72B	30799	* 72B
30331	72B	30512	70B	30674	72B	30800	* 71A
30338	72A	30513	70B	30676	72A	30802	* 71A
30339	70B	30514	70B	30687	70B	30803	* 71A
30346	70B	30515	70B	30689	70B	30804	* 71A
30349	70B	30516	71A	30690	71B	30806	* 71A
30350	70C	30517	71A	30691	72A	30823	72B
30355	70B	30518	70B	30692	72B	30824	72B
30357	71A	30519	70B	30693	70C	30825	72B
30368	70D	30520	70B	30694	70A	30826	72B
30375	71A	30521	70A	30695	71B	30827	72B
30377	71A	30522	72B	30696	70B	30828	72B
30378	70C	30523	72B	30697	70C		

Isle of Wight Locomotives

4	* 70H	20	* 70H	26	* 70H	31	* 70H
14	* 70H	21	* 70H	27	* 70H	32	* 70H
16	* 70H	22	* 70H	28	* 70H	33	* 70H
17	* 70H	24	* 70H	29	* 70H	35	* 70H
18	* 70H	25	* 70H	30	* 70H	36	* 70H

30829	72B
30830	72B
30831	72B
30832	72B
30833	70B
30834	70B
30835	75B
30836	75B
30837	75B
30838	70B
30839	70B
30840	70B
30841	72A
30842	72A
30843	72A
30844	72A
30845	72A
30846	72A
30847	75B
30850 *	71A
30851 *	71A
30852 *	71A
30853 *	71A
30854 *	71A
30855 *	71A
30856 *	71A
30857 *	71A
30858 *	71A
30859 *	71A
30860 *	71A
30861 *	71A
30862 *	71A
30863 *	71A
30864 *	71A
30865 *	71A
30900 *	75A
30901 *	75A
30902 *	75A
30903 *	70C
30904 *	70D
30905 *	70D
30906 *	70C
30907 *	70A
30908 *	70D
30909 *	70C
30910 *	70A
30911 *	70A
30912 *	70A
30913 *	70A
30914 *	75B
30915 *	75B
30916 *	75B
30917 *	75A
30918 *	75A
30919 *	75A
30920 *	73A
30921 *	73A
30922 *	73A
30923 *	73A
30924 *	73B
30925 *	73B
30926 *	73B
30927 *	73B
30928 *	73B
30929 *	73B
30930 *	73B
30931 *	73B
30932 *	73F
30933 *	73F
30934 *	73F
30935 *	73F
30936 *	73F
30937 *	73F
30938 *	73H
30939 *	73H
30950	72A
30951	72A
30952	72A
30953	72A
30954	72A
30955	72A
30956	72A
30957	72A
31004	73H
31005	73J
31019	73A
31027	73H
31037	70C
31048	73H
31054	70C
31061	73J
31065	73H
31067	73A
31068	73B
31086	73B
31102	73B
31112	73H
31113	73H
31145	70A
31150	73H
31161	75E
31162	75F
31177	73J
31193	73J
31218	73F
31223	73F
31229	73A
31242	70A
31244	73J
31246	70A
31247	70A
31255	73F
31256	73F
31258	73H
31261	73A
31263	73J
31265	73A
31266	75F
31267	73B
31268	73C
31271	70A
31276	75A
31278	75F
31280	73J
31287	73C
31293	73B
31298	73C
31305	73B
31306	75F
31307	73F
31308	75A
31310	75F
31317	73A
31322	75A
31323	73H
31324	73F
31326	73H
31328	73H
31400	73F
31401	73F
31402	73F
31403	73F
31404	73F
31405	73F
31406	73F
31407	73F
31408	73F
31409	73F
31410	73A
31411	73A
31412	73A
31413	73H
31414	73H
31480	73B
31481	73H
31487	73J
31489	73J
31494	70A
31495	70A
31497	73B
31498	73C
31500	73J
31505	70A
31507	73B
31510	70A
31512	73J
31517	73J
31518	73J
31519	73J
31520	73J
31521	75F
31522	75F
31523	73J
31530	75A
31533	73J
31542	73H
31543	75A
31544	75F
31545	70A
31550	73A
31551	73A
31552	73F
31553	73J
31556	75A
31573	73C
31575	73A
31578	73A
31579	73C
31583	73A
31584	73A
31588	73J
31589	73F
31590	73J
31592	73J
31610	70C
31611	70D
31612	70C
31613	71A
31614	72C
31615	70C
31616	75B
31617	70A
31618	71A
31619	71A
31620	71A
31621	70A
31622	70C
31623	70C
31624	70A
31625	70C
31626	71A
31627	70C
31628	70C
31629	71A
31630	70C
31631	70C
31632	72C
31633	70C
31634	70A
31635	70C
31636	70C
31637	72C
31638	70C
31639	71A
31682	73C
31684	73J
31686	73C
31689	73C

31690	73C
31691	73C
31693	73C
31694	73C
31695	73C
31714	73A
31715	73A
31716	73J
31717	73B
31719	73A
31720	73H
31721	73C
31722	70C
31723	70C
31724	75A
31725	75A
31727	70A
31735	71A
31739	73B
31749	73B
31753	70A
31754	70A
31756	73J
31757	70A
31759	70A
31760	70A
31764	70A
31765	70A
31766	70A
31768	70A
31771	70A
31776	70A
31780	70A
31782	70A
31783	73J
31786	70A
31787	70A
31789	70A
31790	70C
31791	71A
31792	72C
31793	71A
31794	71A
31795	71A
31796	70A
31797	70C
31798	72C
31799	75B
31800	70C
31801	71A
31802	72C
31803	71A
31804	71A
31805	72C
31806	70D
31807	75B
31808	71A
31809	71A
31810	73H
31811	70C
31812	70C
31813	72B
31814	72B
31815	70C
31816	73C
31817	75B
31818	73H
31819	73H
31820	73H
31821	73H
31822	73J
31823	73B
31824	73B
31825	73B
31826	73B
31827	73B
31828	73B
31829	73B
31830	72A
31831	72A
31832	72A
31833	72A
31834	72A
31835	72A
31836	72A
31837	72A
31838	72A
31839	72A
31840	72A
31841	72A
31842	72A
31843	72A
31844	72A
31845	72A
31846	72A
31847	72A
31848	73F
31849	72A
31850	75B
31851	75B
31852	75B
31853	72A
31854	73F
31855	73C
31856	73C
31857	73C
31858	70C
31859	73C
31860	72A
31861	75B
31862	75B
31863	75B
31864	75B
31865	75B
31866	75B
31867	75B
31868	75B
31869	75B
31870	75B
31871	75B
31872	75B
31873	73B
31874	73B
31875	73B
31876	73J
31877	73J
31878	73J
31879	73J
31880	73J
31890	75A
31891	75A
31892	70B
31893	70B
31894	73A
31895	73A
31896	73A
31897	73A
31898	73A
31899	73A
31900	73A
31901	73J
31902	73J
31903	73J
31904	73J
31905	73J
31906	73J
31907	73J
31908	73J
31909	73J
31910	73J
31911	73C
31912	73C
31913	73C
31914	73A
31915	73A
31916	73C
31917	75C
31918	75C
31919	75C
31920	75C
31921	73A
31922	73C
31923	73C
31924	73C
31925	73C
32100	73A
32101	71I
32102	73A
32103	73A
32104	75C
32105	75C
32106	73A
32107	71I
32108	71I
32109	71I
32337	75E
32338	75A
32339	75A
32340	75A
32341	75A
32342	75A
32343	75A
32344	75E
32345	75E
32346	75E
32347	75E
32348	75E
32349	75E
32350	75E
32351	75E
32352	75E
32353	75E
32408	73B
32410	73H
32415	73H
32416	73B
32417	73B
32418	73B
32438	70B
32441	75A
32443	75C
32445	75C
32446	75C
32448	75C
32449	75A
32450	75B
32451	75B
32468	75A
32469	75E
32470	75E
32472	73B
32473	73B
32474	73B
32475	75A
32479	75A
32484	75A
32487	70A
32491	71A
32495	75A
32498	70A
32500	70A
32503	75A
32504	75A
32505	70A
32506	70A
32509	75F
32510	71A
32512	75A

32515 75A
32521 75C
32522 75E
32523 75E
32525 73B
32527 75E
32528 75E
32532 75E
32534 75E
32535 75E
32536 75E
32538 73B
32539 73B
32541 75C
32543 73A
32544 75C
32545 75C
32546 75C
32547 73A
32548 75C
32549 75C
32550 75C
32552 73B
32553 73B
32556 71A
32557 73B
32559 71A
32562 75A
32563 70A
32564 75E
32565 73B
32578 73J
32580 75A
32581 75F
32635 75A
32636 75A
32640 71A
32646 71A
32650 71A
32655 71A
32661 71A
32662 75A
32670 75A
32678 71A
32694 71I

33001 73J
33002 73J
33003 73J
33004 73J
33005 70C
33006 70B
33007 70B
33008 70B
33009 70B
33010 70B
33011 70B
33012 70B
33013 70B
33014 73J
33015 70A
33016 70B
33017 70A
33018 70B
33019 70C
33020 71A
33021 71A
33022 70C
33023 71A
33024 73J
33025 70C
33026 70B
33027 70B
33028 73J
33029 73J
33030 73J
33031 73J
33032 73J
33033 73J
33034 73J
33035 73J
33036 73J
33037 73J
33038 70A
33039 73J
33040 73J

34001 * 73B
34002 * 72A
34003 * 73B
34004 * 73B
34005 * 73B
34006 * 70A
34007 * 70A
34008 * 75A
34009 * 70A
34010 * 70A
34011 * 72A
34012 * 73B
34013 * 73B
34014 * 73B
34015 * 72A
34016 * 73B
34017 * 73B
34018 * 70A
34019 * 75A
34020 * 70A
34021 * 73B
34022 * 73B
34023 * 72A
34024 * 72A
34025 * 73B
34026 * 73B
34027 * 73B
34028 * 71B
34029 * 71B
34030 * 72A
34031 * 70A
34032 * 72A
34033 * 72A
34034 * 72A
34035 * 72A
34036 * 72A
34037 * 73B
34038 * 72A
34039 * 71B
34040 * 71B
34041 * 71B
34042 * 71B
34043 * 71B
34044 * 71B
34045 * 71B
34046 * 71B
34047 * 71B
34048 * 72B
34049 * 72B
34050 * 72B
34051 * 72B
34052 * 72B
34053 * 71B
34054 * 72B
34055 * 75A
34056 * 72A
34057 * 72A
34058 * 72A
34059 * 72B
34060 * 72A
34061 * 72A
34062 * 72A
34063 * 72A
34064 * 72A
34065 * 72A
34066 * 73A
34067 * 73A
34068 * 73A
34069 * 72A
34070 * 73H
34071 * 73H
34072 * 72A
34073 * 73H
34074 * 72A
34075 * 72A
34076 * 72A
34077 * 73A
34078 * 73B
34079 * 72A
34080 * 72A
34081 * 72A
34082 * 73H
34083 * 73H
34084 * 73H
34085 * 73A
34086 * 73A
34087 * 73A
34088 * 73A
34089 * 73A
34090 * 70A
34091 * 73A
34092 * 73A
34093 * 70A
34094 * 70A
34095 * 70A
34096 * 72A
34097 * 75A
34098 * 75A
34099 * 72B
34100 * 73A
34101 * 73A
34102 * 71B
34103 * 73H
34104 * 72A
34105 * 71B
34106 * 72A
34107 * 72A
34108 * 72A
34109 * 72A
34110 * 72A

35001 * 70A
35002 * 71B
35003 * 72A
35004 * 72B
35005 * 71B
35006 * 72B
35007 * 72B
35008 * 71B
35009 * 72A
35010 * 72A
35011 * 71B
35012 * 70A
35013 * 72A
35014 * 70A
35015 * 70A
35016 * 70A
35017 * 70A
35018 * 70A
35019 * 70A
35020 * 70A
35021 * 71B
35022 * 72A
35023 * 71B
35024 * 71B
35025 * 72A

35026	* 72A	40085	89C	40147	56E	40396	17B
35027	* 71B	40086	89C	40148	55D	40402	15C
35028	* 70A	40087	2B	40149	18A	40411	16A
35029	* 70A	40088	9E	40150	60D	40421	16A
35030	* 70A	40089	9F	40151	67B	40439	18A
		40090	27C	40152	65D	40443	18A
(See *Note* on *page* 4)		40091	24E	40153	65D	40452	15C
		40092	15E	40154	65D	40453	17B
		40093	9A	40155	56A	40454	16A
40001	9F	40094	9F	40156	16B	40487	16A
40003	1A	40095	6G	40157	2B	40489	85E
40006	WW	40097	9F	40158	65D	40491	55A
40007	1A	40098	82E	40159	65D	40501	82E
40009	9E	40099	24E	40161	86K	40502	16A
40010	1A	40100	14B	40162	24D	40504	16A
40011	24L	40101	6C	40164	24E	40511	18A
40012	14E	40102	6C	40165	15E	40537	82E
40014	26A	40103	24E	40166	24E	40540	85E
40015	26A	40104	2B	40167	15E	40543	15C
40016	1A	40105	9F	40168	16B	40548	14B
40018	9E	40106	6A	40170	68B	40552	55A
40020	14E	40107	9A	40171	86K	40557	16A
40022	14A	40108	3E	40173	3A	40563	82G
40024	14B	40109	24E	40174	24E	40564	82G
40026	14E	40110	84G	40175	16B	40566	68C
40028	14B	40111	14B	40176	65D	40569	82G
40029	14A	40112	56C	40177	65D	40570	67B
40031	14A	40113	9F	40178	HW	40571	67B
40032	14B	40114	56C	40179	55E	40572	67B
40033	14A	40115	16B	40180	3D	40574	67B
40034	14B	40116	6C	40181	55D	40575	67B
40035	14B	40117	56A	40182	15E	40577	68B
40036	14A	40118	8D	40183	24C	40578	67D
40037	14B	40119	14B	40184	16B	40579	67D
40038	14A	40120	24D	40185	16B	40580	14B
40041	24L	40121	6C	40186	65D	40581	55D
40042	1A	40122	9A	40187	65D	40583	5C
40049	1A	40123	6G	40188	65D	40584	55C
40050	16B	40124	9F	40189	65D	40585	16A
40051	1A	40126	84G	40190	56C	40586	24G
40053	14B	40128	6G	40191	27C	40588	27A
40054	16B	40129	3E	40192	24C	40592	67B
40062	26A	40130	6G	40193	55A	40593	67B
40063	26A	40131	6C	40194	27C	40595	67B
40064	14B	40132	6H	40195	27C	40596	67A
40071	6H	40133	6G	40196	27C	40597	67B
40072	24E	40134	8D	40197	27C	40602	67A
40073	16B	40135	2B	40198	27C	40603	61C
40074	56C	40136	6H	40199	27C	40604	61C
40075	55E	40137	8D	40200	65D	40609	67B
40076	6H	40138	2B	40201	8D	40612	67B
40077	2B	40140	55A	40202	8D	40613	67A
40078	6H	40141	9E	40203	14B	40614	68B
40079	16B	40142	14B	40205	84G	40615	67A
40080	3A	40143	8D	40206	3D	40618	61B
40081	24L	40144	6C	40207	2B	40619	67B
40082	55D	40145	27C	40208	9E	40620	67A
40083	3A	40146	16B	40209	6C	40621	67A

40622	61C
40623	68C
40624	67D
40625	67D
40626	67B
40627	67A
40628	12B
40629	67A
40630	55E
40631	26F
40632	16A
40634	82G
40635	6G
40637	67A
40638	67D
40640	67C
40641	68C
40642	68C
40643	67B
40645	67B
40646	5C
40647	67B
40648	61A
40650	61A
40651	67A
40652	82G
40657	24K
40659	1C
40661	67B
40663	61A
40664	67C
40665	67B
40668	67D
40669	67D
40670	68B
40671	26F
40672	1C
40675	6G
40678	3A
40681	27D
40682	16A
40683	24K
40684	27A
40685	24H
40686	67B
40687	67B
40689	67B
40690	55A
40691	16A
40692	3A
40694	24K
40695	67A
40696	82F
40697	82F
40698	82F
40700	82F
40907	41C
40936	3E

41063	55F
41157	17A
41162	2A
41168	3E
41200	6H
41201	84H
41202	82A
41203	82A
41204	84H
41205	24F
41206	27A
41207	82E
41208	82E
41209	41C
41210	8B
41211	8G
41212	5A
41213	8B
41214	2A
41215	24J
41216	6K
41217	9A
41218	2E
41219	2E
41220	5A
41221	9A
41222	1E
41223	1C
41224	14E
41225	14E
41226	6C
41227	2A
41228	2A
41229	5A
41230	6H
41231	84H
41232	84H
41233	6H
41234	6H
41235	6G
41236	6G
41237	6H
41238	6G
41239	6H
41240	82E
41241	84H
41242	82F
41243	82F
41244	6H
41245	41C
41246	41C
41247	50F
41248	82G
41249	82A

41250	56F
41251	50F
41252	55H
41253	56F
41254	55C
41255	55C
41256	55C
41257	55F
41258	55C
41259	55C
41260	24F
41261	24F
41262	50B
41263	56F
41264	56D
41265	50F
41266	55F
41267	55A
41268	27A
41269	27A
41270	14D
41271	14E
41272	14D
41273	55F
41274	56F
41275	1E
41276	6K
41277	17B
41278	2E
41279	15C
41280	16D
41281	55B
41282	55D
41283	26F
41284	14D
41285	2A
41286	8G
41287	26F
41288	8G
41289	8G
41290	73A
41291	73A
41292	73A
41293	71A
41294	72E
41295	72E
41296	82G
41297	72E
41298	72E
41299	73B
41300	73B
41301	73B
41302	83H
41303	73B
41304	82E
41305	71A
41306	72A
41307	72A

41308	72A
41309	72A
41310	83H
41311	71A
41312	72E
41313	72E
41314	72E
41315	83H
41316	83H
41317	83H
41318	72A
41319	71A
41320	16D
41321	15C
41322	6C
41323	24J
41324	8B
41325	55F
41326	55F
41327	24G
41328	17B
41329	14D
41528	41E
41529	41E
41531	41E
41532	17B
41533	41E
41535	85E
41536	17B
41537	85E
41702	9G
41708	41E
41712	16B
41734	41E
41739	41E
41763	41E
41769	41E
41773	17A
41804	41E
41835	41B
41844	16B
41875	41D
41900	85E
41947	18A
41981	33B

42050	9E
42051	24H
42052	55A
42053	14D
42054	16A
42055	66A
42056	66A
42057	66A
42058	66A

42059	66A
42060	66A
42061	2A
42062	2A
42063	27C
42064	9E
42065	9E
42066	1E
42067	1E
42068	1A
42069	1E
42070	1A
42071	1E
42072	55F
42073	56A
42074	6H
42075	6H
42076	6H
42077	6C
42078	6C
42079	6A
42080	14D
42081	14D
42082	14D
42083	56E
42084	56F
42085	50A
42086	14D
42087	14D
42088	14D
42089	14D
42090	14D
42091	14D
42092	14D
42093	55F
42094	56E
42095	1C
42096	1C
42097	1C
42098	1C
42099	1C
42100	1C
42101	1C
42102	1C
42103	1C
42104	1C
42105	1E
42106	1E
42107	56F
42108	56F
42109	56F
42110	24A
42111	9E
42112	27E
42113	27E
42114	26E
42115	26E
42116	56F
42117	1A
42118	1A
42119	11A
42120	11A
42121	8A
42122	67C
42123	67D
42124	67D
42125	66B
42126	66B
42127	66B
42128	66C
42129	66C
42130	68D
42131	65D
42132	24H
42133	14D
42134	14A
42135	24J
42136	24J
42137	27F
42138	55A
42139	55F
42140	16A
42141	55F
42142	66E
42143	66A
42144	66A
42145	66E
42146	17A
42147	24D
42148	24E
42149	56E
42150	56E
42151	56E
42152	56D
42153	24A
42154	24D
42155	8A
42156	14B
42157	14D
42158	24C
42159	14D
42160	15C
42161	16A
42162	66E
42163	66E
42164	66C
42165	66C
42166	66C
42167	66C
42168	60B
42169	66B
42170	66A
42171	66A
42172	66A
42173	66E
42174	17A
42175	66D
42176	66D
42177	66E
42178	14D
42179	11A
42180	27D
42181	27F
42182	15C
42183	27F
42184	17A
42185	16A
42186	27F
42187	24C
42188	56F
42189	56F
42190	67A
42191	67D
42192	68D
42193	67A
42194	67D
42195	65D
42196	67C
42197	65D
42198	6A
42199	65J
42200	66B
42201	65D
42202	6A
42203	66B
42204	66E
42205	68D
42206	24E
42207	24E
42208	66B
42209	6C
42210	6C
42211	6C
42212	6A
42213	6A
42214	68D
42215	68D
42216	66E
42217	6A
42218	33C
42219	33C
42220	33C
42221	33C
42222	14D
42223	33C
42224	33C
42225	14D
42226	33C
42227	33C
42228	17C
42229	6A
42230	14D
42231	14D
42232	14D
42233	11A
42234	1A
42235	8F
42236	6A
42237	14B
42238	6A
42239	66A
42240	6A
42241	66D
42242	66A
42243	66A
42244	66A
42245	66A
42246	66A
42247	6A
42248	14D
42249	14D
42250	14D
42251	14D
42252	14D
42253	14D
42254	33B
42255	33B
42256	14D
42257	33B
42258	66D
42259	66D
42260	66D
42261	66D
42262	66D
42263	66D
42264	66D
42265	66D
42266	66D
42267	3E
42268	66A
42269	60B
42270	6A
42271	66E
42272	64C
42273	64C
42274	66A
42275	66A
42276	66A
42277	66A
42278	24H
42279	14D
42280	26A
42281	14D
42282	14D
42283	14D
42284	14D
42285	56D
42286	24C
42287	26B
42288	26A
42289	26C
42290	27C

42291	14D
42292	27C
42293	27C
42294	24A
42295	24A
42296	24C
42297	27D
42298	24C
42299	27D
42300	9E
42301	11C
42302	14B
42303	8F
42304	12A
42305	87E
42306	9D
42307	87E
42309	5C
42310	55G
42311	56F
42313	12A
42314	11C
42315	5D
42316	9B
42317	8F
42318	9C
42319	8E
42320	11A
42322	9B
42323	5D
42324	56D
42325	14B
42326	9G
42327	21A
42328	9E
42329	14B
42330	15C
42331	15C
42332	11A
42333	9E
42334	14B
42335	14B
42336	14B
42337	21A
42338	14B
42339	9E
42340	21A
42342	14B
42343	9B
42344	5D
42345	11C
42346	5D
42347	9C
42348	9C
42349	14B
42350	1A
42351	1A
42352	17A
42353	2E
42355	9C
42356	8E
42357	9B
42358	5F
42359	8E
42360	1A
42361	9E
42362	5D
42363	9C
42364	11A
42365	8E
42366	1A
42367	1A
42368	1A
42369	9A
42370	9D
42371	9D
42372	9B
42373	9G
42374	9G
42375	5F
42376	11A
42377	55A
42378	5D
42379	9B
42380	56E
42381	9A
42382	9C
42383	18A
42384	55G
42385	87E
42386	8E
42387	87E
42388	87E
42389	5C
42390	87E
42391	9B
42392	11A
42393	8E
42394	87E
42395	11A
42396	11D
42397	11A
42398	9A
42399	9A
42400	5C
42401	11A
42402	11A
42403	11D
42404	11D
42405	56E
42406	56D
42407	56D
42408	55D
42409	55A
42410	55G
42411	56E
42412	55G
42413	55G
42414	55G
42415	9B
42416	5B
42417	6A
42419	9E
42420	5D
42421	5D
42422	1A
42423	8E
42424	11D
42425	6H
42426	12B
42427	11A
42428	9E
42429	9G
42430	1A
42431	6A
42432	11A
42433	24C
42434	24C
42435	27C
42436	50D
42437	15E
42438	24B
42439	26F
42440	11A
42441	6C
42442	26F
42443	5D
42444	26D
42445	27F
42446	15C
42447	6C
42448	27F
42449	11C
42450	14D
42451	27C
42452	9E
42453	15E
42454	5D
42455	24E
42456	8F
42457	11C
42458	26F
42459	5D
42460	26D
42461	24E
42462	8F
42463	1A
42464	5D
42465	8F
42466	9E
42467	2A
42468	26F
42469	9E
42470	3D
42471	8F
42472	9G
42473	27D
42474	26B
42475	27D
42476	24C
42477	50A
42478	2A
42479	9E
42480	24C
42481	24C
42482	6A
42483	24D
42484	24H
42485	24D
42486	17C
42487	6H
42488	3E
42489	6H
42490	27F
42491	24H
42492	24H
42493	6C
42494	26F
42500	33C
42501	33C
42502	33C
42503	33C
42504	33C
42505	33C
42506	33C
42507	33C
42508	33C
42509	33C
42510	33C
42511	33C
42512	33C
42513	33C
42514	33C
42515	33C
42516	33C
42517	33C
42518	33C
42519	33C
42520	33C
42521	33C
42522	33C
42523	33C
42534	33C
42525	33C
42526	33C
42527	33C
42528	33C
42529	33C
42530	33C
42531	33C
42532	33C
42533	33C

42534-42765

42534	33C
42535	33C
42536	33C
42537	27C
42538	1A
42539	12B
42540	14D
42541	2A
42542	9A
42543	5D
42544	6H
42545	26C
42546	24B
42547	24B
42548	26A
42549	26A
42550	26D
42551	24D
42552	3D
42553	50A
42554	27D
42555	24B
42556	15E
42557	27D
42558	24D
42559	24D
42560	9E
42561	26F
42562	6H
42563	26F
42564	2A
42565	26C
42566	84D
42567	1B
42568	17C
42569	27D
42570	8A
42571	8F
42572	8F
42573	2A
42574	26F
42575	5A
42576	1A
42577	2A
42578	5A
42579	1A
42580	27F
42581	11A
42582	3B
42583	8A
42584	27F
42585	1A
42586	1A
42587	17A
42588	14D
42589	24J
42590	5D
42591	11A
42592	27D
42593	5D
42594	12B
42595	14B
42596	27F
42597	6C
42598	27F
42599	6C
42600	5D
42601	1B
42602	6C
42603	5D
42604	1A
42605	5F
42606	8B
42607	8B
42608	6C
42609	5D
42610	14B
42611	1A
42612	27F
42613	11C
42614	27D
42615	2E
42616	3D
42617	14B
42618	14D
42619	26A
42620	26A
42621	27D
42622	56A
42623	26A
42624	26A
42625	24E
42626	26C
42627	1A
42628	9E
42629	14D
42630	26C
42631	27D
42632	27D
42633	26C
42634	24C
42635	26C
42636	16A
42637	27C
42638	24E
42639	50A
42640	27D
42641	27D
42642	27D
42643	24A
42644	27D
42645	87E
42646	26B
42647	26B
42648	24H
42649	56C
42650	56C
42651	26A
42652	26C
42653	26C
42654	26C
42655	26C
42656	26C
42657	24E
42658	3D
42659	3B
42660	26A
42661	24C
42662	26F
42663	5D
42664	12B
42665	5F
42666	11A
42667	5D
42668	5D
42669	2A
42670	5D
42671	5D
42672	5D
42673	11A
42674	6H
42675	9E
42676	9E
42677	5A
42678	33C
42679	33C
42680	14A
42681	33C
42682	14B
42683	9E
42684	33C
42685	14B
42686	14A
42687	33C
42688	68D
42689	66B
42690	65J
42691	66D
42692	62B
42693	68D
42694	65D
42695	66A
42696	26A
42697	27D
42698	26A
42699	66B
42700	26D
42701	26A
42702	55F
42703	26A
42704	26A
42705	26A
42706	24B
42707	24F
42708	26A
42709	26A
42710	26A
42711	27B
42712	26D
42713	55C
42714	26A
42715	27D
42716	24B
42717	24B
42718	24D
42719	26D
42720	12A
42721	27B
42722	24F
42723	26B
42724	26B
42725	26B
42726	26A
42727	27B
42728	26A
42729	24D
42730	26D
42731	27D
42732	24F
42733	26A
42734	27D
42735	66C
42736	65F
42737	65F
42738	66A
42739	67B
42740	66D
42741	66D
42742	67D
42743	67B
42744	67B
42745	67C
42746	66C
42747	1A
42748	9G
42749	68C
42750	26A
42751	12A
42752	12A
42753	26B
42754	9G
42755	26B
42756	17B
42757	12A
42758	21A
42759	17B
42760	9G
42761	21A
42762	55F
42763	17B
42764	15B
42765	24F

42766	55C
42767	9G
42768	9G
42769	16D
42770	55F
42771	55A
42772	9A
42773	9B
42774	55C
42775	9G
42776	5A
42777	5D
42778	6C
42779	9B
42780	65F
42781	2B
42782	5D
42783	2B
42784	16D
42785	1A
42786	9A
42787	5B
42788	9G
42789	55C
42790	21A
42791	21A
42792	9G
42793	12A
42794	41B
42795	55C
42796	24D
42797	41B
42798	55A
42799	17B
42800	67C
42801	67C
42802	65F
42803	65F
42804	6C
42805	67C
42806	67D
42807	64C
42808	67C
42809	67C
42810	24J
42811	5D
42812	1A
42813	9G
42814	9A
42815	5A
42816	9G
42817	3D
42818	17B
42819	26B
42820	26D
42821	27D
42822	17B
42823	21A
42824	17B
42825	17B
42826	17B
42827	21A
42828	6C
42829	17B
42830	12A
42831	12A
42832	12A
42833	12A
42834	12A
42835	12A
42836	12A
42837	12A
42838	26B
42839	17B
42840	24F
42841	24F
42842	24F
42843	24F
42844	24F
42845	27B
42846	21A
42847	16D
42848	9B
42849	9B
42850	66A
42851	24J
42852	1A
42853	2B
42854	9B
42855	17B
42856	6C
42857	21A
42858	9A
42859	1A
42860	26B
42861	56A
42862	56A
42863	56A
42864	27D
42865	55C
42866	55C
42867	24F
42868	26B
42869	24B
42870	1A
42871	26A
42872	16D
42873	9G
42874	9G
42875	12A
42876	12A
42877	6C
42878	27B
42879	67C
42880	66C
42881	12A
42882	12A
42883	12A
42884	12A
42885	1A
42886	9B
42887	9A
42888	5D
42889	9A
42890	21A
42891	5D
42892	9B
42893	24J
42894	6C
42895	24J
42896	17B
42897	16D
42898	24B
42899	12A
42900	21A
42901	26A
42902	9G
42903	21A
42904	41B
42905	12A
42906	12A
42907	12A
42908	68B
42909	68B
42910	67C
42911	67D
42912	67C
42913	68B
42914	67C
42915	68B
42916	67C
42917	67C
42918	68B
42919	68B
42920	5D
42921	3D
42922	17B
42923	9A
42924	9A
42925	9A
42926	2B
42927	67C
42928	24J
42929	5D
42930	9A
42931	1A
42932	9B
42933	2B
42934	9A
42935	1A
42936	9A
42937	9B
42938	9A
42939	2B
42940	5A
42941	6C
42942	9D
42943	9D
42944	1A
42945	24K
42946	5B
42947	3D
42948	5B
42949	5B
42950	2A
42951	2A
42952	5B
42953	2A
42954	5A
42955	5B
42956	5B
42957	3D
42958	5A
42959	5B
42960	24K
42961	5B
42962	5B
42963	5A
42964	5B
42965	24K
42966	5A
42967	6B
42968	5A
42969	6C
42970	6C
42971	6B
42972	5B
42973	6C
42974	3D
42975	3D
42976	24K
42977	6C
42978	6C
42979	3D
42980	5B
42981	6B
42982	6B
42983	5B
42984	5B
43000	2B
43001	2B
43002	2B
43003	2B
43004	11B
43005	2B
43006	11B
43007	24J
43008	11B
43009	11B

43010	15A
43011	11D
43012	21A
43013	21A
43014	50A
43015	51C
43016	55F
43017	21A
43018	24J
43019	14A
43020	2B
43021	24J
43022	2B
43023	2B
43024	2B
43025	11B
43026	11B
43027	12D
43028	11D
43029	11D
43030	55F
43031	14A
43032	41C
43033	21A
43034	2B
43035	11D
43036	21A
43037	41C
43038	55B
43039	55A
43040	21A
43041	21A
43042	15B
43043	55A
43044	55B
43045	24J
43046	21A
43047	21A
43048	15B
43049	21A
43050	51A
43051	55H
43052	2B
43053	51C
43054	55H
43055	50A
43056	50A
43057	50A
43058	40F
43059	40F
43060	40A
43061	40F
43062	40F
43063	2F
43064	40F
43065	40F
43066	40F
43067	34E
43068	40F
43069	50B
43070	50A
43071	50A
43072	51L
43073	24J
43074	55E
43075	56A
43076	50B
43077	50B
43078	50B
43079	50B
43080	40F
43081	34E
43082	34E
43083	40F
43084	34E
43085	40F
43086	34E
43087	41H
43088	34E
43089	31C
43090	31C
43091	40F
43092	40F
43093	40F
43094	31C
43095	40B
43096	50A
43097	50D
43098	50D
43099	51A
43100	51C
43101	56A
43102	51L
43103	12D
43104	40A
43105	30A
43106	2F
43107	40F
43108	40E
43109	40F
43110	40F
43111	41B
43112	24J
43113	24J
43114	55E
43115	24J
43116	55E
43117	55A
43118	14A
43119	14A
43120	14A
43121	14A
43122	21A
43123	50B
43124	55A
43125	50D
43126	52B
43127	34E
43128	51C
43129	51A
43130	55A
43131	50B
43132	65E
43133	65E
43134	65E
43135	65A
43136	65A
43137	65A
43138	64F
43139	12C
43140	65B
43141	64G
43142	40F
43143	40F
43144	30A
43145	41H
43146	41B
43147	40F
43148	40E
43149	30A
43150	34E
43151	34E
43152	40E
43153	30A
43154	40A
43155	40E
43156	40E
43157	40F
43158	40A
43159	41B
43160	32A
43161	32A
43185	8G
43187	9G
43189	3A
43194	82G
43200	17A
43203	41B
43207	9G
43211	9E
43212	9F
43213	8G
43214	21A
43216	82G
43225	41D
43234	41B
43235	9G
43240	12A
43242	21A
43243	41B
43245	9F
43250	17C
43254	41B
43257	8B
43261	14E
43263	21A
43266	18B
43267	55D
43268	9D
43277	15C
43282	8B
43284	21A
43295	8B
43306	17A
43307	41B
43309	21A
43321	21A
43325	1C
43326	15C
43329	9D
43330	2F
43333	14E
43340	17B
43342	17C
43344	8G
43359	21A
43361	41B
43368	17A
43371	41D
43373	14E
43374	15C
43386	41E
43389	21A
43394	2F
43395	41B
43399	2E
43400	9G
43405	15C
43410	9B
43411	15C
43427	85E
43428	14E
43435	17A
43436	82G
43444	82E
43446	55D
43449	14E
43453	21A
43457	9G
43459	17A
43464	5B
43468	21A
43474	14E
43482	21A
43484	21A
43496	17C
43499	15B
43507	21A
43510	17A
43514	12A
43515	41E
43521	21A

43523	21A
43529	14E
43548	17A
43562	9D
43565	14E
43570	17A
43572	9E
43574	17B
43579	56A
43580	9E
43583	21A
43585	24H
43586	55F
43593	82E
43594	21A
43599	21A
43605	41E
43608	17B
43615	8B
43618	6K
43620	21A
43621	17A
43624	9G
43627	21A
43634	41B
43637	41B
43639	21A
43644	21A
43645	85E
43650	9E
43652	17B
43657	8B
43658	17A
43668	21A
43669	41B
43673	21A
43679	17A
43680	21A
43681	55D
43682	82G
43687	21A
43705	56A
43709	17B
43714	55E
43715	41B
43721	9G
43729	41E
43734	82G
43735	17A
43737	55D
43751	41B
43754	85E
43756	24H
43760	3A
43762	85F
43763	9G
43766	14E
43773	9G
43778	17A
43784	55F
43789	9G
43793	15C
43800	41B
43808	14E
43809	9G
43812	21A
43814	41D
43822	3A
43825	18B
43826	9G
43832	9F
43840	17A
43843	17B
43844	41B
43845	18A
43846	16A
43848	66A
43849	66A
43850	18B
43853	85E
43854	15D
43855	21A
43856	16A
43859	16A
43861	15D
43863	41E
43865	18A
43868	11B
43869	41E
43870	16A
43871	55B
43872	41B
43876	15D
43880	26D
43882	41D
43883	66B
43884	66B
43885	16B
43887	85E
43888	16A
43893	24G
43899	67A
43900	41E
43902	12A
43903	16B
43905	14A
43906	55D
43908	24L
43911	21A
43913	26D
43914	55D
43915	27F
43917	16A
43918	16A
43920	41E
43921	18A
43922	12A
43923	16B
43924	85E
43925	17A
43928	16A
43929	15A
43931	55B
43932	21A
43933	16B
43935	14A
43937	15C
43938	21A
43940	21A
43942	55D
43944	55F
43945	9F
43947	14A
43948	21A
43949	21A
43950	17C
43951	21A
43952	27D
43953	16A
43954	16A
43955	17A
43957	2E
43958	16A
43960	24G
43962	16A
43963	21A
43964	14B
43967	18C
43968	55B
43969	15C
43971	18A
43972	16B
43973	8F
43975	21A
43976	24D
43977	15F
43979	15D
43981	6K
43982	18B
43983	55D
43985	21A
43986	21A
43987	55B
43988	27E
43991	17A
43994	18A
43995	15A
43996	67A
43999	24G
44001	67A
44002	41D
44003	55B
44004	21A
44007	24G
44008	12A
44009	12A
44010	41E
44011	66D
44012	18A
44013	21A
44015	9G
44016	12B
44019	56A
44020	17A
44022	26A
44023	27E
44025	9G
44026	21A
44027	3A
44028	55B
44029	14A
44030	16A
44031	17A
44033	16A
44034	15C
44035	11B
44036	41E
44037	41D
44038	27E
44039	41B
44040	27E
44041	24G
44042	17C
44043	18A
44044	55B
44045	85E
44046	17C
44047	16A
44048	17A
44049	17A
44051	14A
44052	14B
44053	18C
44054	18C
44055	55F
44056	56D
44057	3E
44059	9D
44060	12B
44061	5E
44062	56F
44063	5E
44065	6B
44066	41E
44067	5E
44068	5D
44069	8F

44070	41E
44071	41D
44074	5D
44075	6H
44076	2E
44078	17C
44079	5E
44080	17C
44081	12B
44082	41D
44083	24L
44085	15D
44086	11A
44087	41B
44088	41E
44089	41D
44090	9F
44091	21A
44092	21A
44094	55B
44096	26D
44097	41B
44098	55E
44099	55E
44100	17B
44101	17C
44102	82G
44104	41E
44105	24G
44106	18A
44107	55B
44109	15D
44110	2E
44111	41D
44112	17A
44113	15D
44114	9G
44115	5D
44117	1E
44118	16B
44119	24D
44121	12B
44122	18C
44123	85E
44124	17B
44125	5E
44126	12B
44127	27F
44128	41D
44129	41E
44130	18B
44131	16A
44132	16A
44133	18A
44134	17C
44135	82E
44137	21A
44138	9E
44139	16A
44141	55D
44143	21A
44146	82F
44147	41E
44148	15D
44149	24H
44150	15D
44151	16A
44152	31B
44153	55B
44154	18B
44155	8E
44156	15A
44157	12C
44158	16A
44159	67A
44160	21A
44162	18A
44163	17C
44164	17A
44165	21A
44166	15D
44167	85E
44168	21A
44169	17A
44170	55E
44171	21A
44172	17C
44174	41B
44176	17A
44177	18B
44178	18A
44179	21A
44180	15D
44181	12A
44182	15A
44183	12A
44184	21A
44185	21A
44186	5D
44187	21A
44188	27E
44189	67A
44190	16A
44191	18B
44192	8G
44193	66A
44194	65B
44195	16A
44196	66B
44197	24G
44198	67A
44199	65B
44200	18A
44202	16B
44203	21A
44205	41E
44206	41D
44207	55B
44208	1A
44209	85E
44210	14B
44211	21A
44212	41B
44213	21A
44214	17A
44215	16A
44216	55F
44218	27E
44219	2E
44220	24G
44221	27D
44222	27D
44223	16A
44224	18A
44226	21A
44228	14A
44229	18B
44231	15C
44232	27F
44233	18B
44234	65F
44235	14B
44236	9G
44237	8B
44238	55B
44239	2E
44240	27D
44241	17B
44242	2E
44243	14B
44244	18C
44245	41D
44246	5D
44247	2E
44248	16A
44249	41E
44250	9F
44251	66A
44252	16B
44253	63A
44254	63A
44255	63B
44256	66A
44257	63A
44258	63A
44259	14A
44260	15D
44261	9F
44262	17C
44263	21A
44264	85E
44265	41B
44266	8G
44267	41E
44268	16B
44269	82E
44270	18A
44271	5D
44272	85E
44273	31B
44274	55D
44275	9G
44276	24H
44277	24G
44278	15A
44279	15D
44280	8F
44281	67B
44282	24G
44283	66A
44284	18A
44286	9F
44287	41B
44288	18C
44289	18B
44290	55D
44292	11B
44294	14B
44295	18A
44296	85E
44297	14A
44299	27E
44300	8G
44301	5B
44302	3D
44303	8F
44304	16A
44305	24L
44307	5D
44308	1E
44309	5D
44310	5D
44311	26A
44312	67B
44314	63A
44315	8G
44318	66A
44319	67C
44320	65F
44321	18B
44322	66A
44323	67A
44324	12A
44325	67B
44327	17C
44328	63A
44329	67C
44330	67A
44331	67C
44332	17B
44333	21A
44334	17A

44335	55B
44336	55E
44337	55E
44338	55E
44339	9D
44340	1A
44341	8E
44342	5E
44344	5D
44345	24L
44346	12B
44347	11A
44348	1C
44349	5E
44350	8G
44351	11A
44352	5E
44353	2E
44354	5E
44355	5F
44356	8B
44358	5D
44359	5B
44362	18B
44363	CW
44364	1E
44367	6K
44368	55B
44370	1E
44371	41E
44373	CW
44374	CW
44375	9D
44376	18A
44377	5D
44378	9F
44379	9F
44380	17B
44381	14B
44384	8B
44386	5E
44387	9F
44388	15A
44389	6G
44390	11B
44392	9E
44393	5D
44394	16A
44395	5D
44396	27F
44397	1E
44398	24D
44399	24L
44400	55F
44401	16A
44402	9E
44403	15C
44404	41E
44405	5E
44407	9F
44408	55E
44409	18A
44411	82E
44413	17C
44414	16A
44416	16B
44417	82G
44418	16B
44419	17A
44420	17A
44421	9F
44422	82E
44424	5D
44425	17A
44426	41B
44428	17A
44429	17C
44431	24H
44432	5D
44433	17B
44434	17B
44435	17B
44436	17B
44437	41B
44439	3D
44440	1C
44441	14A
44442	1C
44443	11A
44444	3E
44445	6B
44446	55D
44447	1E
44448	3A
44449	11B
44450	5E
44451	1A
44452	5E
44454	24L
44455	5D
44456	8E
44457	41B
44458	55E
44460	24D
44461	11B
44462	27E
44463	21A
44464	27D
44465	17A
44466	82E
44467	55B
44468	24G
44469	24L
44470	16B
44472	16A
44474	56D
44475	41E
44476	15C
44477	41B
44478	5D
44479	24D
44481	27E
44482	41E
44484	5D
44485	56A
44486	27D
44487	11A
44489	27F
44490	3E
44491	2E
44492	3D
44493	6B
44494	27F
44497	1A
44499	5D
44500	5D
44501	9F
44504	6H
44505	11B
44508	5D
44509	31B
44512	3A
44514	3E
44516	21A
44517	3D
44518	41B
44519	15C
44520	21A
44521	31B
44522	2E
44523	82F
44524	2E

ALLOCATION OF PRESERVED LOCOMOTIVES RESTORED FOR SPECIAL DUTIES

Pre-Grouping Company	*Type*	*Pre-Grouping Number*	*Allocation*
Caledonian	4-2-2	123	65D
G.N. of S.	4-4-0	49	61C
G.W.	4-4-0	3440	82C
Highland	4-6-0	103	65D
Midland	4-4-0	1000	17A
N.B.	4-4-0	256	61C

44525	6G
44526	17B
44527	17B
44528	17B
44529	14A
44530	14A
44531	14B
44532	14B
44533	16A
44534	82E
44535	41B
44536	5D
44537	11A
44538	17B
44539	15D
44540	17A
44541	17B
44542	17B
44543	26A
44544	27D
44545	17A
44547	41B
44548	5D
44549	11B
44550	55D
44551	17B
44552	17B
44553	82E
44554	9F
44556	17C
44557	82G
44558	82F
44559	82F
44560	82G
44561	82F
44562	17B
44564	9E
44565	9E
44566	9E
44567	24G
44568	41B
44569	82E
44570	55B
44571	21A
44572	14B
44573	41B
44574	15A
44575	15A
44576	41D
44577	16A
44578	16A
44579	24G
44580	21A
44581	14A
44582	55D
44583	21A
44584	55B
44585	16A
44586	55B
44587	27F
44588	17C
44589	27F
44590	41E
44591	17B
44592	5B
44593	5D
44594	11A
44595	5B
44596	12B
44597	17B
44598	18B
44599	17B
44601	11A
44602	17C
44603	18C
44604	55E
44605	27E
44606	41E
44658	16A
44659	21A
44660	21A
44661	6J
44662	55A
44663	21A
44664	16A
44665	9E
44666	21A
44667	15C
44668	12A
44669	12A
44670	12A
44671	12A
44672	12A
44673	12A
44674	12A
44675	12A
44676	12A
44677	65B
44678	5A
44679	5A
44680	5A
44681	5A
44682	6G
44683	5A
44684	5A
44685	5A
44686	9A
44687	9A
44688	9E
44689	24A
44690	15C
44691	14D
44692	24A
44693	56F
44694	56F
44695	56F
44696	26A
44697	26A
44698	63A
44699	63A
44700	66E
44701	66E
44702	65A
44703	61B
44704	63A
44705	63A
44706	67A
44707	65A
44708	26F
44709	24L
44710	3D
44711	2A
44712	2A
44713	5B
44714	5A
44715	2A
44716	2A
44717	9E
44718	60A
44719	60A
44720	63A
44721	63A
44722	60A
44723	60A
44724	60A
44725	12A
44726	12A
44727	12A
44728	27C
44729	27C
44730	24E
44731	24E
44732	24E
44733	24E
44734	26A
44735	26A
44736	26A
44737	24E
44738	6G
44739	6G
44740	6G
44741	9A
44742	9A
44743	27A
44744	27A
44745	27A
44746	9A
44747	9A
44748	9A
44749	9A
44750	9A
44751	9A
44752	9A
44753	55A
44754	55A
44755	55A
44756	55A
44757	55A
44758	8F
44759	5A
44760	2A
44761	5A
44762	5A
44763	5A
44764	5A
44765	5A
44766	3E
44767	27A
44768	8A
44769	8A
44770	5A
44771	2A
44772	8A
44773	8A
44774	14A
44775	21A
44776	21A
44777	14A
44778	24E
44779	24E
44780	8F
44781	26B
44782	26B
44783	60A
44784	60A
44785	60A
44786	65B
44787	65A
44788	60A
44789	60A
44790	12A
44791	67A
44792	12A
44793	66E
44794	61B
44795	12A
44796	63A
44797	63A
44798	60A
44799	60A
44800	6B
44801	63A
44802	6J
44803	26A
44804	21A
44805	21A
44806	16A
44807	3E
44808	26F
44809	9E
44810	21A
44811	15C

44812	21A
44813	21A
44814	21A
44815	15C
44816	14A
44817	14B
44818	21A
44819	14D
44820	63A
44821	14B
44822	14B
44823	26B
44824	55A
44825	21A
44826	55A
44827	6G
44828	55A
44829	3B
44830	14D
44831	2A
44832	5B
44833	2A
44834	5B
44835	84G
44836	2A
44837	11A
44838	1A
44839	21A
44840	5A
44841	21A
44842	9A
44843	15C
44844	5A
44845	26A
44846	14B
44847	14D
44848	15C
44849	55A
44850	66B
44851	17A
44852	55A
44853	55A
44854	55A
44855	9A
44856	16A
44857	55A
44858	21A
44859	21A
44860	2A
44861	16A
44862	2A
44863	2A
44864	6G
44865	6G
44866	2A
44867	2A
44868	5B
44869	5A
44870	2A
44871	5B
44872	3D
44873	3A
44874	24L
44875	1A
44876	3D
44877	12A
44878	12A
44879	63A
44880	65B
44881	65B
44882	12A
44883	12A
44884	12A
44885	63A
44886	12A
44887	27C
44888	21A
44889	24A
44890	26A
44891	26A
44892	24L
44893	26A
44894	24B
44895	26A
44896	55C
44897	3D
44898	12A
44899	12A
44900	12A
44901	12A
44902	12A
44903	12A
44904	24L
44905	24L
44906	8A
44907	8A
44908	65A
44909	2A
44910	3D
44911	5A
44912	56F
44913	6H
44914	3A
44915	2A
44916	1A
44917	6B
44918	16A
44919	21A
44920	21A
44921	63A
44922	65B
44923	65B
44924	63A
44925	63A
44926	24E
44927	24E
44928	27A
44929	26B
44930	24E
44931	63A
44932	16D
44933	26A
44934	26A
44935	6B
44936	12B
44937	9A
44938	2A
44939	12B
44940	24B
44941	14A
44942	3D
44943	55A
44944	21A
44945	21A
44946	56F
44947	24E
44948	24B
44949	24B
44950	24E
44951	56F
44952	66E
44953	66E
44954	62B
44955	66E
44956	65A
44957	65A
44958	12A
44959	63A
44960	63A
44961	63A
44962	21A
44963	21A
44964	9E
44965	21A
44966	21A
44967	65A
44968	65A
44969	66B
44970	65A
44971	6B
44972	63B
44973	63B
44974	63B
44975	63B
44976	63B
44977	63B
44978	63A
44979	63A
44980	63A
44981	21A
44982	24E
44983	55A
44984	14B
44985	14B
44986	6J
44987	26B
44988	24E
44989	27C
44990	56F
44991	60A
44992	60A
44993	12A
44994	64C
44995	68B
44996	65A
44997	63A
44998	63A
44999	63A
45000	5B
45001	5B
45002	5B
45003	5A
45004	5A
45005	8A
45006	14D
45007	67A
45008	66B
45009	66B
45010	67B
45011	66E
45012	12A
45013	12A
45014	24L
45015	3B
45016	65J
45017	8F
45018	12A
45019	8F
45020	1E
45021	5A
45022	64C
45023	64C
45024	1A
45025	12B
45026	8F
45027	1A
45028	6B
45029	66B
45030	64C
45031	6B
45032	8A
45033	5A
45034	3E
45035	8B
45036	64C
45037	5A
45038	3E

45039	8A
45040	21A
45041	8C
45042	6B
45043	6B
45044	5D
45045	5B
45046	5A
45047	63A
45048	5B
45049	65J
45050	2E
45051	3D
45052	3E
45053	67A
45054	24L
45055	6B
45056	6J
45057	8F
45058	3D
45059	14A
45060	5D
45061	27C
45062	14A
45063	55C
45064	1A
45065	3D
45066	66A
45067	5B
45068	24A
45069	8A
45070	5A
45071	3E
45072	24L
45073	5A
45074	5B
45075	55C
45076	26A
45077	24E
45078	24E
45079	55C
45080	55C
45081	12A
45082	12A
45083	12A
45084	65J
45085	66B
45086	64C
45087	66E
45088	21A
45089	1E
45090	63A
45091	2E
45092	5B
45093	5A
45094	3D
45095	26F
45096	26F
45097	5B
45098	66A
45099	66B
45100	12A
45101	26A
45102	26A
45103	26A
45104	26A
45105	26A
45106	12B
45107	24F
45108	8F
45109	8F
45110	6J
45111	9A
45112	12A
45113	3E
45114	3D
45115	65B
45116	16D
45117	60A
45118	12A
45119	65B
45120	12A
45121	66B
45122	12A
45123	60A
45124	60A
45125	65B
45126	12A
45127	64C
45128	5B
45129	26F
45130	5B
45131	5E
45132	5A
45133	26F
45134	5B
45135	8F
45136	60B
45137	1A
45138	12A
45139	1A
45140	12B
45141	11A
45142	5B
45143	84G
45144	6H
45145	84G
45146	1A
45147	2E
45148	5A
45149	5B
45150	24K
45151	66B
45152	66B
45153	65B
45154 *	26A
45155	64C
45156 *	26A
45157 *	65B
45158 *	65B
45159	65B
45160	67C
45161	66E
45162	61B
45163	12A
45164	62B
45165	63A
45166	66E
45167	61B
45168	63A
45169	68B
45170	63A
45171	63A
45172	63A
45173	66E
45174	66E
45175	66E
45176	66B
45177	65B
45178	65B
45179	60A
45180	6G
45181	8A
45182	26F
45183	64C
45184	2A
45185	12B
45186	21A
45187	1A
45188	5B
45189	5A
45190	84G
45191	2E
45192	60A
45193	24L
45194	67C
45195	26F
45196	5A
45197	12B
45198	5B
45199	26F
45200	24E
45201	24E
45202	26A
45203	26A
45204	55C
45205	24B
45206	24F
45207	56F
45208	56F
45209	24B
45210	27A
45211	55C
45212	24F
45213	65J
45214	65J
45215	14D
45216	24B
45217	27F
45218	27C
45219	56F
45220	26A
45221	16A
45222	2E
45223	16D
45224	26A
45225	6H
45226	24A
45227	24E
45228	27C
45229	24B
45230	24L
45231	3D
45232	26A
45233	26A
45234	16D
45235	5A
45236	12B
45237	6A
45238	14A
45239	9E
45240	5A
45241	24L
45242	8A
45243	5A
45244	12B
45245	66E
45246	12B
45247	6H
45248	6G
45249	8A
45250	5A
45251	67D
45252	26F
45253	21A
45254	5A
45255	26F
45256	8B
45257	5A
45258	12B
45259	12B
45260	14D
45261	26B
45262	27F
45263	21A
45264	15C
45265	21A
45266	67B
45267	14E
45268	21A
45269	21A
45270	5B

45271	8B	45329	12A	45387	1A	45445	12B
45272	21A	45330	12A	45388	1E	45446	5A
45273	55A	45331	1E	45389	65J	45447	21A
45274	14A	45332	24K	45390	5B	45448	3D
45275	6B	45333	15C	45391	5B	45449	8F
45276	8B	45334	12A	45392	2E	45450	16D
45277	14B	45335	14A	45393	1E	45451	12B
45278	1A	45336	26A	45394	12B	45452	64D
45279	14B	45337	26B	45395	5A	45453	60A
45280	21A	45338	26B	45396	65J	45454	24K
45281	8A	45339	9A	45397	12B	45455	12A
45282	5A	45340	8F	45398	8A	45456	67D
45283	84G	45341	26A	45399	8A	45457	67D
45284	1A	45342	14E	45400	65J	45458	63A
45285	14B	45343	8B	45401	8A	45459	66C
45286	12B	45344	12B	45402	12B	45460	60A
45287	3B	45345	6H	45403	5B	45461	60A
45288	1A	45346	27F	45404	1A	45462	66B
45289	5A	45347	8F	45405	3B	45463	63A
45290	26A	45348	5A	45406	84G	45464	24E
45291	5B	45349	3D	45407	16A	45465	63A
45292	5B	45350	1A	45408	8F	45466	12A
45293	12B	45351	12B	45409	26F	45467	63A
45294	26F	45352	26F	45410	8B	45468	65B
45295	12B	45353	3D	45411	26F	45469	61B
45296	12B	45354	8B	45412	12B	45470	63A
45297	12B	45355	65B	45413	8A	45471	65B
45298	84G	45356	65B	45414	5B	45472	63A
45299	5B	45357	65J	45415	24E	45473	63A
45300	5B	45358	65B	45416	14D	45474	63A
45301	3E	45359	65J	45417	6H	45475	63A
45302	6H	45360	60A	45418	3D	45476	60A
45303	24L	45361	60A	45419	3A	45477	60A
45304	26F	45362	67A	45420	26F	45478	63A
45305	5A	45363	12A	45421	8A	45479	60A
45306	24L	45364	12A	45422	84G	45480	68B
45307	2E	45365	63A	45423	65J	45481	12A
45308	3E	45366	63A	45424	26F	45482	65B
45309	66B	45367	63A	45425	8F	45483	63A
45310	3B	45368	12B	45426	9A	45484	66B
45311	5A	45369	5A	45427	24L	45485	66B
45312	8C	45370	5B	45428	55C	45486	62B
45313	8F	45371	12B	45429	6H	45487	65J
45314	8F	45372	8F	45430	3D	45488	63A
45315	12B	45373	8F	45431	8F	45489	67A
45316	12B	45374	1A	45432	68B	45490	67D
45317	12B	45375	1A	45433	66B	45491	12A
45318	24E	45376	8A	45434	5A	45492	63A
45319	60A	45377	24F	45435	26A	45493	2A
45320	66A	45378	26F	45436	24E	45494	5B
45321	8B	45379	5A	45437	12B	45495	8B
45322	3D	45380	8A	45438	12B	45496	63A
45323	12B	45381	1A	45439	3B	45497	63A
45324	1A	45382	6J	45440	6C	45498	66B
45325	6B	45383	11A	45441	6J	45499	65B
45326	24L	45384	62B	45442	24F	45500	* 26A
45327	3D	45385	3A	45443	65B	45501	* 8B
45328	8B	45386	11A	45444	27F	45502	* 12B

45503 * 8B
45504 * 82E
45505 * 9A
45506 * 82E
45507 * 12B
45508 * 12B
45509 * 26A
45510 24L
45511 * 8B
45512 * 12B
45513 12B
45514 * 41C
45515 * 26A
45516 * 8B
45517 27A
45518 * 8B
45519 * 82E
45520 * 9A
45521 * 8A
45522 * 14B
45523 * 1B
45524 * 12B
45525 * 8A
45526 * 12B
45527 * 8A
45528 * 5A
45529 * 5A
45530 * 9A
45531 * 8A
45532 * 16A
45533 * 2A
45534 * 6G
45535 * 8A
45536 * 41C
45537 * 2A
45538 * 1A
45539 * 26A
45540 * 3B
45541 * 2A
45542 24K
45543 * 9A
45544 12B
45545 * 5A
45546 * 8B
45547 1A
45548 * 2A
45549 8B
45550 8B
45551 12B
45552 * 8A
45553 * 5A
45554 * 8A
45555 * 12B
45556 * 5A
45557 * 17A
45558 * 26F
45559 * 17A
45560 * 8A
45561 * 14B
45562 * 55A
45563 * 26F
45564 * 55A
45565 * 55A
45566 * 55A
45567 * 8A
45568 * 55A
45569 * 55A
45570 * 41C
45571 * 24E
45572 * 82E
45573 * 55A
45574 * 24E
45575 * 14B
45576 * 41C
45577 * 82E
45578 * 8A
45579 * 14B
45580 * 24E
45581 * 55C
45582 * 24K
45583 * 8A
45584 * 24E
45585 * 15C
45586 * 6G
45587 * 9A
45588 * 12B
45589 * 55A
45590 * 41C
45591 * 5A
45592 * 3B
45593 * 12B
45594 * 41C
45595 * 5A
45596 * 8A
45597 * 55A
45598 * 17A
45599 * 1A
45600 * 26F
45601 * 1A
45602 * 41C
45603 * 1A
45604 * 5A
45605 * 55A
45606 * 24L
45607 * 41C
45608 * 55A
45609 * 41C
45610 * 17A
45611 * 16A
45612 * 17A
45613 * 8A
45614 * 14B
45615 * 15C
45616 * 15C
45617 * 12B
45618 * 17A
45619 * 55A
45620 * 16A
45621 * 63A
45622 * 14B
45623 * 5A
45624 * 1A
45625 * 5A
45626 * 17A
45627 * 17A
45628 * 14B
45629 * 5A
45630 * 5A
45631 * 9A
45632 * 24L
45633 * 24K
45634 * 5A
45635 * 26A
45636 * 15C
45638 * 9A
45639 * 55A
45640 * 12A
45641 * 16A
45642 * 26A
45643 * 5A
45644 * 9A
45645 * 26F
45646 * 55C
45647 * 3D
45648 * 17A
45649 * 17A
45650 * 15C
45651 * 82E
45652 * 15C
45653 * 24E
45654 * 41C
45655 * 5A
45656 * 41C
45657 * 12A
45658 * 55A
45659 * 55A
45660 * 82E
45661 * 26A
45662 * 82E
45663 * 26F
45664 * 41C
45665 * 66A
45666 * 5A
45667 * 16A
45668 * 17A
45669 * 1A
45670 * 8A
45671 * 9A
45672 * 12B
45673 * 63A
45674 * 5A
45675 * 55A
45676 * 24L
45677 * 63A
45678 * 8A
45679 * 5A
45680 * 9A
45681 * 8A
45682 * 82E
45683 * 41C
45684 * 5A
45685 * 82E
45686 * 24L
45687 * 67A
45688 * 12B
45689 * 5A
45690 * 82E
45691 * 12A
45692 * 63A
45693 * 67A
45694 * 55A
45695 * 55C
45696 * 3D
45697 * 12A
45698 * 27A
45699 * 82E
45700 * 26A
45701 * 26A
45702 * 26A
45703 * 12B
45704 * 6G
45705 * 24E
45706 * 26A
45707 * 66A
45708 * 55C
45709 * 3D
45710 * 26A
45711 * 66A
45712 * 14B
45713 * 12A
45714 * 12A
45715 * 12A
45716 * 12A
45717 * 27A
45718 * 12A
45719 * 27A
45720 * 66A
45721 * 12B
45722 * 1A
45723 * 12B
45724 * 12A
45725 * 41C
45726 * 5A
45727 * 63A
45728 * 12A
45729 * 12A
45730 * 12A
45731 * 12A
45732 * 12A
45733 * 6G
45734 * 12B
45735 * 24K

45736 * 5A
45737 * 3D
45738 * 12B
45739 * 55A
45740 * 1A
45741 * 12B
45742 * 12B

46100 * 16A
46101 * 1B
46102 * 66A
46103 * 14B
46104 * 66A
46105 * 66A
46106 * 9A
46107 * 66A
46108 * 9A
46109 * 55A
46110 * 5A
46111 * 9A
46112 * 16A
46113 * 55A
46114 * 8A
46115 * 9A
46116 * 5A
46117 * 55A
46118 * 16A
46119 * 8A
46120 * 5A
46121 * 66A
46122 * 3B
46123 * 14B
46124 * 8A
46125 * 5A
46126 * 24K
46127 * 6J
46128 * 5A
46129 * 5A
46130 * 55A
46131 * 41C
46132 * 14B
46133 * 14B
46134 * 5A
46135 * 5A
46136 * 24K
46137 * 9A
46138 * 6G
46139 * 14B
46140 * 14B
46141 * 3B
46142 * 14B
46143 * 3B
46144 * 1B
46145 * 55A
46146 * 1B
46147 * 41C
46148 * 41C
46149 * 6J
46150 * 6G
46151 * 41C
46152 * 5A
46153 * 3B
46154 * 24K
46155 * 5A
46156 * 6G
46157 * 16A
46158 * 3B
46159 * 5A
46160 * 14B
46161 * 24K
46162 * 14B
46163 * 6J
46164 * 5A
46165 * 24K
46166 * 9A
46167 * 24K
46168 * 24K
46169 * 5A
46170 * 5A
46200 * 5A
46201 * 66A
46203 * 8A
46204 * 8A
46205 * 5A
46206 * 5A
46207 * 1B
46208 * 8A
46209 * 5A
46210 * 66A
46211 * 8A
46212 * 5A
46220 * 5A
46221 * 1B
46222 * 66A
46223 * 66A
46224 * 66A
46225 * 12B
46226 * 12B
46227 * 66A
46228 * 5A
46229 * 1B
46230 * 66A
46231 * 66A
46232 * 66A
46233 * 5A
46234 * 12B
46235 * 5A
46236 * 12B
46237 * 12B
46238 * 12B
46239 * 1B
46240 * 1B
46241 * 5A
46242 * 1B
46243 * 5A
46244 * 12B
46245 * 1B
46246 * 5A
46247 * 1B
46248 * 5A
46249 * 5A
46250 * 12B
46251 * 5A
46252 * 5A
46253 * 5A
46254 * 1B
46255 * 12B
46256 * 12B
46257 * 12B
46400 41C
46401 89A
46402 17A
46403 15B
46404 15B
46405 27B
46406 26D
46407 50D
46408 50D
46409 50D
46410 24J
46411 26A
46412 27B
46413 56F
46414 26D
46415 50D
46416 26D
46417 26D
46418 26A
46419 26A
46420 2A
46421 3A
46422 12D
46423 3D
46424 1A
46425 3A
46426 24J
46427 3D
46428 8F
46429 5D
46430 5D
46431 1C
46432 11B
46433 11B
46434 8F
46435 56F
46436 26D
46437 26A
46438 56E
46439 27B
46440 17A
46441 24J
46442 24G
46443 17A
46444 15B
46445 2A
46446 2A
46447 8F
46448 8F
46449 12B
46450 41B
46451 41B
46452 24G
46453 55A
46454 15C
46455 12B
46456 11B
46457 12B
46458 1A
46459 3A
46460 61A
46461 61C
46462 64A
46463 62B
46464 62B
46465 31A
46466 31A
46467 31A
46468 30F
46469 30F
46470 12D
46471 51F
46472 6A
46473 51A
46474 51A
46475 51A
46476 52D
46477 51A
46478 50D
46479 51A
46480 50A
46481 50A
46482 52D
46483 56E
46484 26A
46485 26B
46486 26B
46487 26A
46488 12B
46489 12B
46490 3A
46491 11B
46492 3D
46493 55A
46494 41C
46495 15B
46496 15B
46497 17A
46498 55A

46499	17A
46500	17A
46501	16B
46502	17A
46503	89A
46504	89A
46505	89A
46506	89A
46507	89A
46508	89A
46509	89A
46510	89A
46511	89A
46512	89A
46513	89A
46514	89A
46515	89A
46516	89A
46517	82B
46518	89A
46519	89A
46520	89A
46521	89A
46522	89A
46523	89A
46524	89A
46525	82B
46526	89A
46527	89A
47000	17A
47001	27A
47002	27A
47003	18C
47004	18C
47005	6C
47006	17A
47007	17C
47008	24K
47009	6C
47160	8C
47161	24F
47163	64C
47164	8C
47165	24F
47166	6F
47167	66D
47168	66D
47190	82F
47200	14B
47201	24A
47202	14B
47203	14B
47204	14B
47207	26A
47209	14B

47211	14A
47212	14B
47213	14A
47217	26A
47218	18C
47221	41E
47223	14A
47224	26A
47225	27E
47228	27E
47230	27A
47231	18A
47235	27E
47236	17A
47239	50A
47241	14B
47248	14A
47250	18B
47254	50A
47255	56F
47257	15C
47259	27B
47260	14B
47261	14A
47262	30A
47263	41E
47264	14E
47265	15A
47266	56D
47267	6H
47268	8B
47269	6B
47270	8F
47271	56A
47272	18C
47273	15A
47275	82F
47276	85F
47277	16A
47278	18C
47279	14E
47280	5B
47281	8F
47282	30A
47283	14B
47284	26A
47285	8A
47286	WW
47287	11A
47288	12B
47289	8A
47290	11B
47292	12B
47293	24K
47294	NCB

NCB: on loan to National Coal Board

47295	12B
47297	6A
47298	8G
47300	31B
47302	1A
47303	27A
47304	1A
47305	27B
47306	30A
47307	1C
47308	85F
47310	3A
47311	30A
47312	30A
47313	15C
47314	8C
47316	82F
47317	11A
47318	2E
47319	24K
47320	27F
47321	6J
47322	11A
47324	6C
47325	27F
47326	12B
47327	27F
47328	33B
47330	5B
47332	12A
47333	82E
47334	50B
47335	56D
47336	8A
47338	6C
47340	12B
47341	9A
47342	12B
47343	6F
47344	5D
47345	11A
47347	24J
47348	1E
47349	3A
47350	6K
47351	33B
47353	8A
47354	3A
47355	1C
47356	11A
47357	8A
47358	12A
47359	5C
47360	24K
47361	11B
47362	8B
47365	26F
47366	8G

47367	27F
47368	6J
47369	24J
47371	6A
47372	6C
47373	11A
47375	6A
47376	8G
47377	12B
47378	26F
47379	56E
47380	5D
47381	24J
47383	6A
47384	5B
47385	3A
47386	24B
47388	8C
47389	6A
47390	11B
47391	5B
47392	8F
47393	8G
47395	9A
47396	3A
47397	3B
47398	3B
47399	3B
47400	9A
47401	5E
47402	8A
47403	50E
47404	8A
47405	56F
47406	8B
47408	12B
47410	6B
47412	8A
47413	24K
47414	5B
47415	12B
47416	8A
47417	85E
47418	50A
47419	55F
47420	55A
47421	50A
47422	85E
47423	18C
47424	41E
47425	27B
47426	41E
47427	24G
47428	24G
47429	17A
47430	26F
47431	9B
47432	14A

47433	14A
47434	14A
47435	14A
47436	50A
47437	14B
47438	50D
47439	6J
47441	17A
47442	14B
47443	56D
47444	8G
47445	5E
47446	56F
47447	17C
47448	50A
47449	14B
47450	5B
47451	5D
47452	8G
47453	8G
47454	24G
47455	41E
47457	17C
47458	17B
47459	17C
47460	17C
47461	17C
47462	50D
47463	56A
47464	17B
47465	82F
47466	18B
47467	5B
47468	24J
47469	24J
47470	24J
47471	24J
47472	24K
47473	3B
47474	3A
47475	5C
47476	6J
47478	WW
47479	WW
47480	27A
47481	24J
47482	1A
47483	1A
47484	33B
47485	15C
47487	8A
47488	8A
47490	8D
47491	26F
47492	12B
47493	8C
47494	3E
47495	6F
47496	82F
47497	6C
47499	2E
47500	1E
47501	1A
47502	15C
47503	11A
47504	6A
47505	11A
47506	85E
47507	6C
47508	56E
47509	56E
47510	56A
47511	6H
47512	33B
47513	41B
47514	1B
47515	12A
47516	5B
47517	11A
47518	11A
47519	8A
47520	11A
47521	1E
47522	1B
47523	5B
47524	5B
47526	5B
47529	1B
47530	6C
47531	11A
47532	24J
47533	17A
47534	15C
47535	18C
47536	66B
47537	12A
47539	85E
47540	12A
47541	66B
47542	82G
47543	15C
47544	82E
47545	41E
47546	26A
47547	26A
47548	41B
47549	14E
47550	27A
47551	18A
47552	82E
47554	14A
47555	33B
47556	50A
47557	82F
47558	6G
47559	1A
47560	8C
47561	3E
47562	24A
47564	11A
47565	6C
47566	8A
47567	56A
47568	55C
47569	55C
47570	55C
47571	56A
47572	56A
47573	56A
47574	26B
47576	24B
47577	24B
47578	26B
47579	26B
47580	50B
47581	50D
47582	56A
47583	26B
47584	26D
47587	5D
47588	5C
47589	50B
47590	5C
47592	CW
47593	11B
47594	8A
47596	5D
47597	8A
47598	5E
47599	12A
47601	8D
47602	12B
47603	8B
47604	11B
47605	11A
47606	5E
47607	50A
47608	5B
47609	5D
47610	11B
47611	27F
47612	8C
47614	12B
47615	6B
47616	8D
47618	5B
47619	41E
47620	41D
47621	26D
47622	6F
47623	85E
47624	41B
47625	41B
47626	41D
47627	6C
47628	6F
47629	17A
47630	41E
47631	6G
47632	50B
47633	5E
47634	50A
47635	56F
47637	41D
47638	17A
47640	56B
47641	17B
47642	14A
47643	17B
47644	17A
47645	14B
47646	6B
47647	8C
47648	5D
47649	5C
47651	8C
47652	8B
47653	5C
47654	8B
47655	27B
47656	8A
47657	8B
47658	5D
47659	8F
47660	17A
47661	5B
47662	11B
47664	5B
47665	5C
47666	12B
47667	12A
47668	1B
47669	8F
47670	5B
47671	8F
47673	9A
47674	6C
47675	11A
47676	11A
47677	6C
47678	82E
47679	17C
47680	5B
47681	27E
48000	21A
48001	16B
48002	17A

48003	16B
48004	16B
48005	17A
48006	16B
48007	15A
48008	17C
48009	16B
48010	15A
48011	16B
48012	2A
48016	2B
48017	8E
48018	2A
48020	2B
48024	16A
48026	41D
48027	15A
48029	41E
48033	18A
48035	2A
48036	41B
48037	41E
48039	8D
48045	8E
48046	6G
48050	15B
48053	15D
48054	6B
48055	56D
48056	18C
48057	18A
48060	18A
48061	15A
48062	18A
48063	16B
48064	16A
48065	18C
48067	55A
48069	15B
48070	55D
48073	16B
48074	6B
48075	55B
48076	56D
48077	2B
48078	55D
48079	17A
48080	55B
48081	17C
48082	18C
48083	17A
48084	55B
48085	2A
48088	16B
48089	18C
48090	2E
48092	16B
48093	55D
48094	8B
48095	18C
48096	16B
48097	16B
48098	16B
48099	18A
48100	16B
48101	21A
48102	16B
48103	41E
48104	55A
48105	21A
48106	8B
48107	15A
48108	16A
48109	18A
48110	84G
48111	2B
48112	18B
48113	55D
48114	16B
48115	26A
48116	18C
48117	16A
48118	18A
48119	16B
48120	2A
48121	17A
48122	2E
48123	55D
48124	17A
48125	18C
48126	55B
48127	18A
48128	18A
48129	1A
48130	55D
48131	2A
48132	18A
48133	15A
48134	1A
48135	8E
48136	8D
48137	16B
48138	56B
48139	8E
48140	41D
48141	15A
48142	14A
48143	15A
48144	41B
48145	18A
48146	55D
48147	2E
48148	26A
48149	15A
48150	41D
48151	41D
48152	8A
48153	17A
48154	2B
48155	8E
48156	16B
48157	55A
48158	55A
48159	55A
48160	55B
48161	9F
48162	55D
48163	18A
48164	41E
48165	9A
48166	8E
48167	18A
48168	17A
48169	55D
48170	16A
48171	1A
48172	84G
48173	2A
48174	5B
48175	6B
48176	41D
48177	16B
48178	41D
48179	41B
48180	15B
48181	41D
48182	17B
48183	18A
48184	18A
48185	18A
48186	18A
48187	18C
48188	2B
48189	41B
48190	9F
48191	9F
48192	16B
48193	16A
48194	18A
48195	18A
48196	18A
48197	18A
48198	17A
48199	41E
48200	41E
48201	18A
48202	56B
48203	2A
48204	18A
48205	18C
48206	8D
48207	1E
48208	9F
48209	41D
48210	41E
48211	16A
48212	18C
48213	41E
48214	16B
48215	16B
48216	41B
48217	16A
48218	16A
48219	16B
48220	21A
48221	18A
48222	55D
48223	16B
48224	16B
48225	16B
48246	6B
48247	8C
48248	5B
48249	8A
48250	8E
48251	2B
48252	2A
48253	6G
48254	8E
48255	5B
48256	5B
48257	5B
48258	2B
48259	6B
48260	6C
48261	16A
48262	5B
48263	2B
48264	6B
48265	56D
48266	15A
48267	16B
48268	8C
48269	2E
48270	17A
48271	18A
48272	16B
48273	9E
48274	55B
48275	9A
48276	56D
48277	16B
48278	9D
48279	16A
48280	8A
48281	55D
48282	16B
48283	55A
48284	18C
48285	15B
48286	16A
48287	2B

48288	9E
48289	2B
48290	2E
48291	2B
48292	5B
48293	16A
48294	5B
48295	8E
48296	8B
48297	5B
48301	14B
48302	17A
48303	18A
48304	14B
48305	2E
48306	14B
48307	84G
48308	8D
48309	87F
48310	3A
48311	55B
48312	2B
48313	14B
48314	18A
48315	21A
48316	9F
48317	16B
48318	8A
48319	18A
48320	2B
48321	12A
48322	9D
48323	6B
48324	14A
48325	1A
48326	8D
48327	9F
48328	87F
48329	9F
48330	87F
48331	41E
48332	18A
48333	18A
48334	16B
48335	1A
48336	21A
48337	55D
48338	18A
48339	21A
48340	8E
48341	41E
48342	21A
48343	2B
48344	9E
48345	2A
48346	41E
48347	84G
48348	6C
48349	6C
48350	18A
48351	21A
48352	55B
48353	18A
48354	84G
48355	15B
48356	15B
48357	56D
48358	56D
48359	18C
48360	2E
48361	18A
48362	18A
48363	18A
48364	17C
48365	2A
48366	3A
48367	14A
48368	8E
48369	84G
48370	18A
48371	18C
48372	26A
48373	8B
48374	15A
48375	3A
48376	15B
48377	16A
48378	14A
48379	16B
48380	15B
48381	15A
48382	15A
48383	16B
48384	18A
48385	15A
48386	15A
48387	18A
48388	21A
48389	9A
48390	17A
48391	41D
48392	16B
48393	16A
48394	55B
48395	16B
48396	41D
48397	41D
48398	2B
48399	55A
48400	87F
48401	18A
48402	84E
48403	17A
48404	82B
48405	16B
48406	9F
48407	41D
48408	3A
48409	87F
48410	81A
48411	2A
48412	81A
48413	16B
48414	18A
48415	84E
48416	1A
48417	84E
48418	84E
48419	87F
48420	82B
48421	9D
48422	2E
48423	2A
48424	84E
48425	8D
48426	8E
48427	2A
48428	9A
48429	9F
48430	84E
48431	81A
48432	16B
48433	8A
48434	82B
48435	2B
48436	82B
48437	2A
48438	87F
48439	55D
48440	2E
48441	6C
48442	16B
48443	55A
48444	84E
48445	2E
48446	1E
48447	16B
48448	6C
48449	2B
48450	86C
48451	9D
48452	87F
48453	3A
48454	55A
48455	6C
48456	2B
48457	8A
48458	6B
48459	82B
48460	84E
48461	87F
48462	8E
48463	87F
48464	12A
48465	9A
48466	55D
48467	15B
48468	84G
48469	55D
48470	87F
48471	84E
48472	12A
48473	55D
48474	84G
48475	84E
48476	1A
48477	3A
48478	84G
48479	8C
48490	18A
48491	26A
48492	15A
48493	2E
48494	18C
48495	15A
48500	8D
48501	9F
48502	8D
48503	9F
48504	2B
48505	9D
48506	8C
48507	18A
48508	41D
48509	8A
48510	17A
48511	3A
48512	8A
48513	8A
48514	3A
48515	41E
48516	5B
48517	14A
48518	1A
48519	9D
48520	8B
48521	8E
48522	8C
48523	21A
48524	87F
48525	87F
48526	2A
48527	18C
48528	16B
48529	2E
48530	18A
48531	8C
48532	55D
48533	41E
48534	2E
48535	8C
48536	12A

48537	55D
48538	18A
48539	41E
48540	55D
48541	16B
48542	55D
48543	9F
48544	1E
48545	18A
48546	41E
48547	18C
48548	5B
48549	1E
48550	1E
48551	1A
48552	16B
48553	26A
48554	8D
48555	8E
48556	3A
48557	9F
48558	8D
48559	2A
48600	1A
48601	1A
48602	3A
48603	1A
48604	18A
48605	8E
48606	18A
48607	18A
48608	56D
48609	15B
48610	1E
48611	15B
48612	12A
48613	9F
48614	16A
48615	18A
48616	14A
48617	15A
48618	41E
48619	15D
48620	18A
48621	16B
48622	55B
48623	2B
48624	1A
48625	15A
48626	5B
48627	15A
48628	1A
48629	1A
48630	5B
48631	8C
48632	2B
48633	5B
48634	9F
48635	16A
48636	18A
48637	18A
48638	18A
48639	16A
48640	18A
48641	55B
48642	41B
48643	16B
48644	15D
48645	15B
48646	2A
48647	21A
48648	1A
48649	1A
48650	18A
48651	15A
48652	55B
48653	16A
48654	17C
48655	5B
48656	1A
48657	1A
48658	2B
48659	5B
48660	84G
48661	18A
48662	17B
48663	41E
48664	55D
48665	1A
48666	16A
48667	6G
48668	2A
48669	21A
48670	55D
48671	15A
48672	18A
48673	16B
48674	3A
48675	16A
48676	9F
48677	9F
48678	14A
48679	9D
48680	9A
48681	18A
48682	9F
48683	8A
48684	6C
48685	18A
48686	2B
48687	21A
48688	1E
48689	55D
48690	15B
48691	6C
48692	5B
48693	5B
48694	17B
48695	9F
48696	16A
48697	6B
48698	18A
48699	15A
48700	21A
48701	16B
48702	55B
48703	55B
48704	15B
48705	3A
48706	87F
48707	87F
48708	12A
48709	8D
48710	55D
48711	8E
48712	9D
48713	3A
48714	8C
48715	8B
48716	26A
48717	8E
48718	3D
48719	3D
48720	26A
48721	55B
48722	3A
48723	2B
48724	84G
48725	3A
48726	3D
48727	3A
48728	17B
48729	12A
48730	87F
48731	9F
48732	87F
48733	3A
48734	5B
48735	87F
48736	2E
48737	84G
48738	84G
48739	84G
48740	9D
48741	9E
48742	8E
48743	5B
48744	9A
48745	26A
48746	8B
48747	8C
48748	16A
48749	6B
48750	18A
48751	2B
48752	3D
48753	6B
48754	2B
48755	3A
48756	12A
48757	2A
48758	12A
48759	15B
48760	87F
48761	87F
48762	3A
48763	16A
48764	8E
48765	41B
48766	3A
48767	3A
48768	84G
48769	3A
48770	18A
48771	6B
48772	41E
48773	66A
48774	66A
48775	66A
48895	8F
48898	1E
48915	8F
48927	8A
48930	3A
48932	9D
48942	8F
48950	3B
48951	1E
48953	1E
48964	3A
49002	2B
49007	8F
49008	8F
49020	8F
49021	3A
49023	8F
49025	8F
49034	26F
49037	3B
49045	3A
49049	8F
49061	1E
49064	8A
49070	1A
49077	3A
49078	1A
49079	2B
49081	5C

49082	8A
49087	26F
49093	1E
49094	1E
49099	3A
49104	24K
49106	3A
49114	3A
49119	26F
49122	1A
49125	3A
49126	5C
49129	8F
49130	5B
49134	2B
49137	8A
49139	8F
49141	8F
49142	2B
49144	8A
49147	26F
49154	8F
49155	8F
49158	5B
49164	1A
49173	8A
49191	8F
49196	24K
49199	26F
49209	26F
49210	9D
49216	3A
49224	8A
49229	3B
49234	5C
49240	3B
49243	8A
49246	3A
49262	8G
49267	8F
49275	3A
49277	9D
49281	9D
49287	1E
49288	8G
49293	2B
49310	1E
49313	3A
49314	2B
49321	8F
49323	26F
49328	3A
49335	26F
49342	2B
49343	3A
49344	1A
49350	2B
49352	8G

49357	5C
49361	3A
49373	3A
49375	8A
49377	5C
49381	8F
49382	24K
49391	9D
49392	8A
49394	8A
49399	8A
49401	9B
49402	8F
49403	1E
49404	8A
49405	8A
49406	9D
49407	5B
49408	8F
49411	3A
49412	8A
49413	1A
49414	2B
49415	2B
49416	8A
49421	26F
49422	8F
49423	9D
49425	2B
49426	26F
49428	8G
49430	2B
49431	2B
49432	2B
49433	9D
49434	8A
49437	8A
49438	8F
49439	5B
49440	2B
49441	2B
49443	1E
49444	15F
49446	5C
49447	15F
49448	8G
49449	8G
49451	8F
49452	3B
49453	9B
49454	5B
49505	26B
49508	26A
49618	26A
49627	26B
49637	26B
49668	26B

50721	27A
50746	27C
50850	27C
51204	26B
51206	27A
51207	26B
51217	82E
51218	82E
51222	50D
51227	27A
51229	27A
51232	27A
51237	27A
51241	50D
51244	50D
51246	27A
51253	27A
51336	24F
51371	26A
51408	26C
51412	CW
51413	26B
51419	24F
51429	HW
51441	8G
51444	CW
51445	8A
51446	CW
51486	26C
51496	26B
51498	26C
51524	24F
51537	27B
52089	56D
52093	CW
52119	6K
52121	56D
52129	26D
52133	56A
52140	26A
52141	26A
52154	50D
52161	26A
52171	27B
52179	24B
52182	26C
52201	26D
52207	26E
52218	CW

52225	8B
52230	26A
52240	26E
52244	50D
52248	26E
52252	50D
52260	27B
52270	26A
52271	26A
52275	26A
52290	24C
52305	50D
52311	27B
52312	CW
52319	50D
52322	26E
52341	26A
52345	26C
52351	56E
52355	56A
52378	27B
52393	26C
52400	56E
52411	56E
52413	56F
52415	26C
52429	24C
52438	6K
52441	CW
52445	24C
52452	56E
52456	24C
52459	CW
52461	56F
52464	CW
52466	26E
52515	56D
52523	26C
52526	26D
53801	82F
53803	82F
53804	82F
53805	82F
53806	82F
53807	82F
53808	82F
53809	82F
53810	82F
54462	66B
54463	60A
54464	66B

54465	66B
54466	60B
54475	65B
54477	66E
54478	64C
54480	60C
54482	60B
54483	65B
54485	63A
54486	63A
54487	60A
54488	60B
54489	63A
54490	66E
54491	60D
54492	68C
54493	60A
54494	63A
54495	60C
54498	66D
54499	63A
54500	63A
54501	65B
54502	68B
54505	66E
54506	66D
54507	68B
55124	68B
55126	63C
55165	64C
55167	66A
55169	66A
55173	60B
55185	61C
55189	66A
55195	65J
55198	60A
55199	60A
55200	63A
55201	66A
55202	64C
55203	67A
55204	65F
55206	67A
55207	66A
55208	63C
55209	63A
55210	64C
55211	67B
55214	65F
55215	63C
55216	60A
55217	63A
55219	67A
55220	63C
55221	61C
55222	65J
55223	66A
55224	63C
55225	67A
55226	63A
55227	60A
55228	66A
55229	64C
55230	63C
55231	67C
55232	68B
55233	64C
55234	68D
55235	67A
55236	60A
55237	66A
55238	65J
55239	63A
55240	67C
55260	68D
55261	66E
55262	67C
55263	63C
55264	67A
55265	66A
55266	67A
55267	66D
55268	66A
55269	60A
56025	RW
56027	CW
56029	65E
56031	66B
56032	CW
56035	66D
56039	65G
56151	65B
56158	66A
56159	66A
56167	66D
56168	65G
56169	65B
56171	65D
56172	66D
56173	66D
56232	67C
56239	66A
56240	61B
56242	66C
56246	63A
56256	66C
56259	67D
56260	66A
56278	61B
56279	67A
56286	66C
56289	65B
56292	66A
56298	66A
56300	60A
56302	68B
56305	60A
56308	66A
56309	66B
56310	68B
56312	64C
56313	64C
56324	66A
56325	61B
56326	61B
56331	63A
56335	66A
56336	66A
56337	66B
56338	66B
56341	60A
56343	65J
56347	63A
56348	61C
56356	66B
56360	66C
56361	67A
56362	66C
56363	67C
56364	67A
56368	67B
56370	65B
56372	67D
56376	65F
57232	65J
57233	65J
57236	67B
57237	66B
57238	68C
57239	66A
57240	65B
57242	66C
57244	66A
57245	65D
57246	65J
57249	67A
57250	66A
57251	65B
57252	65J
57253	65B
57254	67D
57256	66B
57257	65J
57258	65B
57259	65G
57261	65B
57262	67C
57263	67D
57264	65J
57265	65F
57266	67D
57267	66B
57268	66A
57269	65B
57270	66B
57271	66A
57274	67D
57275	66A
57278	66B
57284	67B
57285	65F
57287	65F
57288	66A
57291	66B
57292	66A
57295	67B
57296	65D
57299	66B
57300	67A
57302	68B
57303	66B
57309	67D
57311	65B
57314	65D
57317	66A
57319	66A
57321	66C
57324	65J
57325	66B
57326	66B
57328	66B
57329	68B
57331	67B
57335	66C
57336	65D
57338	65F
57340	68C
57341	65D
57345	63A
57347	66A
57348	67D
57349	68B
57350	65B
57353	67B
57355	67D
57356	67D
57357	67D
57359	67A
57360	66A

57362	68B
57363	66B
57364	67C
57365	66A
57366	65F
57367	66A
57369	66A
57370	66B
57373	65B
57375	68C
57377	66B
57378	68B
57383	67B
57384	66B
57385	66E
57386	66E
57389	66A
57392	67C
57398	66B
57404	66B
57411	65B
57416	66D
57417	66A
57418	66A
57426	65B
57429	65D
57431	66B
57432	66A
57434	65B
57436	66B
57441	63A
57445	68C
57446	66B
57447	66C
57451	66E
57461	66B
57463	66A
57470	65D
57472	65D
57473	63A
57550	64C
57554	65D
57555	66A
57557	65B
57558	65B
57559	64C
57560	64C
57562	67B
57563	66A
57564	66A
57565	64C
57566	67D
57568	68D
57569	67C
57570	67B
57571	63C
57572	67B
57576	65J
57577	67B
57579	67D
57580	67C
57581	66A
57583	66E
57585	60D
57586	60B
57587	60C
57590	67D
57591	60B
57592	65D
57593	66B
57594	60A
57596	67C
57597	60B
57600	68B
57601	68B
57602	68B
57603	66A
57604	66E
57605	60A
57607	65D
57608	66E
57609	66C
57611	67C
57612	65F
57613	66E
57614	67C
57615	67C
57617	65B
57618	66E
57619	66D
57620	67A
57621	68B
57622	66A
57623	68B
57625	66A
57626	66E
57627	67D
57630	66C
57631	65B
57632	60B
57633	67C
57634	61C
57635	66E
57637	67B
57640	67C
57642	65J
57643	67B
57644	67C
57645	64C
57650	67B
57651	67B
57652	65D
57653	12A
57654	64C
57655	66E
57658	67C
57659	66B
57661	60A
57663	66C
57665	66B
57666	66B
57667	63C
57668	66B
57669	67D
57670	66E
57671	67B
57672	67B
57673	67D
57674	66A
57679	65J
57681	66B
57682	66D
57684	67C
57686	65B
57688	66B
57689	67B
57690	66D
57691	65F
58086	82F
58115	11A
58120	8F
58122	3A
58123	8F
58124	3B
58128	3B
58131	14B
58135	3E
58137	17C
58138	21A
58143	21A
58144	17A
58148	3B
58153	18A
58158	17A
58160	11A
58163	15D
58165	17B
58166	18A
58168	3B
58169	3A
58170	41D
58173	18A
58174	3A
58175	18A
58177	8G
58181	3A
58182	8G
58185	3E
58186	17B
58197	55D
58209	15D
58214	14E
58215	2A
58218	2A
58220	3E
58221	2A
58228	17C
58260	55D
58271	3E
58283	3A
58287	11A
58291	8G
58293	11A
58295	3B
58298	15D
58305	17B
58850	17C
60001	* 52A
60002	* 52A
60003	* 34A
60004	* 64B
60005	* 52A
60006	* 34A
60007	* 34A
60008	* 34A
60009	* 64B
60010	* 34A
60011	* 64B
60012	* 64B
60013	* 34A
60014	* 34A
60015	* 34A
60016	* 52A
60017	* 34A
60018	* 52A
60019	* 52A
60020	* 52A
60021	* 34A
60022	* 34A
60023	* 52A
60024	* 64B
60025	* 34A
60026	* 34A
60027	* 64B
60028	* 34A
60029	* 34A
60030	* 34A
60031	* 64B
60032	* 34A
60033	* 34A
60034	* 34A
60035	* 64B
60036	* 55H

60037 * 64B
60038 * 55A
60039 * 34A
60040 * 51A
60041 * 64B
60042 * 52A
60043 * 64B
60044 * 34A
60045 * 52A
60046 * 34F
60047 * 34F
60048 * 34F
60049 * 34F
60050 * 34F
60051 * 52A
60052 * 52A
60053 * 52A
60054 * 34F
60055 * 34A
60056 * 34F
60057 * 64B
60058 * 52A
60059 * 34A
60060 * 52A
60061 * 34A
60062 * 34A
60063 * 34F
60064 * 34F
60065 * 34F
60066 * 34A
60067 * 34A
60068 * 12C
60069 * 52D
60070 * 52A
60071 * 51A
60072 * 52D
60073 * 52B
60074 * 55H
60075 * 52A
60076 * 52A
60077 * 55A
60078 * 52A
60079 * 12C
60080 * 55A
60081 * 55H
60082 * 55A
60083 * 52B
60084 * 55H
60085 * 52B
60086 * 55H
60087 * 64B
60088 * 55A
60089 * 64B
60090 * 64B
60091 * 52A
60092 * 55A
60093 * 12C
60094 * 64B
60095 * 12C
60096 * 64B
60097 * 64B
60098 * 64B
60099 * 64B
60100 * 64B
60101 * 64B
60102 * 34F
60103 * 34A
60105 * 34F
60106 * 34F
60107 * 34F
60108 * 34A
60109 * 34A
60110 * 34A
60111 * 34F
60112 * 34F
60113 * 36A
60114 * 36A
60115 * 52A
60116 * 52B
60117 * 56C
60118 * 56C
60119 * 36A
60120 * 56C
60121 * 50A
60122 * 36A
60123 * 56C
60124 * 52A
60125 * 36A
60126 * 52B
60127 * 52B
60128 * 36A
60129 * 52A
60130 * 56C
60131 * 56C
60132 * 52B
60133 * 56C
60134 * 56C
60135 * 52A
60136 * 36A
60137 * 52B
60138 * 50A
60139 * 36A
60140 * 50A
60141 * 56C
60142 * 52A
60143 * 52B
60144 * 36A
60145 * 52A
60146 * 50A
60147 * 52A
60148 * 56C
60149 * 36A
60150 * 52A
60151 * 52B
60152 * 64B
60153 * 50A
60154 * 52A
60155 * 52A
60156 * 36A
60157 * 36A
60158 * 36A
60159 * 64B
60160 * 64B
60161 * 64B
60162 * 64B
60500 * 34E
60502 * 50A
60504 * 34E
60506 * 34E
60507 * 64B
60508 * 34E
60509 * 64B
60510 * 64B
60511 * 52B
60512 * 50A
60513 * 34E
60514 * 34E
60515 * 50A
60516 * 52B
60517 * 52B
60518 * 52B
60519 * 64B
60520 * 36A
60521 * 52B
60522 * 50A
60523 * 36A
60524 * 50A
60525 * 61B
60526 * 50A
60527 * 63A
60528 * 62B
60529 * 64B
60530 * 64B
60531 * 61B
60532 * 61B
60533 * 36A
60534 * 64B
60535 * 64B
60536 * 64B
60537 * 64B
60538 * 52B
60539 * 52B
60800 * 34A
60801 52D
60802 52B
60803 31B
60804 62B
60805 52B
60806 52B
60807 52B
60808 52B
60809 * 52B
60810 52B
60811 52B
60812 52B
60813 64A
60814 34A
60815 15E
60816 64A
60817 36A
60818 64A
60819 64A
60820 34E
60821 34E
60822 62B
60823 64A
60824 64A
60825 64A
60826 36A
60827 64A
60828 50A
60829 34E
60830 31B
60831 50A
60832 34E
60833 52B
60834 62B
60835 * 52B
60836 64A
60837 50A
60838 62B
60839 50A
60840 64A
60841 36A
60842 50A
60843 52D
60844 62B
60845 34E
60846 52B
60847 * 50A
60848 51A
60849 36A
60850 36A
60851 61B
60852 36A
60853 34E
60854 34A
60855 50A
60856 50A
60857 36A
60858 31B
60859 56C
60860 * 52B
60861 56B
60862 34A
60863 15E
60864 50A
60865 52D
60866 36A
60867 34E
60868 52B
60869 34E

60870	36A
60871	34A
60872 *	36A
60873 *	64A
60874	34E
60875	36A
60876	50A
60877	50A
60878	50A
60879	50A
60880	36A
60881	36A
60882	64A
60883	64A
60884	56B
60885	51L
60886	52B
60887	50A
60888	61B
60889	36A
60890	15E
60891	52B
60892	64A
60893	34E
60894	64A
60895	50A
60896	36A
60897	34E
60898	61B
60899	36A
60900	64A
60901	52B
60902	34A
60903	34A
60904	52B
60905	36A
60906	34E
60907	50A
60908	36A
60909	36A
60910	52B
60911	51L
60912	36A
60913	52D
60914	34E
60915	51L
60916	56B
60917	36A
60918	50A
60919	61B
60920	64A
60921	36A
60922	52B
60923	52A
60924	34E
60925	50A
60926	52D
60927	64B
60928	36A
60929	52A
60930	36A
60931	64A
60932	52B
60933	64A
60934	52A
60935	36A
60936	36A
60937	64A
60938	31B
60939	50A
60940	52B
60941	50A
60942	52A
60943	36A
60944	52B
60945	52B
60946	51L
60947	52A
60948	31B
60949	52A
60950	34A
60951	64B
60952	52A
60953	64A
60954	50A
60955	61B
60956	36A
60957	64B
60958	64A
60959	64B
60960	51L
60961	50A
60962	52B
60963	50A
60964 *	52A
60965	64A
60966	34E
60967	52A
60968	50A
60969	64A
60970	61B
60971	64A
60972	61B
60973	61B
60974	50A
60975	50A
60976	52B
60977	50A
60978	52B
60979	52A
60980	64A
60981	50A
60982	50A
60983	34A
61000 *	36A
61001 *	36A
61002 *	50A
61003 *	36A
61004 *	41A
61005 *	31B
61006 *	31B
61007 *	64B
61008 *	26B
61009 *	40A
61010 *	50B
61011 *	56D
61012 *	52A
61013 *	56B
61014 *	52A
61015 *	56A
61016 *	55H
61017 *	56A
61018 *	51A
61019 *	52A
61020 *	56A
61021 *	51A
61022 *	52A
61023 *	56B
61024 *	51A
61025 *	52D
61026 *	40A
61027 *	41A
61028 *	2F
61029 *	64A
61030 *	51A
61031 *	51L
61032 *	51A
61033 *	41A
61034 *	51L
61035 *	55H
61036 *	36A
61037 *	51L
61038 *	55H
61039 *	56B
61040 *	56D
61041	41A
61042	40A
61043	32A
61044	41A
61045	32A
61046	32A
61047	41A
61048	32A
61049	56D
61050	41A
61051	41A
61052	31B
61053	50A
61054	32C
61055	36A
61056	41A
61058	40A
61059	31C
61060	34E
61061	51C
61062	51L
61063	14D
61064	12C
61065	50B
61066	31A
61067	65C
61068	51L
61069	50A
61070	34E
61071	50A
61072	62C
61073	34E
61074	34E
61075	34A
61076	64B
61077	14D
61078	2F
61079	40B
61080	50B
61081	64B
61082	40B
61083	41F
61084	50A
61085	2F
61086	50A
61087	36A
61088	40E
61089	30A
61090	41A
61091	34D
61092	40E
61093	41F
61094	41A
61095	31B
61096	31B
61097	34D
61098	40B
61099	64A
61100	52A
61101	62C
61102	62B
61103	62A
61104	41A
61105	41A
61106	2F
61107	36A
61108	64A
61109	30A
61110	56B
61111	41A
61112	41A
61113	34E
61114	40B

61115		56C
61116		14D
61117		65C
61118		62A
61119		30A
61120		36E
61121		36A
61122		36A
61123		56B
61124		36A
61125		36A
61126		36E
61127		36A
61128		36A
61129		56C
61130		40B
61131		56A
61132		62A
61133		62A
61134		62A
61135		36A
61136		14D
61137		15E
61138		41D
61139		41A
61140		65A
61141		40E
61142		40E
61143		40B
61144		40B
61145		36A
61146		62A
61147		62A
61148		62A
61149		30F
61150		41A
61151		41A
61152		41C
61153		41A
61154		41A
61155		36A
61156		31B
61157		36A
61158		36A
61159		40B
61160		40A
61161		9G
61162		41A
61163		40E
61164		41A
61165		41F
61166		41F
61167		41F
61168		40B
61169		41A
61170		36A
61171		31A
61172		62B
61173		51L
61174		34A
61175		40B
61176		51A
61177		40E
61178		64B
61179		34A
61180		62B
61181		41A
61182		31A
61183		41A
61184		64A
61185		40B
61186		2F
61187		14D
61188		40E
61189	*	56C
61190		40B
61191		64A
61192		2F
61193		36A
61194		41F
61195		40B
61196		36A
61197		65A
61198		50A
61199		52D
61200		34A
61201		26B
61202		40A
61203		31A
61204		31B
61205		31B
61206		14D
61207		34E
61208		36E
61209		40E
61210		34E
61211		36E
61212		36E
61213		36E
61214		56C
61215	*	50B
61216		55H
61217		12C
61218		55H
61219		64B
61220		51L
61221	*	64B
61222		12C
61223		40A
61224		51A
61225		36E
61226		30F
61227		30F
61228		41A
61229		50A
61230		56D
61231		36E
61232		30F
61233		30A
61234		41A
61235		40B
61236		31A
61237	*	55H
61238	*	52A
61239		12C
61240	*	51L
61241	*	52D
61242	*	61A
61243	*	65A
61244	*	64B
61245	*	64B
61246	*	64A
61247	*	36A
61248	*	40B
61249	*	41A
61250	*	36A
61251	*	34F
61252		31A
61253		31A
61254		31A
61255		51L
61256		50B
61257		51L
61258		40A
61259		55H
61260		64A
61261		65A
61262		62A
61263		62B
61264		30F
61265		9G
61266		36A
61267		51C
61268		56A
61269		26B
61270		36A
61271		2F
61272		34E
61273		50A
61274		56F
61275		51C
61276		50A
61277		62A
61278		62B
61279		36A
61280		31A
61281		40E
61282		34E
61283		31A
61284		40A
61285		36A
61286		31A
61287		31A
61288		50A
61289		50B
61290		12C
61291		50A
61292		62B
61293		62B
61294		61A
61295		56B
61296		56A
61297		56B
61298		26B
61299		40E
61300		31A
61301		31A
61302		34E
61303		51L
61304		51A
61305		50B
61306		50B
61307		64A
61308		64A
61309		56C
61310		56B
61311		30F
61312		41D
61313		41A
61314		36A
61315		41A
61316		41F
61317		40B
61318		40B
61319		50A
61320		56C
61321		51A
61322		52D
61323		31B
61324		61A
61325		40B
61326		36A
61327		41A
61328		40B
61329		30A
61330		62A
61331		34E
61332		64A
61333		65C
61334		41D
61335		30A
61336		30F
61337		50A
61338		51A
61339		56C
61340		65A
61341		64A
61342		65A
61343		62A
61344		65C
61345		61A
61346		61A

61347	61A	61405	40A	61472	50A	61828	40A
61348	40A	61406	40B	61473	50A	61829	36A
61349	64A	61407	62C	61475	50A	61830	34E
61350	61A	61408	40B	61476	50A	61831	31B
61351	64A	61409	40A	61478	50A	61832	2F
61352	61A	61410	50A	61572	32A	61833	40E
61353	51A	61411	55H	61657 *	31B	61834	31A
61354	64A	61412	55H	61660 *	31B	61835	31B
61355	65A	61413	50A	61664 *	31B	61837	40E
61356	64A	61414	55H	61668 *	30A	61839	36A
61357	64A	61415	55H	61728	41A	61840	31B
61358	62A	61416	50A	61730	40B	61841	2F
61359	64A	61417	50A	61740	40B	61842	2F
61360	36A	61418	50A	61742	40F	61843	2F
61361	30F	61419	50A	61745	40B	61844	52B
61362	30F	61420	50A	61747	41A	61845	31B
61363	31A	61421	50A	61756	40B	61846	50B
61364	34A	61422	50A	61760	41A	61847	50B
61365	36A	61423	50A	61761	41A	61848	40A
61366	40B	61424	50A	61763	34E	61849	31A
61367	34F	61425	50A	61764 *	65A	61850	36A
61368	2F	61428	55H	61766	40B	61851	12C
61369	26B	61429	55H	61767	40B	61852	40E
61370	41D	61431	50A	61769	65C	61853	56B
61371	31A	61432	55H	61771	40B	61854	52D
61372	30F	61434	50A	61773	40B	61856	56B
61373	30F	61435	50A	61779	61C	61857	50B
61374	40B	61436	50A	61782 *	61C	61858	12C
61375	30A	61437	50A	61784	63B	61859	40A
61376	15E	61438	50A	61788 *	65A	61860	31B
61377	36A	61439	50A	61792	61C	61861	31B
61378	30F	61440	50A	61794 *	65A	61862	30F
61379 *	40B	61443	50A	61800	36A	61863	30A
61380	15E	61444	50A	61801	31A	61864	34E
61381	15E	61445	50E	61803	36A	61865	2F
61382	51A	61446	55H	61804	2F	61866	40B
61383	56F	61447	55H	61805	34E	61867	36A
61384	40A	61448	50A	61807	40A	61868	41F
61385	56A	61449	50A	61808	40E	61869	50B
61386	56C	61450	50A	61809	2F	61870	40E
61387	56F	61451	50A	61810	31B	61871	50B
61388	50A	61452	50A	61811	41H	61872	50B
61389	34F	61453	50A	61812	36A	61873	40E
61390	36A	61454	50A	61813	50B	61874	50B
61391	34E	61455	50A	61814	50B	61875	50B
61392	34F	61456	50A	61815	30A	61877	40A
61393	34A	61457	50A	61816	41A	61880	31A
61394	34A	61459	50A	61817	31A	61881	64A
61395	12C	61460	50A	61818	52B	61882	2F
61396	65A	61461	50A	61819	50B	61883	50B
61397	64A	61462	50A	61820	41H	61884	52B
61398	64A	61463	50A	61821	40E	61886	31B
61399	41A	61464	50A	61822	41H	61887	36A
61400	61A	61466	50A	61824	2F	61888	40E
61401	62A	61467	50A	61825	41A	61889	40A
61402	62B	61468	50A	61826	41H	61890	31B
61403	65A	61469	50A	61827	31B	61891	40B
61404	65C	61471	55H			61892	50B

61893	50B
61894	40A
61895	36A
61896	40E
61897	50B
61899	50B
61901	52D
61902	50B
61903	50B
61904	50B
61905	40B
61906	52B
61907	40E
61908	41H
61910	2F
61912	40B
61913	2F
61914	40E
61915	31B
61916	12C
61917	52D
61918	32A
61919	40A
61920	50B
61921	30F
61922	50B
61923	50B
61924	64A
61925	36A
61926	40A
61927	50B
61929	31B
61930	52D
61932	50B
61933	64A
61934	52D
61935	50B
61936	12C
61938	41A
61939	32A
61940	36A
61941	50B
61942	30F
61943	40E
61944	40A
61945	50B
61946	31B
61947	40E
61948	31B
61949	32A
61950	40B
61951	30F
61952	52D
61953	32A
61954	31B
61955	64A
61956	40B
61957	32A
61958	41H
61959	41H
61960	40A
61961	36A
61962	52B
61963	30F
61964	36A
61965	50B
61966	40B
61967	41A
61968	64A
61969	52D
61970	32A
61971	32A
61972	31B
61973	41H
61974	40E
61975	56B
61976	41H
61977	30F
61978	34E
61979	34E
61980	56B
61981	41H
61982	40E
61984	52B
61985	52D
61986	52B
61987	52B
61989	41H
61990	64A
61992	64A
61993 *	62A
61994 *	62A
61995 *	62A
61996 *	62A
61997 *	63B
61998 *	62A
62001	51L
62002	52C
62003	51J
62004	51A
62005	50A
62006	52C
62007	51A
62008	51A
62009	50A
62010	52C
62011	63B
62012	63B
62013	36C
62014	36C
62015	30A
62016	31B
62017	31B
62018	36C
62019	30A
62020	36C
62021	52C
62022	52C
62023	52C
62024	52C
62025	52C
62026	52C
62027	52C
62028	52C
62029	52C
62030	52C
62031	63B
62032	36C
62033	31B
62034	63B
62035	31B
62036	30A
62037	31B
62038	31B
62039	31B
62040	31B
62041	51A
62042	51L
62043	51A
62044	51J
62045	51A
62046	50A
62047	50A
62048	51A
62049	50A
62050	52C
62051	31B
62052	63B
62053	30A
62054	31B
62055	31B
62056	50A
62057	50A
62058	51A
62059	51J
62060	52C
62061	50A
62062	51A
62063	50A
62064	51A
62065	50A
62066	31B
62067	31B
62068	31B
62069	31B
62070	30A
62421 *	64A
62426 *	65J
62467 *	62A
62474 *	65A
62479 *	61A
62484 *	63A
62488 *	64G
62493 *	61A
62495 *	64F
62496 *	65A
62613	31B
62660 *	41A
62661 *	41H
62662 *	41A
62663 *	41H
62664 *	41A
62666 *	41A
62667 *	41A
62668 *	41A
62669 *	41A
62670 *	41A
62671 *	65A
62672 *	65A
62674 *	65A
62680 *	65A
62681 *	65A
62682 *	65A
62685 *	64B
62686 *	65A
62687 *	65A
62688 *	65B
62689 *	64A
62690 *	64B
62691 *	64B
62693 *	64A
62710 *	50B
62711 *	64A
62712 *	64G
62716 *	62A
62717 *	50B
62718 *	64A
62723 *	50B
62727 *	50B
62729 *	64A
62733 *	62A
62734 *	12C
62739 *	50E
62740 *	50B
62743 *	64B
62744 *	64G
62747 *	12C
62759 *	50B
62762 *	50E
62763 *	50B
62765 *	50B
63340	51F
63341	51L
63342	52K
63343	51L
63344	51L

63345	52K
63346	52K
63347	51L
63348	55H
63349	51L
63350	52H
63351	51F
63352	52C
63353	51F
63354	52K
63355	51L
63356	52C
63357	52K
63358	52H
63359	52K
63360	51L
63361	51L
63362	52C
63363	52C
63364	51L
63365	52K
63366	52C
63367	51L
63368	52C
63369	51L
63370	51L
63371	51L
63373	51L
63374	51L
63375	51L
63376	52C
63377	52C
63378	52C
63379	52K
63380	51L
63381	52C
63382	51L
63383	51C
63384	52C
63385	52C
63386	52C
63387	52K
63388	51L
63389	51L
63390	52C
63391	51C
63392	51C
63393	51L
63394	52C
63395	51A
63396	51L
63397	51C
63398	51F
63399	51L
63400	52C
63401	51L
63402	52C
63403	51F
63404	52K
63405	51L
63406	52K
63407	51F
63408	52C
63409	51L
63410	51C
63411	51L
63412	51C
63413	52C
63414	51C
63415	51C
63416	51L
63417	51L
63418	52K
63419	51C
63420	51L
63421	51C
63422	51C
63423	51A
63424	51L
63425	52H
63426	51L
63427	52K
63428	51L
63429	52H
63430	51L
63431	52C
63432	51L
63433	52K
63434	52C
63435	51L
63436	55H
63437	52K
63438	51C
63439	52K
63440	51C
63441	52C
63442	51L
63443	51F
63444	52C
63445	51L
63446	51F
63447	51L
63448	52K
63449	55H
63450	51L
63451	51L
63452	51L
63453	52C
63454	51C
63455	52K
63456	52K
63457	51C
63458	52C
63459	51F
63460	52H
63461	52H
63462	52H
63463	52H
63464	52H
63465	52H
63466	52H
63467	52G
63468	52H
63469	52H
63470	52H
63471	52H
63472	52H
63473	52H
63474	52G
63570	56B
63571	41H
63573	9G
63574	41A
63575	9G
63576	36C
63577	41J
63578	16D
63579	16D
63584	56B
63585	40E
63586	41F
63587	40E
63588	56A
63589	40E
63590	41H
63591	16D
63592	40E
63593	41F
63594	40E
63595	36C
63596	41H
63597	41J
63598	9G
63599	41A
63600	9G
63601	36C
63602	36E
63603	9G
63604	41A
63605	56B
63606	36C
63607	40B
63608	36E
63609	41A
63610	16D
63611	41F
63612	41F
63613	36A
63615	40B
63616	40E
63617	36C
63618	36A
63619	41H
63621	41A
63622	41F
63623	41F
63624	41A
63626	36C
63628	41F
63630	41H
63631	9G
63632	41F
63633	56B
63634	40B
63635	41J
63636	41J
63637	36E
63639	40E
63641	9G
63643	40B
63644	40E
63645	41A
63646	41H
63647	36E
63648	41F
63649	9G
63650	41H
63651	40B
63652	41H
63653	36C
63655	36E
63656	41F
63657	40E
63658	41A
63659	41F
63661	41H
63662	36C
63663	41H
63664	41J
63665	36C
63666	36C
63669	41F
63670	41H
63671	36C
63672	41F
63674	40E
63675	40E
63676	16D
63677	36A
63678	41H
63679	41J
63681	9G
63683	41J
63684	41F
63685	41A
63686	9G
63687	31B
63688	36E
63689	16D
63690	36C
63691	41J
63692	40B

63693	36A
63695	41A
63697	41J
63698	36A
63700	9G
63701	41F
63702	41H
63703	41J
63704	41F
63705	41H
63706	41H
63707	40B
63708	40B
63709	9G
63711	16D
63712	52H
63713	9G
63715	41J
63716	9G
63717	41J
63718	41F
63719	9G
63720	41H
63721	9G
63722	41J
63724	56B
63725	31B
63726	41F
63727	41F
63728	36C
63730	36C
63731	41J
63732	41J
63734	41A
63735	41H
63736	36E
63737	41A
63738	40B
63739	41J
63740	16D
63741	36C
63742	41A
63743	9G
63744	36C
63746	31B
63747	36C
63748	36C
63750	40E
63752	16D
63754	40E
63755	52H
63757	41F
63758	40B
63759	40B
63760	52H
63762	41H
63763	41J
63764	36C
63765	41J
63766	9G
63767	9G
63768	40E
63770	40E
63771	41F
63772	41F
63773	41H
63774	41F
63775	9G
63776	41J
63777	16D
63779	41F
63780	31B
63781	36C
63782	36E
63783	41A
63784	41H
63785	36E
63786	31B
63787	41H
63788	36C
63789	16D
63791	41F
63792	16D
63793	36C
63794	9G
63795	41H
63796	16D
63798	41F
63799	36C
63800	41J
63801	41J
63802	41F
63803	31B
63805	9G
63806	16D
63807	36C
63808	16D
63813	41F
63816	40E
63817	16D
63818	36E
63819	40E
63821	41A
63822	41A
63823	56B
63824	36E
63827	41H
63828	41F
63829	41J
63832	41F
63833	41J
63836	36C
63837	40B
63838	16D
63840	41J
63841	41F
63842	41J
63843	41F
63845	41H
63846	41A
63848	9G
63850	41A
63852	41A
63853	41J
63854	16D
63856	52H
63857	56A
63858	36A
63859	40E
63860	40E
63861	41J
63862	9G
63863	40E
63864	56A
63865	16D
63867	16D
63868	31B
63869	16D
63870	41J
63872	31B
63873	40E
63874	52H
63877	41F
63878	40B
63879	31B
63880	36C
63881	41A
63882	41A
63883	41F
63884	41F
63885	56B
63886	16D
63887	31B
63890	31B
63891	41F
63893	41J
63894	41F
63895	9G
63897	41F
63898	41F
63899	41H
63900	40E
63901	16D
63902	41J
63904	41F
63906	36C
63907	41F
63908	41F
63911	41F
63912	41J
63913	41F
63914	36E
63915	9G
63917	36C
63920	56A
63922	36A
63923	34F
63924	36E
63925	36E
63926	36E
63927	36E
63928	36A
63929	34F
63930	34F
63931	34F
63932	34F
63933	34F
63934	36A
63935	36A
63936	34F
63937	36E
63938	34F
63939	36E
63940	34F
63941	36A
63942	36E
63943	36A
63944	36E
63945	36E
63946	34F
63947	36E
63948	34F
63949	36E
63950	34F
63951	36A
63952	36A
63953	36A
63954	36E
63955	36A
63956	36A
63957	34F
63958	36A
63959	36E
63960	34F
63961	36E
63962	36A
63963	34F
63964	36E
63965	36E
63966	34F
63967	36A
63968	36A
63969	36E
63971	36E
63972	36E
63973	36A
63974	36A
63975	36A
63976	36E
63977	36A
63978	36A
63979	36E

63980	36E
63981	36A
63982	36E
63983	36A
63984	36A
63985	36A
63986	36E
63987	36E
64170	56F
64171	40F
64173	56C
64174	36E
64175	34D
64177	34E
64182	56B
64185	36A
64191	40F
64196	34E
64203	56F
64206	34D
64208	56B
64209	36A
64219	40E
64222	56B
64223	34E
64226	56F
64231	40F
64232	36A
64236	36E
64240	34E
64245	36E
64251	34E
64253	34E
64256	9G
64257	40E
64260	34A
64265	34E
64268	56C
64277	56C
64278	40A
64284	40B
64288	9G
64292	41A
64305	40B
64308	36C
64310	9G
64311	9G
64313	41H
64314	41J
64316	41J
64317	41J
64318	40A
64324	41J
64325	40B
64329	41A
64332	41J
64333	41J
64337	9G
64341	9G
64346	40A
64352	41J
64354	36E
64355	40B
64359	9G
64362	40A
64363	9G
64364	41J
64368	9G
64371	36C
64373	41A
64375	16D
64377	41F
64379	41J
64384	41H
64385	36C
64386	40B
64387	41A
64393	41F
64394	41A
64395	36C
64402	41F
64403	41F
64404	36C
64406	41F
64417	41F
64418	9G
64419	41A
64420	16D
64423	36C
64425	41F
64427	41J
64434	9G
64435	9G
64437	9G
64439	9G
64440	9G
64441	36E
64442	41F
64443	41A
64444	41H
64445	41A
64446	40B
64447	41A
64450	36E
64452	41F
64461	65C
64462	64A
64463	64A
64468	64F
64470	65E
64471	66A
64472	65E
64474	62A
64476	62C
64477	66A
64478	12C
64479	64A
64480	62C
64482	64A
64483	64A
64487	62C
64488	62A
64489	64A
64491	64F
64493	62C
64494	64G
64497	64C
64499	12C
64500	64C
64502	65K
64504	64F
64505	62C
64507	65E
64510	64F
64512	64F
64514	65C
64515	64A
64518	64A
64519	64A
64523	65C
64524	64A
64525	62C
64527	64C
64529	64F
64531	65E
64532	64A
64533	64A
64534	65E
64535	64A
64537	65K
64539	64A
64540	65A
64541	65A
64542	65E
64543	62C
64544	65E
64545	62C
64546	62A
64547	64A
64548	65A
64549	62A
64550	62A
64551	65K
64552	64A
64553	64F
64554	64C
64555	64A
64556	62B
64557	64A
64558	65A
64559	65C
64560	62C
64561	64C
64562	64A
64563	65C
64564	62A
64565	62A
64566	64A
64568	62C
64569	64C
64570	65K
64571	65K
64572	64A
64573	65C
64574	65E
64575	62B
64576	64A
64577	64A
64578	65A
64579	65E
64580	65A
64581	65A
64582	64A
64583	64F
64585	62C
64586	64A
64587	62B
64588	65C
64589	65F
64590	64A
64591	64A
64592	65F
64593	65F
64594	64A
64595	64A
64596	62A
64597	62C
64598	62B
64599	64A
64600	62B
64601	64A
64602	62B
64603	64A
64604	62C
64605	64A
64606	64A
64607	64A
64608	64A
64609	65C
64610	65H
64611	65A
64612	64A
64613	64A
64614	64A
64615	62B
64616	62A
64617	62C
64618	62A
64619	62B

64620	62B
64621	65C
64622	65A
64623	65A
64624	64A
64625	64A
64626	65C
64627	62B
64628	65E
64629	62A
64630	62C
64631	62B
64632	65A
64633	65A
64634	64F
64635	62A
64636	65K
64637	64A
64638	65A
64639	65A
64643	32A
64646	31A
64650	30A
64652	30F
64653	30A
64655	31A
64657	30A
64660	30A
64663	30A
64664	30A
64666	30A
64667	30A
64669	31B
64671	31B
64673	31A
64674	32A
64676	30A
64677	30A
64678	30F
64679	30F
64680	30A
64681	30A
64682	30A
64684	31A
64685	30A
64686	30A
64687	31B
64689	30A
64690	31B
64691	31B
64692	31B
64693	30A
64696	31A
64697	31B
64698	31A
64699	31B
64700	52G
64701	52G
64703	52G
64704	52G
64705	56B
64706	51L
64707	52A
64708	30A
64709	50B
64710	52G
64711	52D
64713	52A
64716	36A
64717	9G
64718	9G
64719	41A
64720	56B
64723	36A
64725	51L
64726	40A
64727	9G
64729	40E
64730	51L
64732	56B
64733	12C
64736	40E
64738	9G
64739	16D
64740	9G
64741	40A
64742	9G
64743	9G
64744	9G
64745	9G
64746	40E
64747	9G
64748	9G
64749	56B
64754	56B
64756	51F
64757	56B
64758	51L
64760	56B
64764	31B
64765	30A
64767	30A
64770	31B
64772	31B
64775	30A
64778	51F
64779	31B
64783	30A
64784	30A
64786	62B
64789	31B
64790	62A
64791	56F
64792	62A
64794	64C
64795	64A
64796	56B
64798	16D
64801	56F
64802	40E
64804	40E
64806	52B
64808	41A
64809	9G
64810	36A
64811	56B
64812	52A
64813	52D
64814	52A
64815	52C
64816	52C
64817	56F
64818	51L
64819	50B
64820	56B
64821	51L
64822	62B
64823	40E
64825	52G
64831	50B
64833	52G
64835	51L
64836	56B
64837	52B
64839	56B
64840	56B
64842	52C
64843	52D
64844	52D
64845	51L
64846	52A
64847	52G
64848	51F
64849	52C
64850	51L
64851	52A
64852	52A
64853	52G
64854	52A
64855	51L
64856	52B
64857	51L
64858	52C
64859	51L
64860	52A
64861	51L
64862	51F
64863	55H
64864	52B
64865	52A
64866	52B
64867	50F
64868	52D
64869	52A
64870	51L
64871	52B
64872	56F
64874	36A
64875	9G
64877	12C
64878	41A
64879	56B
64880	12C
64882	36E
64884	12C
64885	36A
64886	56F
64888	12C
64889	40E
64892	12C
64893	36E
64895	12C
64896	40A
64897	52D
64899	12C
64901	31B
64903	56F
64904	50B
64906	36E
64907	56F
64908	36E
64909	36A
64910	50B
64911	56C
64914	50B
64915	52B
64916	52D
64917	52D
64918	56B
64919	56F
64920	55H
64921	52A
64922	55H
64923	52B
64924	52D
64925	52D
64926	52B
64927	51F
64928	50F
64929	52D
64930	9G
64931	52B
64932	12C
64933	55H
64934	55H
64935	55H
64936	52A
64938	52A
64939	52B
64940	50B
64941	52D
64942	52G

64943	50B
64944	55H
64945	52B
64946	64C
64947	50B
64949	52D
64950	62B
64955	16D
64961	40A
64963	64C
64964	12C
64966	40A
64969	56B
64970	36E
64971	50B
64974	40E
64975	64A
64978	51F
64979	56B
64982	51F
64986	64C
64987	36A
65033	52F
65070	52F
65099	52H
65110	52B
65157	8F
65192	8F
65198	8F
65210	65E
65211	65C
65214	65E
65216 *	65E
65217 *	65F
65218	62A
65222 *	65K
65224 *	64A
65227	61A
65228	65A
65229	64F
65230	65C
65232	65E
65233 *	64F
65234	64G
65235 *	64B
65237	12C
65239	62C
65241	65E
65243 *	64B
65246	65C
65249	65E
65251	61A
65252	62A
65253 *	62C
65257	65K
65258	64A
65260	65E
65261	64F
65265	64F
65266	65E
65267	61C
65268 *	64F
65273	65C
65275	64G
65276	64F
65277	61C
65280	65K
65281	62C
65282	64F
65285	65E
65287	65E
65288	64A
65290	64F
65293	12C
65295	65C
65296	65A
65297	61A
65300	63B
65303	61A
65304	61C
65305	61C
65306	65K
65307	62C
65309	62B
65310	61C
65311	65K
65312	12C
65313	63B
65315	65A
65316	65K
65317	64G
65318	64F
65319	62B
65320	62C
65321	12C
65323	62C
65325	65E
65327	64A
65329	64A
65330	62B
65331	64G
65334	64A
65335	65H
65338	61C
65341	64F
65344	64F
65345	62A
65346	64F
65361	30A
65389	30F
65420	31B
65440	30A
65445	30F
65446	30A
65450	31A
65453	30F
65457	31A
65458	31B
65460	32C
65462	32C
65464	30A
65465	30A
65469	32A
65471	32A
65476	30A
65478	31A
65479	34D
65503	30A
65506	30A
65507	30A
65511	30A
65513	31C
65520	31A
65521	31B
65528	31A
65532	31A
65539	30A
65541	31A
65549	31C
65554	31B
65556	31A
65560	31C
65564	30A
65566	32A
65567	32C
65576	31B
65577	31C
65578	31A
65581	32A
65582	31C
65583	31B
65586	32A
65588	32C
65589	31A
65645	52H
65662	52G
65663	52C
65666	52G
65670	52H
65691	50B
65693	50B
65695	52H
65712	52A
65713	52H
65714	50A
65720	51L
65726	52G
65727	52F
65728	52A
65731	51F
65735	51F
65736	51L
65741	51L
65743	51L
65745	51L
65747	51L
65751	51L
65753	51L
65755	51L
65756	51L
65757	51L
65760	51L
65761	51L
65762	51L
65763	51L
65768	51L
65769	51L
65772	51L
65773	51L
65774	51L
65776	51L
65777	51L
65778	51L
65779	51L
65782	51C
65786	52F
65787	51L
65788	51L
65789	52F
65790	51L
65791	52E
65792	52F
65794	52F
65795	52E
65796	52E
65797	52F
65799	52F
65800	52F
65801	52F
65802	52E
65804	52F
65805	51C
65807	52E
65808	52F
65809	52E
65810	52F
65811	52F
65812	52E
65813	52E
65814	52E
65815	52F
65817	52G
65818	51C
65819	52F
65820	51C
65821	52E
65822	52F
65823	52G
65825	52E

65828	52F
65830	51C
65831	52E
65832	52G
65833	52G
65834	52F
65835	52G
65837	52E
65838	52F
65839	52E
65841	52G
65842	52E
65844	50F
65845	50A
65846	51C
65849	50F
65850	52G
65851	52F
65852	52E
65853	51L
65854	52G
65855	51L
65857	52F
65858	52E
65859	51L
65860	51A
65861	52F
65862	52F
65863	52F
65864	52B
65865	51L
65867	52F
65868	51L
65869	52B
65870	51L
65871	52G
65872	52G
65873	52G
65874	50A
65875	52F
65876	52B
65877	52F
65878	52G
65879	52F
65880	52F
65881	52F
65882	52F
65883	50A
65884	51L
65885	50F
65887	50A
65888	50F
65889	52F
65890	50A
65891	52F
65892	52G
65893	52F
65894	50A
65900	62A
65901	62A
65902	62A
65903	62A
65904	62A
65905	62A
65906	64A
65907	62A
65908	62A
65909	65K
65910	62A
65911	62A
65912	64A
65913	62A
65914	64A
65915	64A
65916	64A
65917	65K
65918	64A
65919	64A
65920	64A
65921	62A
65922	64A
65923	62C
65924	62C
65925	62A
65926	62C
65927	64A
65928	62C
65929	64A
65930	62C
65931	62A
65932	62A
65933	62C
65934	64A
67474	65A
67484	62B
67485	65A
67486	62B
67489	64G
67490	62B
67494	65K
67501	62B
67502	62B
67600	65A
67601	65I
67602	65A
67603	65A
67604	65H
67605	65E
67606	64A
67607	65C
67608	65C
67609	65E
67610	64B
67611	65C
67612	65C
67613	65H
67614	65H
67615	64B
67616	65H
67617	64A
67618	65E
67619	65H
67620	64B
67621	65C
67622	65H
67623	65C
67624	64A
67625	65H
67626	65C
67627	65E
67628	65H
67629	65C
67630	65C
67631	65H
67632	65H
67633	65C
67634	52C
67635	50B
67636	52C
67637	52A
67638	50B
67639	52A
67640	50B
67641	52B
67642	52B
67643	65C
67644	65A
67645	52G
67646	52B
67647	52B
67648	65C
67649	64A
67650	65C
67651	52B
67652	52B
67653	52C
67654	52B
67655	65C
67656	52B
67657	52A
67658	52B
67659	64A
67660	65E
67661	65C
67662	65C
67663	50B
67664	65A
67665	65E
67666	64A
67667	65A
67668	64C
67669	62C
67670	64A
67671	65A
67672	62C
67673	52G
67674	65E
67675	65C
67676	65C
67677	50B
67678	65C
67679	65C
67680	65A
67681	65C
67682	50B
67683	52B
67684	50B
67685	52B
67686	50B
67687	52A
67688	52A
67689	52A
67690	52A
67691	52B
67701	30A
67702	30A
67703	30A
67704	30A
67705	30A
67706	30A
67707	40E
67708	30A
67709	30A
67710	40E
67711	30A
67712	31A
67713	31A
67714	30A
67715	30A
67716	30A
67717	32A
67718	31A
67719	34A
67720	31A
67721	31A
67722	31A
67723	31A
67724	30A
67725	30A
67726	30A
67727	40E
67728	30A
67729	30A
67730	30A
67731	30A
67732	30A
67733	34A
67734	31A

67735	30A
67736	30A
67737	30A
67738	32C
67739	30A
67740	2F
67741	40E
67742	51A
67743	2F
67744	34D
67745	34D
67746	34D
67747	9G
67748	9G
67749	34A
67750	51A
67751	9G
67752	34A
67753	40E
67754	51L
67755	51A
67756	9G
67757	34A
67758	40E
67759	51L
67760	40E
67761	34F
67762	9G
67763	51A
67764	51L
67765	51A
67766	51L
67767	34A
67768	34A
67769	40E
67770	34A
67771	2F
67772	34A
67773	34A
67770	34A
67775	40E
67776	34A
67777	51A
67778	30A
67779	34A
67780	34A
67781	15E
67782	15E
67783	34A
67784	34A
67785	34F
67786	34A
67787	34A
67788	40E
67789	2F
67790	40E
67791	34F
67792	34A
67793	34A
67794	34A
67795	9G
67796	9G
67797	34A
67798	9G
67799	40E
67800	34A
68006	17C
68007	51A
68008	51A
68009	40E
68010	52C
68011	50B
68012	17C
68013	17C
68014	52C
68015	51A
68016	52G
68017	51A
68018	40B
68019	52H
68020	36A
68021	51C
68022	36A
68023	51L
68024	51A
68025	51A
68026	41J
68027	51A
68028	40E
68029	52H
68030	17C
68031	52H
68032	51A
68033	40E
68034	17C
68035	52C
68036	52C
68037	51A
68038	52H
68039	51A
68040	51A
68041	52G
68042	50B
68043	51A
68044	52G
68045	51A
68046	50A
68047	51A
68048	52G
68049	51L
68050	51A
68051	51C
68052	51A
68053	51C
68054	51C
68055	51C
68056	51C
68057	51C
68058	52G
68059	52H
68060	51A
68061	50A
68062	51L
68063	6F
68064	9G
68065	6F
68066	6F
68067	34B
68068	9G
68069	36A
68070	40B
68071	36A
68072	40E
68073	34B
68074	40B
68075	34B
68076	40E
68077	34B
68078	40B
68079	9G
68080	41J
68095	64A
68100	65E
68101	62C
68104	65K
68110	65E
68114	65E
68117	65E
68119	64A
68123	65E
68190	61A
68192	61A
68233	51C
68235	51F
68254	51F
68269	51F
68272	51L
68275	55E
68278	52J
68316	52C
68320	64A
68325	65A
68332	62A
68335	64B
68336	65E
68338	64A
68342	64A
68343	65E
68344	65D
68345	65A
68346	62C
68349	65F
68350	65K
68352	65A
68353	62A
68354	65E
68361	50B
68392	50A
68408	52F
68410	51C
68442	65E
68443	65E
68445	65E
68447	65A
68448	64A
68453	64A
68454	64A
68456	65K
68458	67A
68459	62A
68470	64A
68471	65K
68472	64A
68477	64A
68479	65A
68481	64B
68497	41B
68499	31C
68500	30A
68501	40A
68502	36E
68507	36A
68508	36A
68513	30A
68522	40F
68526	30A
68530	36E
68538	30A
68542	31C
68545	40E
68549	30A
68550	40F
68552	30A
68554	40A
68556	41J
68558	36A
68560	40A
68563	30A
68565	30A
68566	31C
68569	41J
68570	40E
68571	30A
68573	30F
68575	30A
68577	30F

68578	30A
68600	30A
68609	31A
68612	30A
68613	30A
68619	30A
68621	41J
68623	41J
68626	40E
68633	30A
68635	40E
68642	32C
68644	30A
68646	30A
68647	30A
68649	30A
68650	30A
68660	30A
68663	30A
68672	50B
68673	NE
68674	52A
68675	52A
68676	NE
68677	50A
68678	52G
68679	51A
68680	52A
68681	55E
68683	51C
68684	51L
68685	51F
68686	50A
68687	50A
68688	51L
68689	51L
68690	51L
68691	51F
68692	51F
68693	52A
68695	52A
68696	51L
68698	51C
68701	55E
68702	52B
68703	51C
68704	52G
68705	50B
68706	52H
68707	51C
68708	52B
68709	65E
68711	51C
68713	52B
68715	51C
68716	50B
68717	61A
68719	61A
68720	52D
68721	51L
68723	52A
68724	51F
68726	55E
68728	52A
68729	51L
68730	52H
68732	52B
68733	65E
68734	51C
68736	50A
68737	52A
68738	52B
68740	51L
68742	52B
68743	52H
68744	51A
68745	NE
68747	52B
68749	61A
68750	61A
68753	50B
68754	51A
68869	56B
68875	56B
68890	56B
68891	34B
68892	56B
68894	34B
68896	34B
68897	56A
68899	30A
68900	56B
68901	56B
68902	56B
68903	34B
68904	56A
68905	30A
68907	34B
68908	56F
68910	56A
68911	56C
68913	56C
68914	56B
68915	56B
68916	56B
68917	34B
68918	34B
68920	34B
68921	34B
68922	56F
68923	56F
68924	30A
68925	56C
68926	34B
68927	40E
68928	34B
68929	34B
68930	34B
68931	34B
68932	56F
68933	56A
68934	56B
68935	56B
68936	34B
68937	56B
68939	56A
68941	56B
68943	56F
68944	56F
68945	34B
68946	34B
68947	56B
68948	56F
68950	34B
68951	51C
68952	65A
68954	65A
68956	65A
68957	65A
68959	56F
68960	34B
68961	34B
68962	36A
68963	36A
68964	36A
68965	36A
68966	34B
68968	34B
68970	34B
68971	34B
68972	34B
68975	40E
68976	34B
68977	36A
68979	34B
68981	34B
68982	34B
68983	34B
68984	56C
68986	34B
68987	34B
68988	56C
68989	34B
68990	34B
68991	34B
69001	52A
69002	52G
69003	50A
69004	51A
69005	52A
69006	51L
69007	51F
69008	50A
69009	NE
69010	NE
69011	NE
69012	62A
69013	64A
69014	64A
69015	65C
69016	50A
69017	51A
69018	51F
69019	51L
69020	50B
69021	51A
69022	51A
69023	52C
69024	52C
69025	52C
69026	52C
69027	52A
69028	52B
69097	52A
69101	52A
69105	52A
69109	52A
69126	65D
69128	61B
69131	65A
69132	66B
69133	64A
69134	64A
69135	64A
69136	62A
69137	65K
69138	61B
69141	64A
69143	66B
69150	64A
69155	12C
69156	64F
69159	64F
69161	65C
69163	65A
69165	65C
69171	65A
69173	64A
69177	65D
69178	65A
69179	65A
69180	61A
69181	65A
69183	65A
69184	65D
69188	65A
69190	65C
69191	65A

69194		65C
69196		66C
69198		65C
69199		65C
69202		62C
69204		62A
69206		65E
69209		65C
69211		64B
69212		65A
69216		64F
69218		65A
69219		64A
69221		62C
69223		66B
69224		61B
69258		41A
69263		41J
69266		34E
69274		34E
69286		41J
69293		34E
69296		41A
69307		9G
69309		41H
69370		41F
69498		34A
69504		34B
69505		34F
69506		34E
69507		65C
69509		65C
69511		65D
69512		34A
69513		34E
69516		34F
69518		65E
69520		34B
69521		34E
69523		34A
69529		34A
69530		34A
69531		34C
69533		34A
69535		34A
69538		34A
69540		34E
69543		34A
69546		34A
69549		34A
69560		34F
69561		34F
69563		65C
69564		12C
69568		34A
69571		34E
69572		34A
69574		34A
69575		34A
69579		34A
69580		34C
69581		34A
69582		34E
69583		34A
69585		34A
69586		34A
69587		34B
69592		34A
69593		34A
69596		65E
69611		30A
69614		30A
69615		30A
69617		30A
69618		34C
69620		30A
69621		30A
69629		34C
69630		30A
69631		34C
69632		34C
69636		30A
69640		34C
69642		30A
69645		30A
69646		30A
69647		30A
69648		34C
69651		30F
69652		30A
69653		30A
69654		30A
69656		30A
69658		30A
69663		30A
69664		30A
69668		30A
69670		30A
69671		30A
69673		30A
69674		30A
69675		30A
69677		30A
69678		34C
69679		30A
69680		30A
69681		30A
69682		30A
69684		30A
69685		30A
69686		30A
69687		30A
69688		30A
69690		30F
69691		30F
69692		34C
69693		30A
69694		31C
69696		34C
69697		30A
69698		34C
69699		30A
69700		30A
69701		30A
69702		30A
69704		30A
69706		30A
69707		30A
69708		30F
69709		30A
69710		30A
69712		30A
69713		30A
69714		30A
69715		30A
69718		30A
69719		30A
69720		30A
69721		30A
69722		30A
69723		30A
69724		30A
69725		30A
69726		30A
69727		30A
69728		30A
69729		30A
69730		30A
69732		30A
69733		30A
69808		40A
69814		34A
69820		40A
69829		40B
69850		52G
69860		51L
69861		50F
69869		51L
69870		52G
69878		52G
69880		51C
69885		50E
69886		50F
69894		51C
69921		52H
70000	*	32A
70001	*	32A
70002	*	32A
70003	*	32A
70004	*	9E
70005	*	32A
70006	*	32A
70007	*	32A
70008	*	32A
70009	*	32A
70010	*	32A
70011	*	32A
70012	*	32A
70013	*	32A
70014	*	9E
70015	*	9E
70016	*	86C
70017	*	9E
70018	*	86C
70019	*	86C
70020	*	86C
70021	*	9E
70022	*	86C
70023	*	86C
70024	*	86C
70025	*	86C
70026	*	86C
70027	*	86C
70028	*	86C
70029	*	86C
70030	*	32A
70031	*	9A
70032	*	9E
70033	*	9E
70034	*	32A
70035	*	32A
70036	*	32A
70037	*	32A
70038	*	32A
70039	*	32A
70040	*	32A
70041	*	32A
70042	*	9E
70043	*	9A
70044	*	55A
70045	*	26A
70046	*	9A
70047		5A
70048	*	26A
70049	*	26A
70050	*	66A
70051	*	66A
70052	*	66A
70053	*	55A
70054	*	55A

71000	* 5A
72000	* 66A
72001	* 66A
72002	* 66A
72003	* 66A
72004	* 66A
72005	* 12A
72006	* 12A
72007	* 12A
72008	* 12A
72009	* 12A
73000	41B
73001	82C
73002	41C
73003	82E
73004	6A
73005	63A
73006	63A
73007	63A
73008	63A
73009	63A
73010	15E
73011	6J
73012	82C
73013	6A
73014	6A
73015	82E
73016	41C
73017	71G
73018	71G
73019	82F
73020	71G
73021	84G
73022	71G
73023	86C
73024	84G
73025	84G
73026	84G
73027	82C
73028	82F
73029	71G
73030	26F
73031	RTS
73032	6C
73033	6A
73034	84G
73035	84G
73036	84G
73037	84G
73038	6A
73039	6C
73040	6A
73041	71G
73042	71G
73043	41B
73044	26F
73045	15E
73046	41C
73047	82F
73048	6A
73049	84G
73050	82F
73051	82F
73052	82F
73053	15E
73054	82E
73055	66A
73056	66A
73057	66A
73058	66A
73059	66A
73060	66A
73061	66A
73062	66A
73063	66A
73064	66A
73065	41C
73066	15E
73067	6J
73068	82E
73069	15E
73070	6A
73071	6A
73072	66A
73073	6J
73074	41B
73075	66A
73076	66A
73077	65A
73078	65A
73079	67A
73080	* 71G
73081	* 70A
73082	* 70A
73083	* 70A
73084	* 70A
73085	* 70A
73086	* 70A
73087	* 70A
73088	* 70A
73089	* 70A
73090	84G
73091	84G
73092	84G
73093	84G
73094	84G
73095	84G
73096	84G
73097	84G
73098	66A
73099	66A
73100	67A
73101	67A
73102	67A
73103	67A
73104	67A
73105	65A
73106	63A
73107	63A
73108	65A
73109	65A
73110	* 70A
73111	* 70A
73112	* 70A
73113	* 70A
73114	* 70A
73115	* 70A
73116	* 70A
73117	* 70A
73118	* 70A
73119	* 70A
73120	63A
73121	67A
73122	67A
73123	67A
73124	67A
73125	26F
73126	26F
73127	26F
73128	26F
73129	26F
73130	26F
73131	26F
73132	26F
73133	26F
73134	26F
73135	17C
73136	17C
73137	17C
73138	17C
73139	17C
73140	17C
73141	17C
73142	17C
73143	17C
73144	17C
73145	65B
73146	65B
73147	65B
73148	65B
73149	65B
73150	65B
73151	65B
73152	65B
73153	65B
73154	65B
73155	41C
73156	41B
73157	17A
73158	17A
73159	17A
73160	55E
73161	55E
73162	55G
73163	55G
73164	55G
73165	55G
73166	55A
73167	55E
73168	55A
73169	55A
73170	55A
73171	55A
75000	82C
75001	81F
75002	85E
75003	85A
75004	82E
75005	84E
75006	84E
75007	81F
75008	81F
75009	85E
75010	6G
75011	6G
75012	6G
75013	6B
75014	6B
75015	27C
75016	27C
75017	27C
75018	27C
75019	27C
75020	89C
75021	82E
75022	82E
75023	85E
75024	84E
75025	85A
75026	89C
75027	82G
75028	11B
75029	82C
75030	1A

75031	6B
75032	6A
75033	11B
75034	6A
75035	6A
75036	1E
75037	1E
75038	1E
75039	6A
75040	15C
75041	15C
75042	15C
75043	15C
75044	15C
75045	27A
75046	27A
75047	27A
75048	27A
75049	27A
75050	6A
75051	6A
75052	1A
75053	6A
75054	6A
75055	15C
75056	16A
75057	15C
75058	15C
75059	15C
75060	15C
75061	15C
75062	16A
75063	16A
75064	16A
75065	71B
75066	71B
75067	71B
75068	71B
75069	73A
75070	75E
75071	82F
75072	82F
75073	82F
75074	73A
75075	75E
75076	70D
75077	70D
75078	70D
75079	70D
76000	66B
76001	66B
76002	66B
76003	66B
76004	66B
76005	72B
76006	71A
76007	72B
76008	72B
76009	71A
76010	71A
76011	71A
76012	71A
76013	71A
76014	71A
76015	71A
76016	71A
76017	72B
76018	72B
76019	71A
76020	8G
76021	51F
76022	12D
76023	12D
76024	52B
76025	71A
76026	71A
76027	71A
76028	71A
76029	71A
76030	30A
76031	30A
76032	30A
76033	30A
76034	30A
76035	14D
76036	14D
76037	14D
76038	14D
76039	14D
76040	14D
76041	14D
76042	14D
76043	14D
76044	14D
76045	51F
76046	51F
76047	12D
76048	9F
76049	51F
76050	51F
76051	12D
76052	12D
76053	72B
76054	72B
76055	72B
76056	71B
76057	71B
76058	71B
76059	71A
76060	71A
76061	71A
76062	71A
76063	71A
76064	71A
76065	71A
76066	72B
76067	72B
76068	71A
76069	71A
76070	66B
76071	66B
76072	68B
76073	68B
76074	65A
76075	8G
76076	8G
76077	8G
76078	8G
76079	8G
76080	24D
76081	24D
76082	24D
76083	24D
76084	24D
76085	9F
76086	9E
76087	9F
76088	9E
76089	9E
76090	67A
76091	67A
76092	67A
76093	67A
76094	67A
76095	67A
76096	67A
76097	67A
76098	67A
76099	67A
76100	65D
76101	65D
76102	65B
76103	65B
76104	61A
76105	61A
76106	61A
76107	61A
76108	61A
76109	62C
76110	62A
76111	62A
76112	68C
76113	65B
76114	65B
77000	50B
77001	50B
77002	51F
77003	51F
77004	50E
77005	66A
77006	66C
77007	66A
77008	66A
77009	66A
77010	50B
77011	52A
77012	50A
77013	50A
77014	52A
77015	67B
77016	67B
77017	67B
77018	67B
77019	67B
78000	89C
78001	85A
78002	89C
78003	89C
78004	85C
78005	89C
78006	89C
78007	89C
78008	85A
78009	85A
78010	51J
78011	51J
78012	51J
78013	12D
78014	51J
78015	51J
78016	51F
78017	12D
78018	12D
78019	12D
78020	16A
78021	16A
78022	41C
78023	41C
78024	41C
78025	41C
78026	41D
78027	41D
78028	16A
78029	16A
78030	5A
78031	6K

78032	12D
78033	6A
78034	8D
78035	8D
78036	24K
78037	24K
78038	8E
78039	8D
78040	27D
78041	27A
78042	27A
78043	27A
78044	27A
78045	61A
78046	64G
78047	64G
78048	64A
78049	64G
78050	66B
78051	66B
78052	60B
78053	61C
78054	61C
78055	6K
78056	6K
78057	8E
78058	6H
78059	6H
78060	27D
78061	27D
78062	27D
78063	27D
78064	27D
80000	67A
80001	66A
80002	66A
80003	66A
80004	61A
80005	67A
80006	66A
80007	66A
80008	67A
80009	67A
80010	75E
80011	75E
80012	75E
80013	75A
80014	75F
80015	75F
80016	75F
80017	75F
80018	75F
80019	75F
80020	61A
80021	61A
80022	66A
80023	66A
80024	67A
80025	67A
80026	66A
80027	66A
80028	61A
80029	61A
80030	67A
80031	75A
80032	75A
80033	75A
80034	73F
80035	73F
80036	73F
80037	73F
80038	73F
80039	73F
80040	73F
80041	73F
80042	73F
80043	73F
80044	67A
80045	6A
80046	67A
80047	67A
80048	6A
80049	6A
80050	6A
80051	6A
80052	67A
80053	6A
80054	66A
80055	66A
80056	66A
80057	66A
80058	66A
80059	73F
80060	63B
80061	26A
80062	63B
80063	63B
80064	73F
80065	73F
80066	73F
80067	73A
80068	73A
80069	33B
80070	33B
80071	33B
80072	33B
80073	33B
80074	33B
80075	33B
80076	33B
80077	33B
80078	33B
80079	33B
80080	33B
80081	73A
80082	73B
80083	73B
80084	73B
80085	73B
80086	6A
80087	73F
80088	75E
80089	75E
80090	62B
80091	6A
80092	63A
80093	63A
80094	75E
80095	75F
80096	33B
80097	33B
80098	33B
80099	33B
80100	33B
80101	33B
80102	33B
80103	33B
80104	33B
80105	33B
80106	66A
80107	66A
80108	66A
80109	66A
80110	66A
80111	61A
80112	61A
80113	61A
80114	61A
80115	61A
80116	55H
80117	55H
80118	55H
80119	55H
80120	55H
80121	61C
80122	61C
80123	62B
80124	62B
80125	65J
80126	63A
80127	67A
80128	67A
80129	66A
80130	66A
80131	33B
80132	33B
80133	33C
80134	33B
80135	33B
80136	33B
80137	75F
80138	75F
80139	75F
80140	75F
80141	75F
80142	75F
80143	75A
80144	75A
80145	75A
80146	75A
80147	75A
80148	75A
80149	75A
80150	75A
80151	75A
80152	75A
80153	75A
80154	75A
82000	89C
82001	6A
82002	6A
82003	6A
82004	82F
82005	6A
82006	82A
82007	82A
82008	85A
82009	82A
82010	72A
82011	72A
82012	71A
82013	72A
82014	71A
82015	71A
82016	71A
82017	72A
82018	72A
82019	72A
82020	89C
82021	89C
82022	72A
82023	72A
82024	72A
82025	72A
82026	50E
82027	50F
82028	50E
82029	50F
82030	82A
82031	89C
82032	6A
82033	82A
82034	6A
82035	82A

90187	6B
90188	86C
90189	36C
90190	41F
90192	86G
90193	65D
90194	26D
90195	41F
90196	33B
90197	26A
90198	66A
90199	66A
90200	56F
90201	86C
90202	41D
90203	41F
90204	27B
90205	26D
90206	26C
90207	87G
90208	31B
90209	41F
90210	56E
90211	41F
90212	24L
90213	50D
90214	8F
90215	34E
90216	27B
90217	50B
90218	2F
90219	26D
90220	41F
90221	40B
90222	26F
90223	34E
90224	40B
90225	86A
90226	26D
90227	6B
90228	50D
90229	66A
90230	56A
90231	24B
90232	36C
90233	56D
90234	66A
90235	40E
90236	56F
90237	2F
90238	18B
90239	34E
90240	51L
90241	24B
90242	8D
90243	55D
90244	33B
90245	27B
90246	34E
90247	55E
90248	26A
90249	55E
90250	41F
90251	18B
90252	41F
90253	34E
90254	55E
90255	36A
90256	33B
90257	8F
90258	24C
90259	40E
90260	50D
90261	84C
90262	50D
90263	40E
90264	24B
90265	50D
90266	24C
90267	26C
90268	84C
90269	34E
90270	41F
90271	26A
90272	50B
90273	51L
90274	24B
90275	41J
90276	41D
90277	24C
90278	27B
90279	31B
90280	40B
90281	56D
90282	27B
90283	27B
90284	18B
90285	40B
90286	41F
90287	40E
90288	40B
90289	26A
90290	41J
90291	26A
90292	26B
90293	31B
90294	40B
90295	24C
90296	40E
90297	27B
90298	33B
90299	2F
90300	56D
90301	41J
90302	41J
90303	40E
90304	41F
90305	31B
90306	26E
90307	26B
90308	55C
90309	55E
90310	56E
90311	41F
90312	81C
90313	84C
90314	24B
90315	85E
90316	27B
90317	8F
90318	55E
90319	67C
90320	66A
90321	56A
90322	56F
90323	86C
90324	26B
90325	55G
90326	56A
90327	27B
90328	26A
90329	56E
90330	41F
90331	24C
90332	55G
90333	56F
90334	55C
90335	24C
90336	55D
90337	55E
90338	26A
90339	56A
90340	31B
90341	56A
90342	56A
90343	27B
90344	51C
90345	55G
90346	2F
90347	55G
90348	56A
90349	34E
90350	62A
90351	56F
90352	50B
90353	56A
90354	26B
90355	81C
90356	81C
90357	55E
90358	41F
90359	26B
90360	56E
90361	56A
90362	55E
90363	56A
90364	26D
90365	2F
90366	26A
90367	24C
90368	41D
90369	6C
90370	56A
90371	24B
90372	26B
90373	51L
90374	24A
90375	27B
90376	26A
90377	51L
90378	50B
90379	56A
90380	56A
90381	27B
90382	56A
90383	40B
90384	41F
90385	56A
90386	66B
90387	66A
90388	26A
90389	26A
90390	26A
90391	41D
90392	6C
90393	40B
90394	40B
90395	55D
90396	56A
90397	56F
90398	24C
90399	26F
90400	41F
90401	41F
90402	26E
90403	2F
90404	56A
90405	56A
90406	51L
90407	55C
90408	26D
90409	51L
90410	41F
90411	41D
90412	56E
90413	24C
90414	41D
90415	56A
90416	27B
90417	56A
90418	41B
90419	26D

90420	24B
90421	41F
90422	36C
90423	8D
90424	50A
90425	36C
90426	51L
90427	50B
90428	34E
90429	56A
90430	51A
90431	41J
90432	40E
90433	2F
90434	51L
90435	51L
90436	65D
90437	40E
90438	40E
90439	34E
90440	65D
90441	62A
90442	33B
90443	40B
90444	62B
90445	56A
90446	51L
90447	31B
90448	2F
90449	41J
90450	50B
90451	51L
90452	51L
90453	36A
90454	34E
90455	61B
90456	36C
90457	56D
90458	50B
90459	51L
90460	40B
90461	51L
90462	51L
90463	67C
90464	12A
90465	51L
90466	81C
90467	50A
90468	66B
90469	36C
90470	56E
90471	41D
90472	62A
90473	40E
90474	2F
90475	50A
90476	40E
90477	31B
90478	50D
90479	51L
90480	34B
90481	51L
90482	50B
90483	84C
90484	31B
90485	85E
90486	2F
90487	55E
90488	55D
90489	65A
90490	36C
90491	41F
90492	40E
90493	65D
90494	33B
90495	41F
90496	40E
90497	56A
90498	30A
90499	41F
90500	51L
90501	31B
90502	34E
90503	51L
90504	2F
90505	67C
90506	41F
90507	2F
90508	41F
90509	8F
90510	40B
90511	55D
90512	36C
90513	62A
90514	33B
90515	62B
90516	2F
90517	51L
90518	50A
90519	41F
90520	2F
90521	41F
90522	31B
90523	26A
90524	2F
90525	26E
90526	41F
90527	27B
90528	31B
90529	87G
90530	26F
90531	50D
90532	6B
90533	26A
90534	62A
90535	27B
90536	66A
90537	36A
90538	36A
90539	65F
90540	36C
90541	24C
90542	62C
90543	56A
90544	86A
90545	40E
90546	26B
90547	62C
90548	26A
90549	66A
90550	36C
90551	30A
90552	27B
90553	62C
90554	40E
90555	26D
90556	24C
90557	24B
90558	26B
90559	31B
90560	62C
90561	26A
90562	55C
90563	2F
90564	26B
90565	85E
90566	6B
90567	41F
90568	26D
90569	36A
90570	26A
90571	50B
90572	86C
90573	86C
90574	2F
90575	62C
90576	27B
90577	40E
90578	50A
90579	86C
90580	41F
90581	56A
90582	41F
90583	40B
90584	24H
90585	84C
90586	50B
90587	41F
90588	55C
90589	26A
90590	41F
90591	55C
90592	24B
90593	51L
90594	40E
90595	24J
90596	66A
90597	36C
90598	36C
90599	27B
90600	62C
90601	36C
90602	36A
90603	51L
90604	56A
90605	55D
90606	6B
90607	56A
90608	41F
90609	50B
90610	55E
90611	55D
90612	41F
90613	34E
90614	62A
90615	56A
90616	66A
90617	55E
90618	34E
90619	55G
90620	56A
90621	55G
90622	56D
90623	50B
90624	55G
90625	56A
90626	26D
90627	50B
90628	66B
90629	40E
90630	81C
90631	56A
90632	26B
90633	56A
90634	40E
90635	56A
90636	36A
90637	55E
90638	2F
90639	56A
90640	66A
90641	26C
90642	56D
90643	27B
90644	56A
90645	55C
90646	36C
90647	36C
90648	40E
90649	55G
90650	55C
90651	56A

90652	55E
90653	33B
90654	56A
90655	56D
90656	56A
90657	41J
90658	24C
90659	34E
90660	34B
90661	55E
90662	34E
90663	50A
90664	55E
90665	34E
90666	55G
90667	8F
90668	41F
90669	26F
90670	50B
90671	26E
90672	2F
90673	55E
90674	40B
90675	24C
90676	86A
90677	50B
90678	56D
90679	56A
90680	55G
90681	24C
90682	55E
90683	31B
90684	55C
90685	85E
90686	8F
90687	27B
90688	50B
90689	24C
90690	66A
90691	86C
90692	56A
90693	86C
90694	55G
90695	50B
90696	36C
90697	2F
90698	56D
90699	55C
90700	41F
90701	2F
90702	8F
90703	34E
90704	50D
90705	66A
90706	24J
90707	56D
90708	26E
90709	31B
90710	56A
90711	56F
90712	27B
90713	26B
90714	36C
90715	26A
90716	18B
90717	34E
90718	26E
90719	41D
90720	24C
90721	56D
90722	55E
90723	56D
90724	27B
90725	26C
90726	55C
90727	62C
90728	55C
90729	26C
90730	34E
90731	56D
90732 *	36C
90750	66B
90751	66A
90752	66B
90753	66E
90754	66B
90755	65F
90756	66B
90757	65F
90758	66B
90759	65F
90760	66B
90761	66B
90762	66B
90763	6F
90764	66B
90765	65F
90766	65F
90767	66A
90768	66E
90769	65F
90770	66B
90771	66B
90772	66C
90773	65F
90774	65F
92000	86A
92001	86A
92002	86A
92003	86C
92004	81C
92005	86C
92006	86A
92007	86A
92008	17C
92009	17C
92010	16D
92011	16D
92012	16D
92013	16D
92014	21A
92015	26A
92016	26A
92017	26A
92018	15A
92019	15A
92020	15A
92021	15A
92022	15A
92023	15A
92024	15A
92025	15A
92026	15A
92027	15A
92028	15A
92029	15A
92030	16D
92031	16D
92032	16D
92033	16D
92034	34E
92035	34E
92036	34E
92037	34E
92038	34E
92039	40B
92040	34E
92041	34E
92042	34E
92043	16D
92044	34E
92045	6F
92046	6F
92047	6F
92048	17C
92049	17C
92050	17C
92051	17C
92052	15A
92053	15A
92054	15A
92055	15A
92056	15A
92057	18B
92058	15A
92059	15A
92060	52H
92061	52H
92062	52H
92063	52H
92064	52H
92065	52H
92066	52H
92067	16D
92068	16D
92069	16D
92070	21A
92071	16D
92072	16D
92073	16D
92074	16D
92075	16D
92076	16D
92077	18A
92078	18A
92079	85F
92080	15A
92081	15A
92082	15A
92083	15A
92084	15A
92085	15A
92086	18A
92087	16D
92088	16D
92089	16D
92090	16D
92091	16D
92092	16D
92093	16D
92094	16D
92095	16D
92096	16D
92097	52H
92098	52H
92099	52H
92100	18B
92101	15C
92102	15C
92103	15C
92104	15C
92105	15B
92106	15B
92107	15A
92108	15C
92109	15C
92110	15C
92111	15C
92112	15C
92113	18B
92114	18B
92115	18B
92116	18B
92117	18B
92118	15A
92119	15C
92120	15C
92121	15C
92122	15C

92123	15C	92155	21A	92187	34E	92219	86C
92124	15A	92156	18A	92188	34E	92220 *	86C
92125	15A	92157	21A	92189	36A	92221	84C
92126	15A	92158	18A	92190	36A	92222	84C
92127	15A	92159	15A	92191	36A	92223	84C
92128	15C	92160	15B	92192	36A	92224	83D
92129	18A	92161	26A	92193	40B	92225	86A
92130	18A	92162	26A	92194	40B	92226	84C
92131	18B	92163	15B	92195	40B	92227	84C
92132	15A	92164	15B	92196	40B	92228	84C
92133	15A	92165	21A	92197	36A	92229	86A
92134	15A	92166	21A	92198	36A	92230	86A
92135	21A	92167	21A	92199	36A	92231	86C
92136	21A	92168	36A	92200	36A	92232	84C
92137	21A	92169	36A	92201	36A	92233	84C
92138	21A	92170	36A	92202	40B	92234	84C
92139	21A	92171	36A	92203	82B	92235	86A
92140	34E	92172	36A	92204	82B	92236	86C
92141	34E	92173	36A	92205	82B	92237	86C
92142	34E	92174	36A	92206	82B	92238	81A
92143	34E	92175	36A	92207	81C	92239	81A
92144	34E	92176	36A	92208	81C	92240	81A
92145	34E	92177	36A	92209	86C	92241	81A
92146	34E	92178	34E	92210	86C	92242	86A
92147	34E	92179	34E	92211	81A	92243	86A
92148	34E	92180	34E	92212	84C	92244	81A
92149	34E	92181	34E	92213	84C	92245	81A
92150	21A	92182	34E	92214	84C	92246	81A
92151	21A	92183	34E	92215	84C	92247	81A
92152	21A	92184	34E	92216	86C	92248	21A
92153	18A	92185	36C	92217	82B	92249	86A
92154	15A	92186	40E	92218	82B	92250	86A

ALLOCATION OF SERVICE LOCOMOTIVES

Service No.	*Region*	*B.R. No.*	*Type*	*Allocation*
2† ...	E.	68816	J52	Doncaster Works.
7† ...	E.	68166	Y3	Boston Sleeper Depot.
9† ...	E.	68840	J52	Doncaster Works.
21† ...	E.	68162	Y3	Cambridge Engineer's Dept.
32† ...	E.	68370	J66	Stratford Works.
33† ...	E.	68129	Y4	Stratford Works.
39† ...	E.	68131	Y1	Norwich Engineer's Dept.
40† ...	E.	68173	Y3	Lowestoft Engineer's Dept.
41† ...	E.	68177	Y3	Lowestoft Engineer's Dept.

ALLOCATION OF SERVICE LOCOMOTIVES—(*Continued*)

Service No.	*Region*	*B.R. No.*	*Type*	*Allocation*
42† ...	E.	68178	Y3	Cambridge Engineer's Dept.
44† ...	E.	68498	J69	Stratford Works.
45† ...	E.	68543	J69	Stratford Works.
52† ...	N.E.	11104	0-4-0 Diesel	West Hartlepool P.W. Depot.
54† ...	N.E.	68153	Y1	Darlington P. W. Depot.
57† ...	N.E.	68160	Y3	Faverdale Works, Darlington.
81† ...	E.		0-4-0 Diesel	Cambridge Engineer's Dept.
91† ...	E.		0-6-0 Diesel	Cambridge Engineer's Dept.
92† ...	E.		0-6-0 Diesel	Cambridge Engineer's Dept.
100† ...	E.	26510	Bo-Bo Electric	Ilford Depot.
11304 ...	M.		L.Y.R. 0-6-0 ST	Horwich Works.
11305 ...	M.		L.Y.R. 0-6-0 ST	Horwich Works.
11324 ...	M.		L.Y.R. 0-6-0 ST	Horwich Works.
11368 ...	M.		L.Y.R. 0-6-0 ST	Horwich Works.
11394 ...	M.		L.Y.R. 0-6-0 ST	Horwich Works.
E.D.1 ...	M.		0-4-0 Diesel	Beeston Creosote Works.
E.D.2 ...	M.		0-4-0 Diesel	Ditton Creosote Works.
E.D.3 ...	M.		0-4-0 Diesel	Lenton P.W. Depot.
E.D.4 ...	M.		0-4-0 Diesel	Northampton.
E.D.5 ...	M.		0-4-0 Diesel	Castleton P.W. Depot.
E.D.6 ...	M.		0-4-0 Diesel	Castleton P.W. Depot.
E.D.7 ...	M.		0-4-0 Diesel	Fazakerley.
E.D.10...	M.		0-4-0 Diesel	Beeston Creosote Works.
BEL1 ...	M.			Poplar Docks.
BEL2 ...	M.			Oakamoor.
ZM32 ...	M.		0-4-0 Diesel	Horwich Works.
DS74 ...	S.		Bo-Bo Electric	Durnsford Rd. Power Station.
DS75 ...	S.		Bo Electric	Waterloo & City Line.
DS680 ...	S.		A1	Lancing Carriage Works.
DS681 ...	S.		A1X	Lancing Carriage Works.
DS1169	S.		0-4-0 Diesel	Eng. Dept., Broad Clyst.
DS1173	S.		0-6-0 Diesel	Engineer's Dept.
DS3152	S.	30272	G6	Meldon Quarry.
24 ...	W.		0-4-0 Petrol	Taunton Engineer's Dept.
27 ...	W.		0-4-0 Petrol	Reading Signal Works.
PWM650	W.		0-6-0 Diesel	
PWM651	W.		0-6-0 Diesel	Radyr.
PWM652	W.		0-6-0 Diesel	Taunton.
PWM653	W.		0-6-0 Diesel	Hayes.
PWM654	W.		0-6-0 Diesel	Hookagate.

† Numbered in E. & N.E. Region Departmental stock.

First published 1960
Reprinted 2017
Reprinted 2018

ISBN 978 0 7110 3864 6

Printed in Malta by Gutenberg Press Limited

Published by Crécy Publishing Ltd
1a Ringway Trading Est
Shadowmoss Rd
Manchester M22 5LH

This is a facsimilie reprint of original editions first published in 1960, and as such, all advertisements are no longer valid.

Visit the Crécy Publishing website at www.crecy.co.uk

Front cover:
The last standard gauge steam locomotive built for British Railways was Standard Class 9F No 92220 *Evening Star*, constructed at Swindon in March 1960. It is seen here in June that year at Ealing Broadway at the head of the Capitals United Express. *A. C. Sterndale / Colour-Rail (BWR1796)*

Rear cover:
Built by British Thompson-Houston with Paxman engines the first D8200-series Bo-Bo locomotives entered traffic in November 1957. *Ian Allan Library*